ULTRA-VIOLET AND VISIBLE SPECTROSCOPY

CHEMICAL APPLICATIONS

A

ULTRA-VIOLET

AND

VISIBLE

SPECTROSCOPY

CHEMICAL APPLICATIONS

C. N. R. RAO

D.Sc., Ph.D., F.R.I.C., F.A.Sc.,

Professor of Chemistry, Indian Institute of Technology, Kanpur, India
(formerly of Purdue University and Indian Institute of Science)

SECOND EDITION

NEW YORK
PLENUM PRESS
LONDON
BUTTERWORTHS
1967

A*

Published in the U.S.A. by
PLENUM PRESS
a division of
PLENUM PUBLISHING CORPORATION
227 West 17th Street, New York, N.Y. 10011

First published by
Butterworth & Co. (Publishers) Ltd.

First Edition, 1961
Reprinted, 1964
Second Edition, 1967

©

Butterworth & Co. (Publishers) Ltd.

1967

Suggested U.D.C. No.: 543, 422. 5/6
Library of Congress Catalog Card Number 67-26707

Printed in Great Britain by Page Bros. (Norwich) Ltd.

To My Parents

PREFACE TO THE SECOND EDITION

Encouraged by the good reception for the first edition (1961, reprinted 1964) of this monograph, I have now attempted to revise it to suit the needs of post-graduate students beginning research as well as of practising chemists. While this book is not intended for the theoretician and the spectroscopist, they may find a fairly good collection of references and spectra-structure correlations of value. In this revision, many of the sections in the book have been modified. In addition, a new chapter on the absorption spectra of molecules of biological interest has been included.

I am thankful to the various reviewers and colleagues from all parts of the world who have offered a number of valuable suggestions. I take this opportunity to thank Kagaku Dojin Sha, Tokyo, for the Japanese translation and the Mir Publishers, Moscow, for the Russian translation of the first edition of this book.

C. N. R. RAO

Kanpur, India
January, 1967

PREFACE TO THE FIRST EDITION

It would be superfluous to stress the importance of electronic spectroscopy in structural or analytic research. It has now become a matter of routine to record the ultra-violet or visible spectra of compounds for purposes of identification or structure elucidation. The spectrophotometric methods of analysis have replaced the conventional methods in ever so many instances. The number of publications in the different branches of chemistry, reporting data on or making use of electronic spectroscopy, is ever-increasing and it would be impossible to review the field completely. In this book, I have tried to introduce the basic concepts of electronic spectroscopy and to present its applications in analytical, structural and physico-chemical problems. As far as possible, the material has been selected to illustrate the basic principles of modern theories in chemistry. While surveying the data on organic molecules, several empirical generalizations have been discussed. Many of the more recent developments like the far ultra-violet spectra of organic molecules, fluorescence spectra, charge transfer spectra, ligand field theory, optical rotatory dispersion etc., have been briefly discussed in the latter part of the book. All through the discussion, the recent notations of electronic transitions have been used, although the other commonly encountered notations have also been mentioned. I shall be most gratified if this book can be of help to chemists in using electronic spectroscopy more effectively in research or routine work.

With such a voluminous literature on the chemical applications of electronic spectroscopy, it is rather difficult to credit properly every person who has made a valuable contribution to the field and I have, doubtless, overlooked some important contributions. If so, I wish to apologize for any oversights or errors in judgment which have been made.

I am most grateful to Dr. R. M. Mallya, Miss N. Rajalakshmi, Messrs. K. Srinivasan, A. Balasubramanian and S. R. Yoganarasimhan for their kind collaboration in writing some of the sections in the book. I am specially grateful to Professor S. Bhagavantam, Director, Indian Institute of Science, for his keen interest and encouragement and to Professor M. R. A. Rao for his helpful criticism and suggestions. I am indebted to my various colleagues and co-workers, both past and present, for innumerable discussions which have contributed to this book. I must particularly thank Professors D. K. Banerjee, H. C. Brown, E. Lieber, R. L. Livingston, E. T. McBee and K. S. Pitzer, who have taken continuing interest in my research. Finally, I wish to express my sincere appreciation to my wife, Indu, who not only improved many of these sentences, but also gave the encouragement necessary for their writing.

C. N. R. RAO

Bangalore, India
July, 1961.

CONTENTS

ix

INTRODUCTION

MODERN methods of spectroscopy in the different regions of the electro-magnetic spectrum have provided the chemist with powerful tools for analysis and investigation of structure. The methods include, electronic (ultra-violet and visible) spectroscopy, infra-red and Raman spectroscopy, microwave spectroscopy and nuclear magnetic resonance spectroscopy. The choice of the type of spectroscopy for a specific problem depends upon, among other factors, the structure and properties of the specimen and the information sought. Thus, the detailed structural information on certain types of molecules may be obtained from microwave spectroscopy. Infra-red spectroscopy is best for structural investigations because of the ideal wave-length region it covers in the electromagnetic spectrum. The infra-red spectra of molecules have both group character and considerable structural character. Electronic spectroscopy, on the other hand, does not give much information on the detailed structural features of molecules, but throws light on their group character. However, by studying the electronic spectra of a large number of different types of molecules, it has been possible to correlate the spectra with structure.

Identification of organic compounds by their absorption spectra has become a routine procedure for the past several years. It is a standard practice now, to record either the infra-red or the ultra-violet spectrum while proposing a structure for a new compound or while reporting its physical properties. Electronic absorption spectroscopy has been used as confirmatory evidence for the identity of a previously known substance, just as any other physical property (e.g., melting point, refractive index). Many examples may be cited where a particular structure of a compound was selected from several possibilities on the basis of its ultra-violet or visible spectrum. The high intensity of many of the absorption bands in the near ultra-violet and visible regions not only permits the identification with minute quantities of material, but also serves as an aid in the control of purification of substances. In this book, an attempt has been made to present the basic concepts of electronic spectroscopy and to survey its analytical and structural applications in the different branches of chemistry.

CHAPTER 1

BASIC CONCEPTS AND EXPERIMENTAL METHODS

THE electronic spectra of molecules are found in the wavelength range 1000–8000 Å of the electromagnetic spectrum. The visible region to which the human eye is sensitive, corresponds to the range of wavelengths between 4000 Å and 8000 Å. The ultra-violet region is subdivided into two spectral regions. The range between 2000 and 4000 Å is referred to as the near ultra-violet region. The region below 2000 Å, is called the far or vacuum ultra-violet region.

The unit of wavelength commonly used in visible or ultra-violet spectroscopy is the angstrom unit, Å, or the millimicron, mμ, equal to 10 Å. Sometimes the wave number, $\bar{\nu} = 1/\lambda$, is also used. The unit of wave number is the reciprocal centimetre, cm^{-1}.

Elementary Theory

There are two classes of spectra, namely emission and absorption spectra. An emission spectrum is obtained by analysing the light emitted by a luminous source. An absorption spectrum is obtained by the spectroscopic analysis of the light transmitted by an absorbing medium which is placed between the light source and the spectroscope.

When a molecule absorbs radiation, its energy increases. This increase is equal to the energy of the photon as expressed by the relation

$$E = h\nu = hc/\lambda$$

where h is the Planck's constant, ν and λ are the frequency and the wavelength of the radiation respectively and c is the velocity of light. The change in energy may be in the electronic, vibrational or rotational energy of the molecule. Changes in electronic energy involve relatively large quanta. Changes in vibrational energy involve smaller quantities of energy and changes in rotational energy involve quanta even smaller than those of vibrational energy. The electronic energy level of a molecule under normal conditions is called its ground state and the higher electronic levels represent the first and second excited states respectively. For each electronic level there are the ground and several possible excited vibrational states and similarly, for every vibrational level there are the ground and excited rotational levels (*Figure 1.1*). The energies associated with electronic transitions are indeed very large. 20,000 cm^{-1} is approximately 56 kcal mole^{-1} and this energy is sufficient for the dissociation of many molecules. Since electronic transitions occur at even higher frequencies, it becomes obvious that these transitions are accompanied by changes in the electronic distributions of molecules. These ideas are pictorially represented in *Figure 1.2* for a diatomic molecule.

If a molecule absorbs a small amount of energy from a source of radiation in the far infra-red or the microwave region, only its rotational energy will change, no matter which vibrational or electronic state it is in. If the radiation source is of greater energy, say in the near infra-red region, then both the

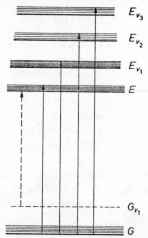

Figure 1.1. Energy levels for a polyatomic molecule and the origin of absorption lines. *G*, ground electronic state; *E*, excited electronic state; V_1, V_2, V_3, different vibrational states. The closely spaced lines represent rotational levels

vibrational and rotational energies of the molecule will change. If the energy from the radiation is much greater, as in the case of ultra-violet light, changes in the electronic, vibrational and rotational energies will take place. Consequently, the ultra-violet spectrum of a molecule will be more complicated than its rotational or rotational-vibrational spectrum. There will be such a large number of closely spaced sublevels as to make the ultra-violet spectra of polyatomic molecules even in the gaseous state appear only as broad

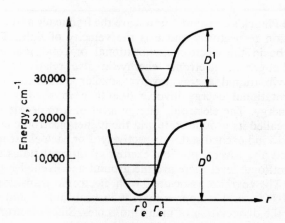

Figure 1.2. Potential energy curves for ground and electronically excited states of a diatomic molecule: D = dissociation energy; r_e = equilibrium distance. Horizontal lines show vibrational levels

2

absorption bands or band envelopes. The complex nature of the electronic spectra of polyatomic molecules renders their complete analysis very difficult or nearly impossible. However, in some simple molecules, the fine structure has been recorded using spectrometers of high resolution and the observed positions and intensities of the absorption bands have been interpreted. The loss of vibrational and rotational structure becomes more prominent in the spectra of liquids and solutions because of the interaction between neighbouring molecules and by solvation. Most of the measurements in chemistry refer to such conditions. Usually polar solvents produce greater changes in the absorption bands than non-polar solvents.

In an electronic transition, the excited molecule may return to the ground state by giving up its excess energy as heat or as fluorescent radiation of longer wavelength. Another possibility is for the excited molecule to undergo homolytic dissociation or ionization. While the former process can take place by absorption of radiation in the 2000–8000 Å range, the latter process usually takes place by absorption in the vacuum ultra-violet region. Beyond the ionization potential, there will be a region of continuous absorption.

Absorption Intensity

Before the development of adequate theory, Beer and Lambert had proposed laws of light absorption. These laws are well-known in their combined form as the Beer–Lambert law of light absorption which states that the fraction of the incident light absorbed is proportional to the number of molecules in the path. That is, if a substance is dissolved in a solvent, the absorption by the solution will be proportional to its molecular concentration, provided the solvent itself does not have any absorption in that region. This law is expressed as

$$\text{Absorbance or extinction or optical density} = \log_{10} \frac{I_0}{I} = \epsilon c l$$

where ϵ is the absorption coefficient, c is the concentration and l is the path length. If c is expressed in gram moles per litre and l in cm, then the absorption coefficient becomes a molar extinction coefficient. The absorption intensity is usually expressed in terms of ϵ and the majority of the applications in spectrophotometry are based on the above-mentioned equation. If the molecular weight of the substance is not known, the expression $E_{1\%}^{1\,cm}$ is often used. This is related to ϵ by the equation

$$E_{1\%}^{1\,cm} = \frac{\epsilon \times 10}{\text{Molecular weight}}$$

According to Beer–Lambert law, the optical density of a solution should remain constant as long as the product of the concentration and the path length is constant. For example, the optical density of a 1 cm layer of an x molar solution should be the same as that of a 10 cm layer of an $x/10$ molar solution. But this is not always true. Quite often, the molar extinction coefficient varies appreciably with the concentration of the solute. These deviations may be due to one of many possible causes: molecular association of the solute at high concentrations; ionization of the solute in the case of

3

acids, bases and salts; fluorescence of the solute; poor transmission of the solvent etc. It is now an accepted rule in spectrophotometry that one should not assume Beer–Lambert law to hold good for any substance without confirming it. Whenever a spectrophotometric method is being developed for the quantitative determination of a substance, one should test the validity of Beer–Lambert law in the particular solvent over the entire range of concentrations likely to be used.

The absorption intensity of an electronic transition at any wavelength is governed by the probability of the transition and the size of the absorbing molecule. The absorption maximum of a band therefore corresponds to the most probable transition in that region of absorption. The extinction coefficient may be expressed as

$$\epsilon = k\,Pa$$

where k is a constant of the order of 10^{20}, P is the probability and a is the area of cross-section of the molecule[1]. Assuming that the probability of an electronic transition is unity, the maximum theoretical extinction coefficient for an average organic molecule ($a = 10$ Å^2) may be calculated to be of the order of 10^5. In fact, the largest extinction coefficients experimentally observed are also of the order of 10^5.

While the extinction coefficient of an absorption band may change markedly with solvent or phase, the band area, $A = \int \epsilon d\nu$, generally remains the same. Band area is a measure of absorption intensity, although extinction would normally suffice for most of the structural work or quantitative analysis. The band area is related to the oscillator strength, f, which is the number of oscillators of mass m and charge e responsible for absorption. The oscillator strength[18] is given by

$$f = (8\pi^2 mc/3h)G_f \nu\mu_{if} = 1\cdot096 \times 10^{11} G_f \nu\mu_{if}$$
$$= 0\cdot102\,(mc^2/N\pi e^2)\int \epsilon d\nu$$
$$= 4\cdot315 \times 10^{-9}\int \epsilon d\nu$$

where m is the mass of the electron, N the Avogadro number, G_f the degeneracy of final state (generally unity and therefore omitted), ν the frequency of absorption and μ_{if} the dipole strength of the transition from the initial state i to the final state f. The intensity of absorption band, I, is proportional to μ_{if}, or to the square of the transition moment, Q. The transition moment is given by

$$\sqrt{I} \propto \sqrt{\mu} = Q = \int \Psi_i \vec{M}\,\Psi_f d\tau$$

where Ψ_i and Ψ_f are the total electronic wave functions of the initial and final states, M is the dipole moment vector and $d\tau$ the product of the volume elements in the coordinates of all the nuclei and electrons. $\vec{M} = \Sigma e\vec{r}$ where $\vec{r}$ is the average distance between the centre of positive charge to the electron. By replacing the total electronic wave function by one electron functions, the above equation may be written as

$$Q = \int \Psi_{i(j)} M_i \Psi_{f(j)} d\tau_j$$

for an electron j. In doing so, one assumes that only a single electron is

4

excited and that Ψ_i remains the same for the initial and final states. Some of these assumptions are rather serious approximations. When the above integral becomes zero, the translation is called 'forbidden'. However, forbidden transitions do occur and non-zero values of the intensities can be obtained by more refined calculations. The intensity of a forbidden transition is much smaller in magnitude than that of an 'allowed' transition. While allowed transitions may exhibit extinction coefficients of the order of 10^4 or greater (P of 0·1 to 1), forbidden transitions usually exhibit extinction coefficients less than 10^3(P of 0·01 or less).

Selection Rules

Although it is out of the scope of this book to discuss the selection rules[2, 3, 15] in detail, a brief summary of the important selection rules will be presented in this section. The first selection rule applies to all molecules with centres of symmetry and deals with the parity-forbidden transitions ($g \rightarrow g$ or $u \rightarrow u$). The second rule is related to the multiplicity of states. According to this rule, singlet–triplet transitions should be forbidden. The third rule pertains to forbidden transitions arising from the symmetry of states (e.g., 260 mμ band of benzene or the long wavelength bands of C=O, C=S and other chromophores). In addition to these three types of forbidden transitions, there are also other weak transitions which have low intensities. In the above discussion we have assumed that transitions involve only single electron excitation. Transitions involving many electron excitations are usually forbidden but configurational interactions do lend some intensity to such transitions.

Many forbidden transitions are observed with finite intensity in many molecules due to some intramolecular or intermolecular perturbations. Thus, singlet–triplet transitions occur with increased intensities in the presence of paramagnetic substances (NO or O_2) or in solvents containing heavy atoms such as ethyl iodide. Vibration interactions induce allowed character to forbidden transitions in some molecules. For example, the forbidden band of benzene at 260 mμ becomes weakly allowed due to the distortion of the D_{6h} symmetry of benzene by bending vibrations. Similarly, the intensity borrowing mechanism of the long wavelength band (290 mμ) of formaldehyde, is ascribed to the mixing of electronic states by the C—H out-of-plane bending vibration. Analysis of the vibrational and rotational structure of electronic absorption bands often gives information on the nature of the perturbing vibrations and on the changes in molecular shape and size resulting from electronic excitation.

In the case of allowed bands, the symmetric vibrations of the molecules give rise to progressions in the excited state frequency starting from the zeroth vibrational level of the electronic ground state and the relative intensities give a measure of the change in molecular size and shape on excitation. In forbidden transitions which become allowed by a bending or some other vibration, the band origin (which arises from the electronic energy change without any vibrational energy changes) is not found. Rotational structure of an absorption band is dependent on the direction of the transition moment and, the values of moments of inertia of the molecule. The direction of the transition moment can be found by the nature of the rotational structure. This can also be found by examining oriented molecules with polarized radiation. The dipole moment vector $\vec{M}$ will then be replaced by only one component in the direction of the incident polarized light and the molecule absorbs only the radiation which has an electric vector parallel to the transition moment.

Franck and Condon[19, 20] have proposed an important rule for understanding the nature of electronic transitions. According to the Franck–Condon principle, transitions from the vibrational levels of one electronic state to the vibrational levels of another occur so rapidly that the positions and velocities of the nuclei have no time to change. That is, the nuclei remain fixed in position for the duration of the electronic rearrangement. The potential function of a vibrational mode of a molecule will depend on the electronic state of the molecule and the internuclear distance in the electronic excited state will therefore differ from the ground state value. In *Figure 1.3*, the potential energy curves for upper and lower electronic states are shown for cases where the difference in the equilibrium distances in the two states is zero, small or large. The Franck–Condon principle states that electronic transitions will take place only when the internuclear distances are not significantly different in the two states and where the nuclei have little or no velocity. In case (a), 0–0, 1–1 . . . v–v transitions can all occur, although ordinarily at room temperatures only the lowest vibrational states will be populated. The spectrum will mainly consist of a strong line due to the 0–0 transition and weak lines due to the 0–1, 0–2 . . . transitions. As the upper curve is displaced, there will be transitions to higher levels of the upper state (0–3, 0–4 etc.) as in case (b), until in the extreme case (c), a continuous absorption may arise. In polyatomic molecules where there will be a number

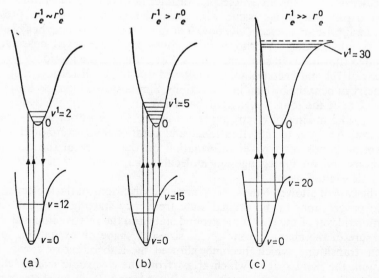

Figure 1.3. Diagram illustrating the Franck–Condon principle in three cases with increasing difference between the equilibrium distances in the electronically excited and ground states

6

of vibrational modes, transitions corresponding to the excitation of various vibrations will appear.

Presentation of Absorption Spectra*

The data on absorption spectra are usually presented as absorption curves. The units of absorption are plotted as ordinates and the units of wavelength as abscissae. The convention normally employed is to plot ϵ, log ϵ, $E_{1\%}^{1\ cm}$ or log $E_{1\%}^{1\ cm}$ against the wavelength in Å or mμ. When tabulating the results, most authors record the positions of the absorption maxima (λ_{max}) and the extinction coefficients at the maxima (ϵ_{max}). The absorption minima (λ_{min}) are also often recorded. For physical studies, some workers prefer to use the wave numbers (cm^{-1}) instead of wavelengths since the wavenumber scale is linearly related to energy units (see reference 12 for details).

Experimental Methods and Instruments

The basic parts of any type of spectroscopic equipment are the radiation source, the sample container, the monochromator, the detector and the detector output measuring instrument. In the ultra-violet and visible regions, the sources are incandescent lamps or discharge tubes. Prisms or gratings are used as monochromators. If prisms are used, the prism material will vary from one region of electronic spectra to the other. Calcium fluoride or lithium fluoride prisms are used in the vacuum ultra-violet region while quartz prisms are used in the near ultra-violet region. For the visible region, glass prisms are employed. The eye, the photographic plate and the photo-electric cells are used as detectors for the visible region and the last two also for the ultra-violet region. For the past few years, photoelectric spectro-photometers have been widely used and they have almost completely replaced spectrographs employing photographic plates. The uncertainty in the measurement of absorption intensity is much less with an instrument employing a photo-cell (less than 1%). Neither the historical methods of recording absorption spectra nor the detailed descriptions of the modern instruments will be discussed here. Only a brief account of the photoelectric instruments in vogue will be given. Details of the design and construction of spectroscopic equipment have been dealt with in several books[4,5,6]. However, for informa-

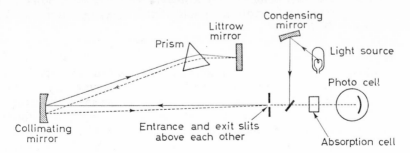

Figure 1.4. Optical system in a simple photoelectric spectrophotometer

* It has not been possible to follow any particular convention in presenting the spectral curves in this book since many of them have been reproduced from different sources in the literature.

7

tion on the more recent instruments one will have to refer to the articles in the literature or to the pamphlets supplied by the manufacturers.

The photographic methods of spectrophotometry are not merely slow and expensive, but are also limited in accuracy in the measurement of absorption intensity. The accuracy will be in the range of ± 2 to $\pm 5\%$. The modern photoelectric spectrophotometers are claimed to be accurate within $\pm 0.2\%$ for intensity measurement. The photoelectric instruments incorporate one or

Table 1.1. Some of the Commercially Available Photoelectric Spectrophotometers

Instrument	Wavelength range, mμ	Manufacturers
Beckman DU, manual	210–1000	Beckman Instruments, U.S.A.
Unicam SP500, manual	210–1000	Unicam Instruments Ltd., England
Hilger Uvispeck, manual	200–1000	Hilger and Watts, England
Beckman DB, recording, low cost	210–770	Beckman Instruments, U.S.A.
Cary, Model 14, recording*	185–3000	Applied Physics Corp., U.S.A.
Beckman, Model DK-1 and DK-2, recording*	185–3500	Beckman Instruments, U.S.A.
Perkin-Elmer, Model 350, recording*	175–2700	Perkin-Elmer Corp., U.S.A.
Perkin-Elmer, Model 202, recording, low-cost	190–750	Perkin-Elmer Corp., U.S.A.
Spectronic 505, recording, low-cost	210–800	Bausch and Lomb Optical Co., U.S.A.
Zeiss RPQ20A, recording	200–2500	Carl Zeiss, Germany
General Electric, recording	380–700	General Electric Co., U.S.A.
Rapid Scanning, No. 10175, with cathode-ray oscillograph indicator	400–700	American Optical Co., U.S.A.

*High resolution (~ 0.1 mμ around 250 mμ)

more photo-cells with suitable sensitivity over the whole wavelength range of interest and electrical devices are used in place of the photographic plate recorders. In these instruments the intensities are read off directly at different wavelength settings. The optical system of a typical photoelectric spectrophotometer is shown in its simple form in *Figure 1.4*. The manual recording of an absorption curve is time-consuming and several automatic recording instruments have been commercially available for some time. Some of the manually operated and recording photoelectric spectrophotometers have been listed in *Table 1.1*.

Standards

It is desirable to calibrate every photoelectric instrument against a standard and to repeat the calibration from time to time. This is necessary because of the possible effects of ageing on optical surfaces, on the spectral distribution of the lamp radiation and on the photo-cell. For wavelength calibration, didymium glass has been recommended[5,7]. For spectral transmission, the National Bureau of Standards[7], U.S.A., has recommended standard solutions of copper sulphate, cobalt ammonium sulphate and potassium chromate. Potassium chromate is most suitable since it absorbs both in the near ultraviolet and the visible regions. The absorbance data for a standard solution of potassium chromate[7] are given in *Table 1.2*.

8

Instruments are usually found to be less accurate at low wavelengths due to stray radiation. However, it is possible to estimate corrections for stray radiation. The careless handling of the instrument and of the cells also result in anomalous readings. Finger prints should be avoided on the cells since

Table 1.2. Standard Values of Absorbency, A_s, for Standard Potassium Chromate Solution*

Wavelength, mμ	A_s	Wavelength, mμ	A_s
220	0·4559	370	0·9914
230	0·1675	380	0·9281
240	0·2933	390	0·6841
250	0·4962	400	0·3872
260	0·6345	410	0·1972
270	0·7447	420	0·1261
280	0·7235	430	0·0841
290	0·4295	440	0·0535
300	0·1518	450	0·0325
310	0·0458	460	0·0173
320	0·0620	470	0·0083
330	0·1457	480	0·0035
340	0·3143	490	0·0009
350	0·5528	500	0·0000
360	0·8297		

* 0·0400 g per litre of K_2CrO_4 in 0·05N KOH solution at ~25°C in 1 cm cell.

they badly affect the measurement of absorption intensity. If the photoelectric spectrophotometers are in good working condition and are used with sufficient care, the absorption curves may be reproduced very accurately, the accuracy being greater at longer wavelengths.

Slit Width

Slit width is one of the important variables in spectrophotometry. Slit width determines the resolution and the measured extinction coefficients of the absorption bands. The possibility of the lack of resolution of absorption bands necessitates a statement with regard to the slit width employed while reporting the data. If slit widths are mentioned, it will make it easier to compare results on poorly resolved absorption bands from other laboratories. Serious errors result if the variation of the extinction coefficient with slit width is large. The measured extinction coefficients will be lower at the maxima and higher at the minima than the actual values. It is not easy to apply slit width corrections and in important cases it is better to record the spectra with different slit widths until a further decrease in the slit width does not produce major changes in the extinction coefficient. Thus, it is not possible to quote a general value for the slit width to be employed. The importance of slit width in spectrophotometry has been discussed by West[5].

Overlapping Bands

Overlapping bands are frequently seen in the ultra-violet and visible absorption spectra of molecules. The extinction coefficients of these bands are often taken to be the measured values. This is not really correct, although it would suffice for most qualitative and quantitative work. Since the measured absorbance values will actually have contributions from more than one band,

9

it becomes necessary to resolve the band into components for obtaining the true values of extinctions. In *Figure 1.5*, the analyses of three types of composite bands where the relative intensities and spacings of the component bands vary are shown from the work of Vandenbelt and Henrick[16]. The

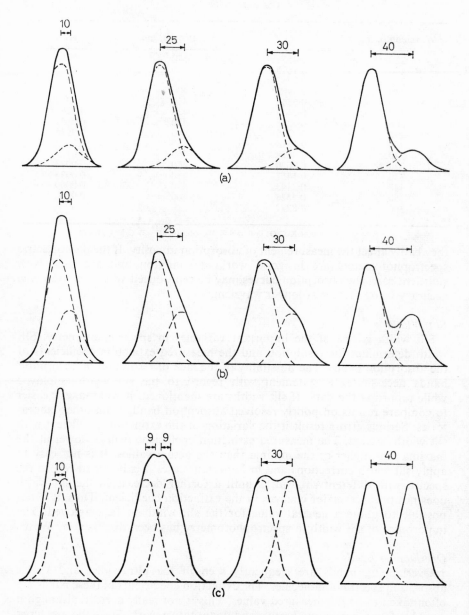

Figure 1.5. Band shapes resulting from two overlapping bands[16]. The numbers above the curves are in mμ units.

10

analysis of overlapping bands by derivative spectroscopy have been discussed by Giese and French[17].

Cells, Solvents, Accessories

In recording the absorption spectra, two cells are used, one as the reference cell and the other as the sample cell. In the case of solution spectra, the reference cell is filled with the solvent and the sample cell with the solution. Such an arrangement compensates for solvent absorption and also for losses of radiation by scattering and reflection. Absorption cells of different dimensions made of glass or quartz are available. While quartz cells may be used in the entire near ultra-violet-visible region, glass cells can be used only for the visible region. Cells of thickness anywhere from 0·1 cm to 10 cm are available, although 1 cm cells are most generally used for everyday work. Some of the recent instruments accommodate even 20 cm long cells. Cells of variable length (micrometer Baly cells) are also available (see reference 13).

Spectra of gases are taken using enclosed cells, with an evacuated cell as a reference. Spectra of solids may be taken in the form of pellets. Potassium bromide pellets similar to those used in infra-red spectroscopy have been found suitable. Pellet holders for measurements on solids are commercially available. In order to avoid complications due to nonparallel sides of solid samples, a rough-ground quartz 'diffuser' is placed in front of the photo-cell.

Most of the spectrophotometric studies are made in solution and the important factor in deciding the choice of solvents is that the solvent should not absorb in the same region as the solute. Of course, one should keep in mind the effect of solvents on the absorption bands (see Chapters 2 and 12 for a discussion of solvent effects). The solvents one can use for the near ultra-violet and visible regions are: water, alcohols (methyl, ethyl, *iso*-propyl etc.), acetonitrile, chloroform, dioxane, hexane, heptane, *iso*-octane and cyclohexane. The lower wavelength limit for these solvents is in the range 220–240 mμ. The near ultra-violet cut-off wavelengths in mμ for some of the solvents (1 cm cells) are given below:

Acetone	330	Ethanol	210
Acetonitrile	210	Ethyl ether	210
Benzene	280	Iso-octane	210
Bromoform	360	Methanol	215
Butanol	210	Methylcyclohexane	210
Carbon tetrachloride	265	Methylformate	260
Chloroform	245	Nitromethane	380
Cyclohexane	210	*i*-propanol	210
1,2-Dichloroethane	235	Pyridine	305
Dichloromethane	235	Tetrachloroethylene	290
N,N-Dimethylformamide	270	Water	210

However, purified hexane and heptane may also be used in the vacuum ultra-violet region down to 170 mμ. Below 170 mμ, spectra will have to be studied only in gas phase. For studies in the visible region or in the near ultra-violet region beyond 280 mμ one may also use carbon tetrachloride and aromatic solvents like benzene, toluene etc. as solvents.

11

Small changes in laboratory temperature do not affect the absorption spectra and a thermostat is normally unnecessary. But in certain physical studies like the determination of the kinetics or the equilibrium of a reaction, one has to control the temperature carefully. Thermostated cell holders are available for several commercial instruments. Large changes in temperature do produce marked changes in the spectra of some compounds (see Chapter 12). Specially designed cells for low temperature spectrophotometry are sold for the Cary instruments (see reference 14).

Normally, about 0·10 to 100 mg of a substance is sufficient for taking a spectrum. The substance, if necessary, may be recovered. If it is very scarce, one can minimize the quantity of the material even to about 0·001 mg by using reflecting microscopes[8,9]. Another important micro-technique has been the examination of spots on paper chromatograms by spectrophotometry[10,11].

The usefulness of the modern spectrophotometer is made greater by the availability of a number of accessories and attachments. Attachments are available for measuring reflectance of diffusely reflecting materials, and for fluorescence spectra. Attachments have been described for commercial spectrophotometers in order to cover the vacuum ultra-violet region down to 170 mμ. Some instruments which cover the range from vacuum ultra-violet to visible are commercially available.

REFERENCES

[1] BRAUDE, E. A., *Nature*, 1945, **155**, 733; *J. Chem. Soc.*, 1950, 379.

[2] DUNCAN, A. B. F. and MATSEN, F. A. in *Chemical Applications of Spectroscopy*, Edited by West, W., Interscience, New York, 1956, Chapter V.

[3] BAK, B., *Elementary Introduction to Molecular Spectra*, North Holland Publishing Co., Amsterdam, 1954.

[4] HARRISON, G. R., LORD, R. C. and LOOFBOUROW, J. R., *Practical Spectroscopy*, Prentice-Hall, New York, 1948.

[5] WEST, W., *Physical Methods of Organic Chemistry*, Part II, Edited by Weissberger, A., Interscience, New York, 1949, Chapter 21.

[6] GILLAM, A. E. and STERN, E. S., *Electronic Absorption Spectroscopy*, Edward Arnold, London, 1957, Chapter 2.

[7] GIBSON, K. S., 'Spectrophotometry', *Natl. Bur. Standards (U.S.) Circ.* 484, 1949.

[8] BARER, R., HOLIDAY, E. R. and JOPE, E. M., *Biochim. et. Biophys. Acta*, 1950, **6**, 123.

[9] LOOFBOUROW, J. R., *J. Opt. Soc. Amer.*, 1950, **40**, 304, 317.

[10] PARKE, T. V. and DAVIES, W. W., *Anal. Chem.*, 1952, **24**, 2019.

[11] CAMPBELL, H. and SIMPSON, J. A., *Chem. and Ind. (Rev.)*, 1953, 342.

[12] CAWLEY, J. D. and UNGNADE, H. E., *Anal. Chem.*, 1959, **31**, 42A (No. 2).

[13] GLICK, D. and GREENBERG, L. J., *Anal. Chem.*, 1960, **32**, 736.

[14] MARTIN, H. J. and GORIN, G., *Anal. Chem.*, 1960, **32**, 892

[15] JAFFE, H. H. and ORCHIN, M., *Theory and Applications of Ultraviolet Spectroscopy*, John Wiley and Sons, New York, 1962.

[16] VANDERBELT, J. M. and HENRICH, C., *Appl. Spectrosc.*, 1953, **7**, 173.

[17] GIESE, A. T. and FRENCH, C. S., *Appl. Spectrosc.*, 1955, **9**, 78.

[18] MULLIKEN, R. S., *J. Chem. Phys.*, 1939, **7**, 14.

[19] CONDON, E. U. and MORSE, P. M., *Quantum Mechanics*, McGraw-Hill, New York, 1929.

[20] FRANCK, J., *Trans. Faraday Soc.*, 1925, **21**, 536.

CHAPTER 2

CHROMOPHORES AND TRANSITIONS

IT has been known for quite some time that coloured substances owe their colour to the presence of one or more unsaturated linkages. These linkages or groups conferring colour on substances were called *chromophores*. Some groups which by themselves did not confer colour on a substance were found to increase the colouring power of a chromophore. Such groups were called *auxochromes*. Typical examples of chromophores would be, $C=C$, $C=O$, $N=N$ etc. and of auxochromes, $C-Br$, $C-OH$, $C-NH_2$ etc.

If one surveys the data on the electronic spectra of organic molecules, some generalities become evident. Saturated organic molecules do not exhibit any absorption in the near ultra-violet and visible regions (200–800 mμ). Introduction of an auxochrome in a saturated system usually shifts the absorption maximum to a longer wavelength. However, the presence of a chromophore, i.e. a multiple bond, generally causes absorption in the 200–800 mμ region. The wavelength corresponding to the absorption maximum, λ_{max}, varies from chromophore to chromophore. Thus, in simple molecules one can easily identify the presence of chromophoric groups by the examination of their electronic spectra. The factors governing the λ_{max} of chromophores are the difference in the electronegativities of the elements forming the double bond and the relative ease in forming the double bond. These are exemplified by the λ_{max} for some of the simple compounds below:

Compound	λ_{max}, mμ
$H_2C = CH_2$	180
$(CH_3)_2C = O$	277
$CH_3N = NCH_3$	347
$(CH_3)_2C = S$	400
$C_4H_9N = O$	665

The location of the absorption bands due to chromophores depends markedly on environmental factors. By studying the displacements of the λ_{max} of the chromophores by the introduction of other groups, one can understand the nature of substituent effects. The interpretation of the spectra of organic molecules often becomes difficult because of the presence of more than one chromophore. Typical examples of such complex chromophores would be dienes, $\alpha\beta$-unsaturated ketones, substituted benzenes etc. However, by a study of the electronic spectra of a large number of different types of molecules, it has been possible to correlate the spectroscopic data with the structure of molecules.

Instead of discussing the electronic spectra of organic molecules empirically in terms of chromophores and auxochromes, one is now in a position to systematize the spectral properties of molecules in this region according to the types of valence electrons they contain. Electrons forming single bonds are called σ electrons (according to the molecular orbital notation). The characteristic functions and charge densities of these electrons are rotationally symmetrical with respect to the valency axis[1]. The electrons responsible for double bonds are called π electrons; the characteristic functions and charge densities of which have an oscillation nodal plane through the valency axis[1]. In unsaturated systems, π electrons predominantly determine the energy states of the electron sheaths which are excited by the absorption of visible or ultra-violet light. There are, then, the unshared electrons or non-bonded electrons in molecules containing atoms like nitrogen, oxygen etc. These electrons are usually called n electrons. The n electrons in the case of the elements of the first two rows of the periodic table are the p electrons. These three types of valence electrons are illustrated by formaldehyde:

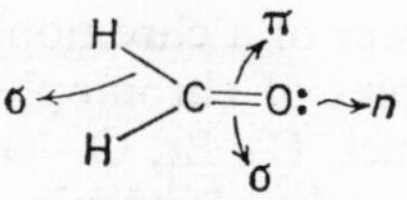

$$\sigma \leftarrow \underset{H}{\overset{H}{\diagup}} C = O: \to n \quad (\pi, \sigma)$$

While the interaction between σ and π electrons may be ignored, that between n and π or π and π electrons is considerable. Nonbonded electrons are bound less strongly than the bonding electrons. In the bonding electrons, the σ electrons are more strongly bound than the π electrons while in the antibonding levels, the σ^* level has higher energy compared to the π^* level. These ideas are pictorially represented in *Figure 2.1*.

	Level	Symbol	
	Antibonding σ	σ^*	————
	Antibonding π	π^*	————
E	*Non-bonded*	n	————
	Bonding π	π	————
	Bonding σ	σ	————

Figure 2.1. Electronic energy levels in a molecule

Having discussed the different types of valence electrons, we shall now mention the various transitions responsible for electronic spectra. Here again, we shall use the molecular orbital language without going into its details. The transitions have been discussed in detail by Duncan and Matsen[2], Jaffe and Orchin[9] and Murrel[10]

First, there are the N $\to$ V transitions which are from the bonding orbital in the ground state of a molecule to a higher energy orbital (antibonding orbital)[2]. The class of N $\to$ V transitions is large and one or more may occur for a molecule. For a transition between σ orbitals as in the case of paraffins, the N $\to$ V transition may be written as a $\sigma \to \sigma^*$ transition. For transitions between π orbitals as in the case of olefins, the N $\to$ V transitions are called $\pi \to \pi^*$ transitions. The $\sigma \to \sigma^*$ transitions are observed only in the far ultra-violet region. While some of the $\pi \to \pi^*$ transitions are observed in the far ultra-violet region, as in ethylene, many of them are observed in the near

14

ultra-violet region. The $\pi \to \pi^*$ bands are displaced to longer wavelengths by suitable substitution on the molecule.

The second type of transition denoted by $N \to Q$ results from the excitation of a nonbonding orbital localized on an atom to an antibonding orbital[2]. The $N \to Q$ transitions are usually weaker as a class than the $N \to V$ transitions. For transitions to σ orbitals, the $N \to Q$ transitions are called $n \to \sigma^*$ transitions and for transitions to π orbitals they are called $n \to \pi^*$ transitions. While the $n \to \sigma^*$ transitions are usually found in the far or the near ultra-violet region, the $n \to \pi^*$ transitions are always found at fairly long wavelengths in the near ultra-violet or the visible region. The $n \to \sigma^*$ transitions are found in the case of saturated molecules which contain singly bonded basic groups with atoms having unshared pairs of electrons (i.e. the traditional auxochromes like C—OH, C—NH_2, C-halogen etc.). The $n \to \pi^*$ transitions are found in molecules when a hetero atom with unshared electrons is multiply bonded to another atom. Most of the traditional chromophores like C=O, C=S, —N=N— etc. exhibit $n \to \pi^*$ transitions. In addition, they also exhibit the $n \to \sigma^*$ and $\pi \to \pi^*$ transitions at lower wavelengths. The $n \to \pi^*$ transitions are forbidden transitions and the intensities are usually very low compared with the corresponding $n \to \sigma^*$ and $\pi \to \pi^*$ transitions. Recently, Sidman[3] has written an excellent review on $n \to \pi^*$ transitions where he tabulates the general features of $n \to \pi^*$ transitions as compared to $\pi \to \pi^*$ transitions.

Lastly, there is the $N \to R$ transition which occurs from an orbital in the ground state to one of high enough energy for the molecule ion core to resemble an atomic ion[2]. Such a transition is seen as a progression of bands

Table 2.1. Classification of Electronic Transitions

Transition	Description	Region of electronic spectra
$N \to V$	From a bonding orbital in the ground state to an orbital of higher energy (a) $\sigma \to \sigma^*$ (between σ orbitals)	Vacuum ultra-violet e.g., methane at 125 mμ
	(b) $\pi \to \pi^*$ (between π orbitals) (often called K or A or E bands in different systems)	Ultra-violet e.g., ethylene at 180 mμ or benzene at 203 mμ
$N \to Q$	From a nonbonding atomic orbital to a high energy molecular orbital (a) $n \to \pi^*$ (to π orbitals) (often called R bands)	Near ultra-violet and visible e.g., acetone at 277 mμ, nitrosobutane at 665 mμ
	(b) $n \to \sigma^*$ (to σ orbitals)	Far ultra-violet and sometimes near ultra-violet e.g., acetone at 190 mμ, methylamine at 213 mμ
$N \to R$	From an orbital in the ground state to one of very high energy in the direction of the ionization of the molecule	Vacuum ultra-violet

(Rydberg series) which terminates in ionization (continuum). The N → R transitions are found in the far end of the vacuum ultra-violet region.

The N → V bands in π systems have also been termed as K-bands (K for Konjugation) in the literature. In the benzene system, N → V bands have been called E-bands or A-bands. The $n \to \pi^*$ transition bands have also been called the R-bands (R for Radical). Electronic transitions were in fact originally classified by Burawoy[11] in terms of the K and R bands. The spectra of aromatic compounds was classified by Clar[12] who defined three main types of bands α, p and β in the order of increasing intensity. One finds that the literature is full of terminologies, some having theoretical bases and others only empirical.

Kasha[5] and Platt[4] have made a plea for the adoption of a systematic nomenclature for the states and transitions of organic molecules. According to their terminology, the low excited states of aromatics and their derivatives are denoted by ^1L_a, ^3L_a, ^1L_b, ^3L_b. The ground states and low 'classical-oscillator' states are denoted by ^1A, ^1B, ^1C, ... For particular states of $n\pi$ excited configurations, the symbols ^1U, ^3U, ^1W, ^3W have been suggested. According to this new system, the $n \to \sigma^*$ and the $n \to \pi^*$ bands of the carbonyl group will be denoted by $^1W - {}^1A$ and $^1U - {}^1A$ respectively. Similarly, the $\pi \to \pi^*$ band of ethylene will be denoted by $^1B - {}^1A$. Since this book only deals with the chemical applications of electronic spectroscopy, only the more common notations will be used. Wherever possible, alternative notations will also be mentioned. Chemists using electronic spectra for structure elucidation etc. should not get confused with the various terminologies for the bands found in the literature. A little patient examination will indicate what transitions the particular authors are discussing.

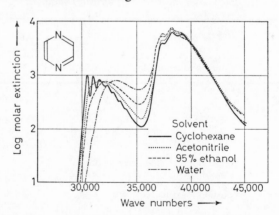

Figure 2.2. Solvent effect on pyrazine spectrum[7]

The transitions discussed above have been summarized in *Table 2.1*. Substitution or structural changes in organic compounds result in changes in the wavelength and in the intensity of absorption bands. Wavelength changes to longer wavelengths are called *bathochromic* shifts and changes to shorter wavelengths are called *hypsochromic* shifts. An increase in the intensity of a band is called a *hyperchromic* effect, while a decrease is called a *hypochromic* effect.

16

The structural character and the position of absorption bands depend on the nature of the solvent. Generally, polar solvents tend to shift the position of the bands and diminish the vibrational structure of the bands. Particularly in hydroxylic solvents, the structure gets completely blurred. Non-polar solvents produce little change in the bands compared to the gas phase spectra. Recently, solvent effects have been employed for the characterization of electronic transitions. Solvent and substituent effects were first employed by Burawoy[11] to characterize electronic transitions. These ideas have been revived by Kasha[5] and McConnell[6] who have suggested that solvent effects may be of value in distinguishing between $\pi \rightarrow \pi^*$ and $n \rightarrow \pi^*$ transitions. The wavelengths of the $n \rightarrow \pi^*$ bands are generally found to decrease (blue-shift) with the increase in the polarity of the solvent. The vibrational structure of the $n \rightarrow \pi^*$ bands is completely blurred in polar solvents. Polar solvents generally (but not always) shift the $\pi \rightarrow \pi^*$ transitions to longer wavelengths (red-shift). A typical exception would be the $\pi \rightarrow \pi^*$ bands of benzene. The vibrational structure of some $\pi \rightarrow \pi^*$ bands is retained even in polar solvents. Solvent effects on spectra are discussed in greater detail in Chapter 12. In *Figure 2.2* the near ultra-violet spectrum of pyrazine[7] in different solvents has been reproduced. The low frequency (long wavelength) band is due to the $n \rightarrow \pi^*$ transition while the high frequency band is due to the $\pi \rightarrow \pi^*$ transition. The solvent effects on the near ultra-violet spectrum of mesityl oxide[8] are given in *Table 2.2* and the absorption curves in heptane, alcohol and water are reproduced in *Figure 2.3*. This molecule

$$\begin{array}{c} H_3C \\ \diagdown \\ \\ \diagup \\ H_3C \end{array} \begin{array}{c} O \\ \| \\ C = CHC\!-\!CH_3 \end{array}$$

exhibits a $\pi \rightarrow \pi^*$ band due to C=C and an $n \rightarrow \pi^*$ band due to C=O, both in the near ultra-violet region. Recently it has been found that even $n \rightarrow \sigma^*$ transitions (as in alkyl iodides and amines) show solvent blue-shifts similar to $n \rightarrow \pi^*$ transitions.

Table 2.2. Solvent Effects on the Ultra-violet Spectrum of Mesityl Oxide[8]

Transition	λ_{max} , mμ, in				
	iso-octane	Aceto-nitrile	Chloro-form	Methanol	Water
$\pi \rightarrow \pi^*$ (K-band)	230·6	233·9	237·6	236·8	242·6
$n \rightarrow \pi^*$ (R-band)	321·0	314·0	315·4	308·8	submerged

It may be generalized at this point that the absorption bands of almost all organic molecules normally found in the near ultra-violet and visible regions arise from either $\pi \rightarrow \pi^*$ or $n \rightarrow \pi^*$ transitions. The $\pi \rightarrow \pi^*$ transitions may be very intense (allowed) or weak (forbidden). But the $n \rightarrow \pi^*$ transitions are generally forbidden and consequently of weak intensity. As far as possible, one should use non-polar solvents while recording solution spectra. If highly polar solvents are used, one may miss the $n \to \pi^*$ bands in some cases. This is particularly true of compounds in which the $n \to \pi^*$ bands are preceded by intense $\pi \to \pi^*$ bands (*Figure 2.3*).

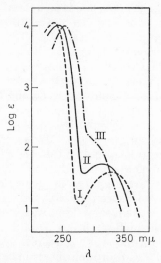

Figure 2.3. Solvent effect on mesityl oxide spectrum.
I, Heptane; II, Ethanol and III, Water

When comparing two absorption curves, one should use the same solvent. The pH of the medium is an important factor in the case of acids and bases (see Chapter 7).

In the following few chapters the electronic spectra of various types of molecules have been discussed. The electronic spectra of molecules are modified by substitution with different groups. Both electronic and steric interactions of groups are important in electronic spectra. The term, electronic interaction, includes both inductive and resonance (mesomeric) interactions, although the influence of the latter may be more prominent. The substituent effects on the spectra of different chromophores and molecules will be discussed appropriately in the following chapters. Steric effects on electronic spectra have been dealt with separately in Chapter 8.

REFERENCES

[1] CARTMELL, E., and FOWLES, G. W. A., *Valency and Molecular Structure*, Butterworths, London, 1956.
[2] DUNCAN, A. B. F. and MATSEN, F. A., in *Chemical Applications of Spectroscopy*, Edited by West, W., Interscience, New York, 1956, Chapter V.
[3] SIDMAN, J. W., *Chem. Revs.*, 1958, **58**, 689.
[4] PLATT, J. R., *Ann. Rev. Phys. Chem.*, 1959.
[5] KASHA, M., *Discussions Faraday Soc.*, 1950, **9**, 14.
[6] McCONNELL, H., *J. Chem. Phys.*, 1952, **20**, 700.
[7] HALVERSON, F. and HIRT, R. C., *J. Chem. Phys.*, 1951, **19**, 711.
[8] KOSOWER, E. M., *J. Amer. Chem. Soc.*, 1958, **80**, 3261.

[9] JAFFE, H. H. and ORCHIN, M., *Theory and Applications of Ultraviolet Spectroscopy*, John Wiley and Sons, New York, 1962.

[10] MURREL, J. N., *The Theory of the Electronic Spectra of Organic Molecules*, Methuen and Co., London, 1963.

[11] BURAWOY, A., *Ber.*, 1963, **63**, 3155; *J. Chem. Soc.*, 1939, 1177.

[12] CLAR, E., *Aromatische Kohlenwasserstoffe*, Springer Verlag, Berlin, 1952, 2nd edition.

[13] KIMURA, K. and NAGAKURA, S., *Spectrochim, Acta*, 1961, **17**, 166.

B

CHAPTER 3

SIMPLE MOLECULES

IT is clear from the discussion in the previous chapter that the electronic spectra of simple molecules may easily be characterized. In this chapter, we shall deal with the spectra of simple molecules with a single chromophore.

Paraffins and Saturated Compounds containing Auxochromes

Since paraffins contain only single bonds, i.e. σ electrons, the only transitions that may be expected in these molecules would be the $\sigma \to \sigma^*$ transitions. These occur at very low wavelengths in the vacuum ultra-violet region. For example, the first absorption bands of methane and ethane are found at 125 and 135 mμ respectively. The excitation in ethane is thought to lie in the C—C bond while it is in the C—H bond in methane. The bond strength of the C—C bond is less than that of the C—H bond and consequently the absorption in ethane is at a longer wavelength. The ionization energies of methane and ethane are also different, with values of 13·1 and 12·6 eV respectively.

Cyclopropane is found to exhibit absorption at a much longer wavelength (190 mμ) than the corresponding straight-chain compound. This is explained as due to the unsaturation resulting from the strain in the molecule.

Saturated compounds containing atoms with unshared pairs of electrons, exhibit absorption bands at longer wavelengths than the corresponding saturated hydrocarbons. This is because of the excitation of one of the electrons in the nonbonding orbital. Such substituted saturated molecules generally seem to exhibit two absorption bands, one in the vacuum ultra-violet region and another at a longer wavelength. Absorption data[41] of several saturated compounds with auxochromes are given in *Table 3.1* along with the data on related molecules. The short wavelength bands may be due to $N \to V$ ($\sigma \to \sigma^*$) transitions while the long wavelength bands may result from the excitation of the unshared electrons (possibly $n \to \sigma^*$ type transitions). The ionization energies of the molecules vary in the same direction as the wavelengths corresponding to the absorption maxima. The $n \to \sigma^*$ transitions are generally weaker than the corresponding $\sigma \to \sigma^*$ transitions. This is particularly true of VI and VII group elements where the n-electrons are p-electrons and the $n \to \sigma^*$ transitions are forbidden. In molecules where there is an overlap of lone-pair orbitals (e.g. halogens, hydrazine) the character of the $n \to \sigma^*$ transition changes and the transition is shifted to longer wavelengths. For example, the $n \to \sigma^*$ transition of an alkyl halide becomes essentially a $\pi^* \to \sigma^*$ transition in halogens. Among the halogens, the intensity of absorption increases from fluorine to iodine (*Table 3.1*).

The $n \to \sigma^*$ transitions of alkyl iodides (~ 260 mμ) have been studied in detail[42, 43] and the λ_{max} varies in the order t-Bu $>$ CF$_3$ $>$ i-Pr $>$ s-Bu $>$ n-Bu $>$ n-Pr $>$ Et $>$ Me. Both inductive and hyperconjugative effects of

20

Table 3.1. Absorption Data on Saturated Compounds with Auxochromes and other Related Compounds (From Mason, S. F.[41] by courtesy of The Chemical Society)

Compound	Solvent*	$\lambda_{max}(m\mu)$†	ϵ_{max}†
B_2H_6	V	182	20
		135	10,000
$B_{10}H_{14}$	CH	272	3,200
CH_4	V	122	strong
C_2H_6	V	135	strong
$Me_3C \cdot CH_2 \cdot CHMe_2$	V	154	10,000
NH_3	V	194	5,600
		152	strong
$MeNH_2$	V	215	600
		174	2,200
Me_2NH	V	220	100
		191	3,300
Me_3N	V	227	900
		199	3,950
$(NHMe)_2$	V	245	1,000
H_2O	V	167	1,480
$MeOH$	V	184	150
Me_2O	V	184	2,520
Me_2S	E	*229*	*140*
		210	1,020
$Pr^nS \cdot SPr^n$	E	252	475
$S \cdot [CH_2]_3S$	E	334	160
EtS_4Et	E	290	2,400
S_8	E	275	8,000
CH_3Cl	V	173	weak
CH_3Br	V	204	200
CH_3I	PE	258	365
CH_2I_2	PE	292	1,320
CHI_3	HX	349	230
F_2	V	285	6
Cl_2	V	330	66
Br_2	V	420	200
I_2	V	520	950
ICl	FA	450	121
IBr	FA	487	308
Cl_2O	CT	260	600
$ClOEt$	CT	310	30
ClO_2	V	360	1,300
Br_2O	CT	320	250
SCl_2	CT	304	1,150
PI_3	ET	360	8,800
AsI_3	PE	378	1,600

*The following abbreviations are used in this table for the solvents listed: V vapour, S unspecified solvent, E ethanol, CH cyclohexane, PE light petroleum, ET diethyl ether, CT carbon tetrachloride, HX hexane, FA trifluoroacetic acid
†Values in italics refer to shoulders or inflections.

alkyl substituents seem to be operative. The $n \to \sigma^*$ transition wavelength of alkyl iodides is shifted to lower wavelengths in polar solvents although the magnitude of the shift is smaller than encountered in the case of $n \to \pi^*$ transitions. Some absorption data are given below for a few alkyl iodides.

The absorption spectra of mono-, di- and poly-sulphides have been studied[44-46]. Monosulphides containing the C—S—C linkage show the $n \to \sigma^*$ transition around 215 mμ. This band shows solvent blue shifts and in alkyl sulphides the λ_{max} varies in the order t-Bu > Et > Me. Sulphur

21

dichloride, SCl_2, and dipiperidinesulphide containing the N—S—N linkage do not show the band corresponding to the $n \to \sigma^*$ transition of alkyl sulphides because of the interaction of the lone pair electrons on the chlorine and nitrogen respectively. In addition to the $n \to \sigma^*$ transition, alkyl sulphides show a

	Heptane		Water
	λ_{max} (mμ)	ϵ_{max} (mμ)	λ_{max} (mμ)
CH_3I	257·5	378	249
C_2H_5I	258·5	444	251
$i\text{-}C_3H_7I$	262·5	531	256
$t\text{-}C_4H_9I$	269	400	—
CH_2I_2	212	1,580	240
	240	600	285
	290	1,300	—
CHI_3	207	1,860	—
	274	1,300	—
	349	2,170	—

weaker band around 227 mμ which is solvent insensitive, but sensitive to substitution. Dipiperidinesulphide shows two bands at 213 and 230 mμ. Thioketals show a characteristic weak band (log ϵ 2·6) around 254 mμ.

Alkyl disulphides absorb at higher wavelengths (~ 250 mμ, ϵ 300–500) than the monosulphides. This band is sensitive to substitution and does not vary with the solvent. The open-chain disulphides probably have a staggered conformation due to repulsion of the non-bonding electrons and the overlap of the n-orbitals will be small. Interestingly, trimethylenedisulphide absorbs at a longer wavelength than open-chain disulphides. Tetraethyldithiodiamine, Et_2N—S—S—NEt_2, shows an intense band ($\epsilon \sim 4,000$) around 258 mμ. The λ_{max} of both the alkyl and piperidine polysulphides increase with the number of sulphur atoms in the chain.

The $n \to \sigma^*$ absorption bands of water, ammonia, hydrogen sulphide and phosphine have been found to show blue-shifts in water solution compared to the spectra in vapour phase or in aprotic solvents[47].

Multiple Bonds

Compounds with multiple bonds in them have lower ionization energies and absorb at longer wavelengths than saturated systems. Simple carbon–carbon double bonds are found in olefins. Ethylene itself exhibits a strong $\pi \to \pi^*$ band around 165 mμ ($\epsilon \sim 10,000$) and another weak (forbidden) $\pi \to \pi^*$ band around 210 mμ ($\epsilon \sim 1,000$). With suitable substitution, the bands of ethylene are shifted to longer wavelengths. Of the two bands, the long wavelength band undergoes greater shifts. The intensity of this band is also enhanced in unsymmetrically substituted ethylenes.

Substitution of ethylene with basic groups (auxochromes) containing unshared electrons like Cl, OH, NH_2 etc. shifts the spectrum towards longer wavelengths. These bathochromic shifts are explained mainly in terms of the

substituent	NR_2	OR	SR	Cl	CH_3
shift in mμ	40	30	45	5	5

22

resonance interactions of these groups since inductive effect lowers both the π and π^* levels equally (*Figure 3.1*). Substitution of ethylene with alkyl groups also results in bathochromic shifts, although alkyl groups do not contain any unshared electrons. The shifts were explained as due to 'hyperconjugation'[2] of the alkyl groups. Hyperconjugation in propylene for example, is explained in terms of resonance between the structures:

$$H_3C—CH = CH_2 \qquad H_2C = CH—CH_2$$
$$\qquad\qquad\qquad\qquad H^+ \quad C^-$$

Increase in the branching of the alkyl groups will decrease the C—H hyperconjugation because of the decrease in the number of α-hydrogens. Thus, the C—H hyperconjugating ability of methyl > ethyl > *i*-propyl > *t*-butyl. The C—C hyperconjugation of these groups will vary in the reverse order. The observed ionization energies and absorption spectra[3] of alkyl substituted ethylenes, however, do not prove the importance of hyperconjugation.

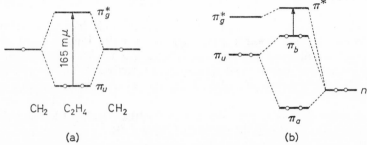

(a)   (b)

Figure 3.1. Energy levels for ethylene (a) and substituted ethylene with resonance effect (b)

All compounds with an isolated ethylenic linkage exhibit an intense absorption band ($\epsilon \sim 10,000$) around 190 mμ due to the $\pi \to \pi^*$ transition[4]. For all practical purposes, an isolated ethylenic linkage need not be considered a 'chromophore', since it gives rise to a band in the not easily accessible far ultra-violet region. End-absorption data have been made use of to decide the extent of substitution of ethylenic linkages[31–34]. Thus, the trisubstituted olefinic linkages show extinctions in the ranges 1,400–4,700, 600–3,500 and 250–1,800 at 210, 215 and 220 mμ respectively, while tetrasubstituted linkages show extinctions in the ranges 4,400–10,000, 3,900–9,200 and 3,400–6,700 at these wavelengths. Cyclic olefins, like cyclopentene and cyclohexene, exhibit spectra very similar to those of disubstituted olefins.

	λ_{max}*	ϵ_{max}
HC≡CH	220	weak
	182	moderate
	152	strong
alkyl-C≡CH	187	450
alkyl-C≡C-alkyl	191	850
HC≡N	160–200	overlapping
	155–170	bands
H₃CC≡N	167	weak

*In mμ.

Although molecules with triple bonds contain two sets of π orbitals, all the $\pi \to \pi^*$ transitions are not observed due to the operation of selection rules. If molecules become non-linear on excitation, then one of the transi-

23

tions becomes allowed. Some absorption data[41] on triple-bonded systems are shown on page 23. The intensity of the acetylene band system is sensitive to substitution. Thus 2-alkynes show increased intensity compared to 1-alkynes.

Multiple Bonds with Atoms Containing Unshared Electrons

The electronic spectra of molecules with such multiple bonds should be expected to be more complicated than those of simple multiple bonds or saturated compounds containing atoms with unshared electrons (auxochromes). One finds low intensity bands at long wavelengths due to $n \to \pi^*$ transitions in addition to bands at lower wavelengths due to $n \to \sigma^*$ transitions similar to saturated molecules containing auxochromes and $\pi \to \pi^*$ transitions characteristic of simple multiple bonds. A great number of the traditional chromophores belongs to this class. The most characteristic transition of these chromophores is the $n \to \pi^*$ transition. We shall now survey[5] the available data on the $n \to \pi^*$ transitions (R-bands or $^1U \to {}^1A$ transitions) of different chromophores.

Carbonyl group. Saturated carbonyl compounds like acetone exhibit three bands: a weak band around 280 mμ, a more intense band around 190 mμ and a still more intense band around 150 mμ, which are assigned to the $n \to \pi^*$, $n \to \sigma^*$ and $\pi \to \pi^*$ transitions respectively[5]. The $n \to \pi^*$ transitions of a large number of carbonyl derivatives have been reported in the literature[5].

The position of the $n \to \pi^*$ band of the carbonyl group varies with the substituents R_1 and R_2 on the molecule (*Table 3.2*):

$$R_1 \atop \diagdown$$
$$C = 0$$
$$\diagup \atop R_2$$

Substitution of a halogen, a hydroxyl or an amino group (auxochromes) for hydrogen, shifts the band to shorter wavelengths. This is because these groups donate electrons by resonance interaction and raise the

Table 3.2. $n \to \pi^*$ Transitions of Carbonyl Derivatives ($R_1R_2C = O$)

R_1	R_2	in heptane		in methanol*
		λ_{max}, mμ	ϵ_{max}	λ_{max}, mμ
CH$_3$	H	293	12	285
CH$_3$	OH	210	40	204
CH$_3$	NH$_2$	<220	—	<220
CH$_3$	Cl	235	53	—
CH$_3$	Ph	325	54	submerged
Ph	Ph	348	110	333
CH$_3$	CH$_3$	276·5	12	270
CH$_3$	C$_2$H$_5$	277·5	15	272
CH$_3$	i-C$_3$H$_7$	283·5	17	278
CH$_3$	t-C$_4$H$_9$	286	18	282
CH$_3$	CF$_3$	277·5	40	—

* ϵ_{max} are of the same magnitude as in heptane.

energy of the excited state relative to the ground state. In addition, these groups withdraw electrons by virtue of their inductive effect and lower the energy of the ground state, thus shifting the spectrum in the same direction.

Alkyl substitution also shifts the $n \rightarrow \pi^*$ band to lower wavelengths. The wavelengths of the $n \rightarrow \pi^*$ bands of aliphatic ketones (*Table 3.2*) cannot be explained merely in terms of inductive effects of groups. But they may be quantitatively correlated if the C—H and C—C hyperconjugation of the alkyl groups are taken into account in addition to the inductive effects. While the bands are shifted to lower wavelengths due to hyperconjugation, they are shifted to longer wavelengths by the inductive interaction of the alkyl groups[6]. The $n \rightarrow \pi^*$ frequencies in saturated ketones and aldehydes have been correlated by the expression[6]

$$\nu' = \nu'_0 + \Sigma\sigma^*\rho^* + n_h h_h + n_c h_c$$

where ν is the observed $n \rightarrow \pi^*$ frequency in cm^{-1}, σ^* is the Taft aliphatic substituent constant, n_h and n_c are the number of α-hydrogen and α-carbon atoms available for C—H and C—C hyperconjugation and h_h and h_c are the

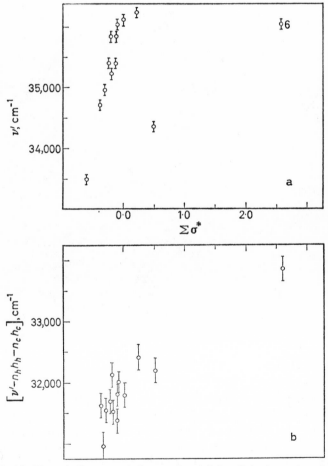

Figure 3.2. (a) Plot of the $n \rightarrow \pi^*$ frequencies (ν') in aliphatic carbonyl derivatives against the polar substituent constants of Taft $\Sigma\sigma^*$. (b) Plot of ($\nu' - n_h h_h - n_c h_c$) against $\Sigma\sigma^*$. The maximum limits of uncertainty on the frequencies have been shown

25

corresponding hyperconjugative contributions. Generally h_h is much larger than h_c. The correlation can be seen in *Figure 3.2*.

The $n \rightarrow \pi^*$ transitions of a number of aliphatic ketones have been reported in the literature[6,7]. Most of the aliphatic ketones do not exhibit fine structure in the $n \rightarrow \pi^*$ bands even in heptane solution. The $n \rightarrow \pi^*$ band of acetalde-hyde in heptane, however, possesses a structural character similar to the gas phase spectrum. The fine structure is completely lost in polar solvents (*Figure 3.3*) and the band is also shifted to lower wavelengths.

The $n \rightarrow \pi^*$ transitions of alicyclic ketones have been studied[8] (*Table 3.3*). Cyclopentanone exhibits the highest λ_{max} of the ring ketones studied. In non-polar solvents the bands show fine structure.

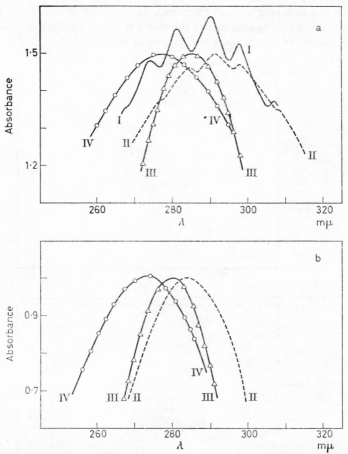

Figure 3.3. Ultra-violet absorption spectra of (a) acetaldehyde and (b) methyl *i*-propyl ketone in different media[6]: I, gas phase; II, heptane; III, alcohol and IV, water

Acetophenone, benzophenone and benzaldehyde absorb at higher wave-lengths (325, 348 and 328 mμ respectively) compared to acetone (277 mμ). This is due to conjugation in these molecules. The $n \rightarrow \pi^*$ bands in these systems are seen immediately next to the very intense $\pi \rightarrow \pi^*$ bands and often the former bands completely merge into the latter in polar solvents.

Cookson[9] has found that the shift in the position of the λ_{max} of a ketone due to α-halogen substitution is a function of the angle between the carbonyl group and C-halogen bond. Thus, the shift for an equatorial α-bromocyclohexanone is -5 mμ and $+28$ mμ for a polar one. The shift produced by bromination of camphor is intermediate. The relation has been employed to assign conformations to some steroid and triterpenoid α-bromoketones. α-Hydroxy and α-acetoxy groups also cause shifts similar to the α-bromo group when they are in equatorial and axial positions[35,36].

Table 3.3. $n \rightarrow \pi^*$ Transitions of Alicyclic Ketones[8]

Compound	In iso-octane*		Methanol† λ_{max}, mμ
	λ_{max}, mμ	ϵ_{max}	
Cyclobutanone	281	19·2	278
Cyclopentanone	300	19·1	287·5
Cyclohexanone	290	15·8	282·5
Cycloheptanone	292	18·6	283
Cyclo-octanone	290	16·8	283
Cyclononanone	288	16·2	281·5
Cyclodecanone	289	15·4	283
2,2-Dimethylcyclopentanone	298	—	292·5
3-t-Butylcyclopentanone	300	—	287
2-Methylcyclohexanone	289	—	283
3-Methylcyclohexanone	289	—	282·5
4-Methylcyclohexanone	291	—	282·5

* Centre of the band.
† ϵ_{max} values are similar in magnitude to those in iso-octane solution.

Very marked effects of double bonds on the carbonyl $n \rightarrow \pi^*$ frequencies have been noticed even though they are not formally conjugated. Cookson and co-workers[40] have found that the carbonyl absorption is considerably intensified by intramolecular charge transfer from isolated C=C in bicyclo (2,2,2) octenones. In such systems, the p-orbitals of the carbonyl carbon and of the C=C point towards each other. The intensity is further increased if the olefinic double bond is substituted. Similar effects are found in the long-wavelength $n \rightarrow \pi^*$ band of α-diketones. Many $\beta\gamma$-unsaturated ketones exhibit absorption in the 200–260 mμ region where normally $\alpha\beta$-unsaturated ketones show their intense $\pi \rightarrow \pi^*$ transitions having charge-transfer character. For example, ketone (I) absorbs at 202 (ϵ 3,000) and 290 mμ (ϵ 110), where the former is likely to be due to a charge-transfer $\pi \rightarrow \pi^*$ transition[48].

(I)

5-Cyclodecene-1-one[49] (II) also shows such effects

(II)

27

with the $n \to \pi^*$ band at 302 mμ (ϵ 73) and another band at 260 mμ (ϵ 423)· Solvent effects have been employed to identify such transannular double bond-carbonyl interactions[50]. β-Diketones also show similar effects due to the mixing of $n \to \pi^*$ and $\pi \to \pi^*$ transitions. Thus, the diketone (IV) shows $n \to \pi^*$ absorption at 310 mμ (ϵ 121) while (III) shows bands at 350 and 309 mμ (ϵ 17 and 35) even though in IV the two C=O groups are orthogonal[41, 51].

(III)   (IV)

Transannular nitrogen–carbonyl interactions have been studied by Leonard and co-workers in aza-acyloins and aminoketones. In the 8-, 9- and 10-membered rings of these compounds, new bands are found around 226 mμ due to the interaction of the nitrogen lone pair and the π electron of the carbonyl[52].

Thiocarbonyl group. The thiocarbonyl group ($>$C=S) exhibits an absorption band due to the $n \to \pi^*$ transition similar to the carbonyl group, but at longer wavelengths. The intense $\pi-\pi^*$ transition is similarly found at longer wavelengths than the corresponding carbonyl compounds. This is understandable since the ionization potential of the sulphur lone pair is smaller than

Table 3.4. *Electronic Absorption Spectra of Thiocarbonyl Derivatives*

Compound	X	Y	Solvent (c)	$n \to \pi^*$ band		Other bands (a)			
				λ_{max}, mμ	log ϵ_{max}	λ_{max}, mμ	log ϵ_{max}	λ_{max}, mμ	log ϵ_{max}
Thiocamphor	C	C	C	493	1·09	244	4·06	214	3·62
Thiofenchone	C	C	C	488	1·04	240	4·00	215	3·60
Ethyl dithioacetate	C	S	H	460	1·25	305	4·08	—	—
Ethylene trithiocarbonate	S	S	H	467	—	315	—	252	—
			A	451	1·92	318	4·20	243	3·00
Thioacetamide	C	N	E	358	1·25	268	4·05	—	—
			A	325	1·58	265	4·14	—	—
Di-*i*-propyl-dixanthogen	S	O	H	365	1·03	285	4·21	243	4·38
			A	362	—	286	—	240	—
Thiazolidinethione	S	N	A	326	2·12	276	4·18	—	—
Thiourea	N	N	E	291*	1·85	254	4·10	—	—
Benzylthiourethane (b)	N	O	H	295*	2·13	—	—	—	—

* Shoulder.
(a) These bands are probably due to the $n \to \sigma^*$ and $\pi \to \pi^*$ transitions of the thiocarbonyl group.
(b) Other bands are not listed because of the interference by the benzenoid band.
(c) A, Alcohol; C, Cyclohexane; E, Diethyl ether; H, Heptane.

that of the oxygen lone pair. In the C=S group while the π^* level has lower energy, the n level has higher energy compared to the C=O group. Recently, electronic transitions of the thiocarbonyl group have been investigated in detail[10, 22, 53]. The absorption data of several derivatives are summarized in *Table 3.4*. The absorption curves of ethylene trithiocarbonate have been given in *Figure 3.4*. From the data in *Table 3.4* it can be seen that the position of the $n \rightarrow \pi^*$ band depends markedly on the elements (X and Y) directly linked to the thiocarbonyl group. The $n \rightarrow \pi^*$ wavelength decreases with the increasing electronegativity of the two elements. To be more precise, the wavelength varies in the order of increasing mesomeric electron release, S > O > N. Thiophosgene exhibits the $n \rightarrow \pi^*$ band around 572 mμ[5]. Thiobenzophenone[11] shows the $n \rightarrow \pi^*$ transition at 605 mμ (ϵ 66) and a $\pi \rightarrow \pi^*$ transition at 315 mμ (ϵ 17,000). Electron donating groups shift the $\pi \rightarrow \pi^*$ transition in thiobenzophenones to longer wavelengths and the $n \rightarrow \pi^*$ transitions to shorter wavelengths. Thus, in the *p*-ethoxy and *p*-diethylamino derivatives, the $n \rightarrow \pi^*$ bands are found at 592 (ϵ 360) and 573 mμ (ϵ 850) while the $\pi—\pi^*$ transitions are found at 354 (ϵ 30,900) and 434 mμ (ϵ 43,800) respectively. It should be pointed out that in thiobenzophenones there is likely to be mixing of $n \rightarrow \pi^*$ and $\pi \rightarrow \pi^*$ transitions.

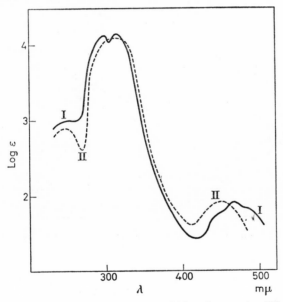

Figure 3.4. Absorption spectrum of ethylene trithiocarbonate in different solvents[22]: I, heptane; II, alcohol

Nitrogen–oxygen linkages. The nitro group exhibits a strong band around 210 mμ and a weak band due to the $n \rightarrow \pi^*$ transition around 270 mμ. The $n \rightarrow \pi^*$ transitions of the nitro group have been reported in several aliphatic derivatives[12,13]. The wavelengths of the $n \rightarrow \pi^*$ bands of the aliphatic nitro compounds (*Table 3.5*) can be explained if the C—H and C—C hyperconjugation and the inductive effects of alkyl groups are taken into account[13]

29

and an equation similar to that proposed for the carbonyl group has been proposed for the $n \to \pi^*$ frequencies of aliphatic nitro compounds (*Figure 3.5*).

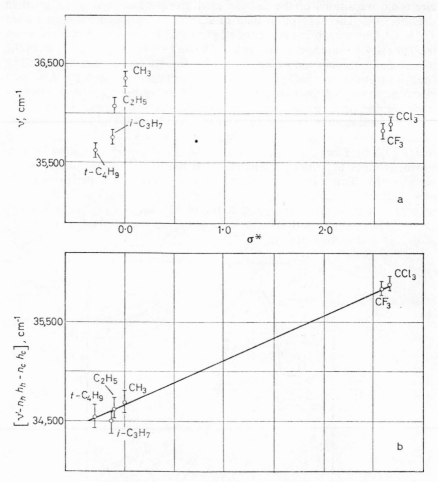

Figure 3.5. Correlation of $n \to \pi^*$ frequencies of aliphatic nitro compounds with Taft σ^* constants

Table 3.5. $n \to \pi^*$ *Transitions of Aliphatic Nitro Compounds* (RNO_2)

R	$n \to \pi^*$ in heptane		$n \to \pi^*$ in methanol*	Other bands	
	λ_{max}, mμ	ϵ_{max}	λ_{max}, mμ	λ_{max}	ϵ_{max}
CH_3	275	14·5	271·5	201	5,000
C_2H_5	277	19·8	274		
i-C_3H_1	279·5	21·4	277		
t-C_4H_9	280·5	22·5	279		
CF_3	279	52	—		

* The ϵ_{max} values are of the same magnitude as in heptane.

The $n \rightarrow \pi^*$ bands of nitroparaffins do not possess any fine structure even in nonpolar solvents, but exhibit solvent blue-shifts in polar solvents, though not comparable to the carbonyl derivatives in magnitude (*Table 3.8*).

The other nitrogen–oxygen linkages which exhibit weak bands due to $n \rightarrow \pi^*$ transitions are alkyl nitrites[12,14], alkyl nitrates[12], nitroso compounds[14-18] and azoxy compounds[19]. The absorption maxima and extinction coefficients of a few typical compounds have been summarized in *Table 3.6*.

Table 3.6. $n \rightarrow \pi^*$ Transitions of a few Nitrogen–oxygen Linkages

Compound	$n \rightarrow \pi^*$ λ_{max}, mμ	ϵ_{max}	Other bands λ_{max}, mμ	ϵ_{max}
n-Heptyl nitrite[12]	356(a)	85	—	—
i-Butyl nitrate[12]	355(a)	76	222	1,700
1-Octyl nitrate[12]	270(b)	15	—	—
Cyclohexyl nitrate[12]	270(b)	22	—	—
Diethylnitrosoamine[14]	366(a)	105	233	6,000
t-Nitrosobutane[15] (monomer)	665	20	300	~100
			220	~5,000
Nitrosobenzene[16](monomer)	755	53	280	9,000(c)
t-Butylthionitrite	599	15	339	980
			229	10,500
Nitrosylchloride	460	13	258	420
Dinitrogentetroxide*	343	233	270	240
Dinitrogen trioxide[29]	662	20	—	—
Azoxymethane[19]	274(b)	54	217	7,250

(a) There is considerable structural character in the band. Only the absorption maximum of highest intensity is indicated.
(b) Appears as an inflection. (c) Other bands: ~320 mμ (ϵ5,200) and two bands in for u.v. (190 and 170 mμ)
* Assignment doubtful.

Alkyl nitrites exhibit a weak band ($\epsilon_{max} \sim 80$) with fine structure (nearly six or seven well defined maxima) in the region of 370 mμ[12]. The fine structure

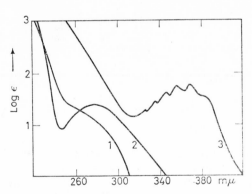

Figure 3.6. Ultra-violet absorption spectra of (1) 2-butyl nitrate in ethanol; (2) 2-nitrobutane in ethanol and (3) 2-butyl nitrite in ether[12]

is not affected by polar solvents like alcohol or water. Alkyl nitrates give an inflection around 270 mμ ($\epsilon \sim 20$) in alcohol solution. It is likely that distinct absorption maxima will result if the spectra were to be taken in less polar solvents. The near ultra-violet spectra of a nitro compound, a nitrite and a nitrate are reproduced in *Figure 3.6*. Azoxy compounds[19] exhibit only an inflection around 275 mμ in alcohol solution, which may appear as well-defined maxima in non-polar solvents.

Monomeric aliphatic nitroso compounds are blue while the aromatic derivatives are green in colour. The aliphatic monomers show bands in the region 630–790 (ϵ 1–20) and 270–290 mμ ($\epsilon \sim 80$) due to the $n_N \rightarrow \pi^*$ and $n_0 \rightarrow \pi^*$ transitions respectively and a band around 220 mμ ($\epsilon \sim 5,000$) due to the $\pi - \pi^*$ transition.[15, 16] Dimerization markedly affects the $n_N - \pi^*$ band and a new band appears around 270 mμ. The absorption data on *cis* and *trans* dimers are available along with the thermodynamics of dimerization.[17] Data on the electronic absorption spectra of nitrosamines have been reported.[14, 18] Basicities of nitrosamines have been examined by electronic spectroscopy.[58]

Nitrogen–nitrogen linkages. Some of the straight chain compounds containing nitrogen–nitrogen multiple bonds give rise to low intensity bands in the near ultra-violet and visible regions (*Table 3.7*). The long wavelength bands may arise from $n \rightarrow \pi^*$ transitions. In aliphatic azides the long wavelength band at 285 mμ has been assigned to the $\pi \rightarrow \pi^*$ transition while the 215 mμ band is considered to be due to a $s - p \rightarrow \pi^*$ transition[54]. Solvent effects on the 287 mμ band are not typical of $n \rightarrow \pi^*$ transitions[54], but substituent effects are similar. Thus, electron donating groups shift the $n \rightarrow \pi^*$ transition wavelength to lower wavelengths in azido derivatives, the effect varying in the order $NR_2 > OR > SR$[55].

Table 3.7. *The Absorption Bands of Some Nitrogen-nitrogen Multiple Bonds*

Compound	λ_{max}, mμ	ϵ_{max}	λ_{max}	ϵ_{max}
Aliphatic azides[20, 54]	285	20	215	500
Azobis-1-cyclohexylnitrile[21]	350	11	—	—
Azomethane	347	5	—	—
Azobenzene (*trans*-)	443	500	320	21,300
Azobenzene (*cis*-)	433	1,520	281	5,260
Perfluoroazomethane	360	2	267	2
Diphenylaldazine	340	125	—	—
Diazomethane[40]	400	3	—	—

In Ph—P≡P—Ph, two bands have been observed at 320 (ϵ 2,300) and 254 mμ (ϵ 25,000), of which the former is likely to have considerable $n \rightarrow \pi^*$ character[41].

The ultra-violet absorption spectra of nitrogen containing heteroaromatic compounds (see Chapter 6) like pyridine[23], diazabenzenes (pyridazine, pyrimidine, pyrazine)[23], triazenes[24] and diazanaphthalenes[25] have been studied by Hirt and co-workers. All of them show long wavelength bands due to $n \rightarrow \pi^*$ transitions in addition to intense $\pi \rightarrow \pi^*$ transitions at lower wavelengths (*Figure 2.2*). In non-polar solvents, the $n \rightarrow \pi^*$ bands show fine structure which becomes completely blurred in polar solvents. There is considerable shift of the absorption maxima to lower wavelengths in polar solvents.

Sulphur–Oxygen linkages. Sulphur dioxide shows two bands at 360 (ϵ 0·05) and 290 mμ (ϵ 342) due to singlet-triplet and singlet-singlet $n \rightarrow \pi^*$ transitions. Dialkyl sulphones (RSO_2R') are transparent down to 200 mμ. This is because the oxygen electrons are tightly bound and sulphur has no non-bonding electrons in these compounds. Aliphatic sulphoxides ($RSOR'$) show fairly intense absorption around 220 mμ (log ϵ 3·5) and a weak band around 150 mμ. Diaryl, aryl alkyl and other unsaturated sulphones and sulphoxides show absorption bands in the ultra-violet region due to the aromatic or olefinic groups (see Chapters 4 and 5).

Inorganic molecules and ions. McConnell[26] pointed out that the absorption bands of nitrate, carbonate and trithiocarbonate ions at 313, 217 and 500 mμ respectively, are due to $n \rightarrow \pi^*$ transitions. McGlynn and Kasha[27] have predicted that many inorganic molecules containing oxygen or sulphur should exhibit $n \rightarrow \pi^*$ transitions at long wavelengths. According to them, molecules or ions like AsO_4^{3-}, CrO_4^{2-}, MnO_4^-, ReO_4^-, UO_4^{2-}, OsO_4, RuO_4, RuO_4^- RuO_4^{2-} should exhibit strong $n \rightarrow \pi^*$ bands ($\epsilon > 1000$), while molecules or ions like NO_3^-, CO_3^{2-}, CS_3^{2-}, SiO_3^{2-}, SO_3, BrO_3^-, IO_3^-, SO_3^{2-} should exhibit weak $n \rightarrow \pi^*$ bands ($\epsilon < 50$). The long wavelength band around 355 mμ ($\epsilon_{max} \sim 20$) in sodium nitrate[28] and the band at 476 mμ ($\epsilon \sim 120$) in ClO_2[27] have been shown to be due to $n \rightarrow \pi^*$ transitions. The $n \rightarrow \pi^*$ transitions of xanthate ion around 390 mμ have been studied in potassium alkyl xanthates[56]. The spectrum of the nitrite ion has been studied[57] and the bands around 360, 280 and 210 mμ have been assigned to $n \rightarrow \pi^*$, $n \rightarrow \pi^*$ and $\pi \rightarrow \pi^*$ transitions from solvent effect studies. The band at 230 mμ (ϵ 430) of azide ion is assigned to the $'\Sigma_g^+ \rightarrow '\Delta_u$ transition characteristic of linear triatomic molecules[54]. The absorption of many monatomic and quasi-monatomic ions (e.g. OH^-, Cl^-, I^-) in the ultra-violet region is ascribed to anion-solvent charge-transfer[41] (see Chapter 11).

Solvent Effects on $n \rightarrow \pi^*$ Transitions

The solvent effects on the position of the $n \rightarrow \pi^*$ absorption maxima of a few compounds have been summarized in *Table 3.8*. The intensities also vary with the solvents, but only to a slight extent.

Table 3.8. Solvent Effects on $n \rightarrow \pi^*$ Transitions (R-bands), λ_{max} *in* mμ

Compound	Heptane	Chloroform	Acetonitrile	Ethyl alcohol	Water
Acetone[6]	276·5	274·5	274	270	264·5
Nitromethane[22]	275	274·5	273	272	268·5
Diethylnitrosoamine[14]	358	—	—	350	338
s-Triazene[24]	272	—	268	267	260
Ethylene trithiocarbonate[22]	467	457	453	451	424

REFERENCES

[1] MATSEN, F. A. in *Chemical Applications of Electronic Spectroscopy*, Edited by West, W., Interscience, New York, 1956, Chapter V.

[2] BAKER, J. W., *Hyperconjugation*, Oxford University Press, 1953.

RAO, C. N. R., *Nature*, 1960, **187**, 913.

[3] MULLIKEN, R. S., *Rev. Mod. Phys.*, 1942, **14**, 265.
[4] CARR, E. P. and STUCKLEN, H., *J. Chem. Phys.*, 1936, **4**, 760.
[5] SIDMAN, J. W., *Chem. Rev.*, 1958, **58**, 689.
[6] RAO, C. N. R., GOLDMAN, G. K. and BALASUBRAMANIAN, A., *Canad. J. Chem.*, 1960, **38**, 2508.
[7] MARONI, P., *Ann. Chim. (Paris)*, 1957 (13), **2**, 757.
[8] RAO, C. N. R., GOLDMAN, G. K. and RAMACHANDRAN, J., *J. Indian Inst. Sci.*, 1961, **43**, 10.
[9] COOKSON, R. C., *J. Chem. Soc.*, 1954, 282.
[10] JANSSEN, M. J., *Rec. Trav. chim. Pays-Bas*, 1960, **79**, 454, 464, 1066.
[11] BROCKLEHURST, P. and BURAWOY, A., *Tetrahedron*, 1960, **10**, 118.
[12] UNGNADE, H. E. and SMILEY, R. A., *J. Org. Chem.*, 1956, **21**, 993.
[13] BALASUBRAMANIAN, A. and RAO, C. N. R., *Chem. & Ind.* (London), 1960, 1025.
[14] HASZELDINE, R. N. and JANDER, J., *J. Chem. Soc.*, 1954, 691.
[15] GOWENLOCK, B. G. and LÜTTKE, W., *Quart. Revs (London)*, 1958, **12**, 321.
[16] NAGAKURAS, S. and co-workers., *Bull. Chem. Soc. (Japan)*, 1965, **38**, 965; 1966, **39**, 766.
[17] (a) GOWENLOCK, B. G. and TROTMAN, J., *J. chem. Soc.*, 1956, 1670.
(b) KEUSSLER, V. V. and LÜTTKE, W., *Z. Elektrochem*, 1959, **63**, 614.
[18] NAKAMOTO, K. and SUZUKI, K., *J. Chem. Phys.*, 1952, **20**, 1971.
[19] LANGLEY, B. W., LYTHGOE, B. and RAYNER, L. S., *J. Chem. Soc.*, 1952, 4191.
[20] LIEBER, E., RAO, C. N. R., CHAO, T. S. and WAHL, W. H., *J. Sci. Industr. Res. (India)*, 1957, **16B**, 95.
[21] OVERBERGER, C. G., O'SHAUNESSY, M. T. and SHALIT, H., *J. Amer. Chem. Soc.*, 1949, **71**, 2661.
[22] RAO, C. N. R. and BALASUBRAMANIAN, A. and RAMACHANDRAN, J., *J. Sci. Indstr. Res. (India)*, 1961, **20B**, 382.
[23] HALVERSON, F. and HIRT, R. C., *J. Chem. Phys.*, 1951, **19**, 711.
[24] HIRT, R. C., HALVERSON, F. and SCHMITT, R. G., *J. Chem. Phys.*, 1954, **22**, 1148.
[25] HIRT, R. C., KING, F. T. and CAVAGNOL, J. C., *J. Chem. Phys.*, 1956, **25**, 574.
[26] McCONNELL, H., *J. Chem. Phys.*, 1952, **20**, 700.
[27] McGLYNN, S. P. and KASHA, M., *J. Chem. Phys.*, 1956, **24**, 481.
[28] SIDMAN, J. W., *J. Amer. Chem. Soc.*, 1957, **79**, 2669, 2674.
[29] MASON, J., *J. Chem. Soc.*, 1959, 1288.
[30] BRINTON, R. K. and VOLMAN, D. H., *J. Chem. Phys.*, 1951, **19**, 1394.
[31] BLADON, P., HENBEST, H. B. and WOOD, G. W., *J. Chem. Soc.*, 1952, 2737.
[32] HALSALL, T. G., *Chem. and Ind. (London)*, 1951, 867.
[33] LEDERER, E., *J. Chim. Phys.* 1954, **51**, D119.
[34] DEV, S., *Tetrahedron*, 1960, **8**, 171.
[35] COOKSON, R. C. and DANDEGAONKER, S. H., *J. Chem. Soc.*, 1955, 352.
[36] BAUMGARTNER, G. and TAMM, C., *Helv. chim. Acta*, 1955, **38**, 441.
[37] DORFMAN, L., *Chem. Revs.*, 1953, **53**, 71.
[38] BARTON, D. H. R., LEWIS, D. A. and McGHIE, J. F., *J. Chem. Soc.*, 1957, 2907.
[39] BIRD, C. W., COOKSON, R. C. and DANDEGAONKER, S. H., *J. Chem. Soc.*, 1956, 3675.
[40] COOKSON, R. C. and co-workers, *J. Chem. Soc.*, 1956, 2302;1961, 1224; *Chem. & Ind. (London)*, 1961, 589.
[41] MASON, S. F., *Quart. Revs. (London)*, 1961, **15**, 287.
[42] KIMURA, K. and NAGAKURA, S., *Spectrochim. Acta*, 1961, **17**, 166.
[43] BALASUBRAMANIAN, A., *Indian J. Chem.*, 1963, **1**, 329.
[44] KOCH, H. P., *J. Chem. Soc.*, 1949, 387, 394.
[45] SICE, J., *J. Phys. Chem.*, 1960, **64**, 1573.
[46] BALASUBRAMANIAN, A., *Indian J. Chem.*, 1963, **1**, 415.

[47] STEVENSON, D. P., COPPINGER, G. M. and FORBES, J. W., *J. Amer. Chem. Soc.*, 1961, **83**, 4350.

[48] LABHART, H. and WAGNIERE, G., *Helv. chim. Acta*, 1959, **42**, 2219.

[49] LEONARD, N. J. and OWENS, F. H., *J. Amer. Chem. Soc.*, 1958, **80**, 6039.

[50] KOSOWER, E. M., CLOSSON, W. D., GOERING, H. L. and GROSS, J. C., *J. Amer. Chem. Soc.*, 1961, **83**, 2013.

[51] CRAM, D. J. and STEINBERG, H., *J. Amer. Chem. Soc.*, 1954, **76**, 2753.

[52] LEONARD, N. J. and OKI, M., *J. Amer. Chem. Soc.*, 1955, **77**, 6241.

[53] FABIAN, J. and MAYER, R., *Spectrochim. Acta*, 1964, **20**, 299.

[54] CLOSSON, W. D. and GRAY, H. B., *J. Amer. Chem. Soc.*, 1963, **85**, 290.

[55] LIEBER, E. and THOMAS, A. E., *Appl. Spec.*, 1961, **15**, 144.

[56] JANSSEN, M. J., BALASUBRAMANIAN, A. and RAO, C. N. R., *J. Sci. Indstr.* (*India*), 1961, **20B**, 349.

[57] STRICKLER, S. J. and KASHA, M., *J. Amer. Chem. Soc.* 1963, **85**, 2899.

[58] LAYNE, W. S., JAFFE, H. H. and ZIMMER, H., *J. Amer. Chem. Soc.*, 1963, **85**, 435, 1816.

Chapter 4

CONJUGATED MOLECULES

THE electronic spectrum of a compound containing two ethylenic linkages which are separated from each other by several methylene groups will not be different from the spectrum of a molecule with only one isolated ethylenic linkage. This is because methylene groups *insulate* the two ethylenic linkages. If the two ethylenic linkages are on adjacent pairs of carbon atoms, as in the case of 1:3-butadiene, CH_2=CH—CH=CH_2, the spectrum is shifted to longer wavelengths due to *conjugation*. In general, two chromophores or two multiple bonds in conjugation almost always give rise to intense bands ($\epsilon \sim$ 20,000) around 220 mμ due to the $\pi \to \pi^*$ transition (K-band). (see *Figure 4.1*).

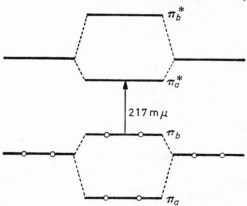

Figure 4.1. Energy levels of butadiene

In some of the linearly conjugated carbonyl molecules, the $\pi \to \pi^*$ band is not found above 210 mμ, but a low intensity ($\epsilon < 100$) $n \to \pi^*$ band (R-band) is observed at fairly long wavelengths (*Table 4.1*). If three chromophores or multiple bonds are linearly conjugated, both the $\pi \to \pi^*$ and the $n \to \pi^*$ bands are shifted to much longer wavelengths. In the case of the elongated open chain conjugated systems, the $\pi \to \pi^*$ bands are progressively displaced to longer wavelengths. The extinction coefficient also increases progressively. The absorption data of a few typical conjugated molecules[1] have been given in *Table 4.1*. We shall now discuss the spectra of different types of conjugated molecules.

Dienes

Simple derivatives of 1:3-butadiene generally exhibit a high intensity ($\epsilon \sim$ 20,000) band between 217 and 230 mμ. Cyclic dienes absorb at much longer wavelengths (230–280 mμ) than linear dienes, but the intensity is lower in the former case. Among the simple cyclic dienes, cyclohexa-1:3-diene exhibits the $\pi \to \pi^*$ band at the longest wavelength with maximum intensity.

In the case of semicyclic dienes where one of the ethylenic linkages forms part of a ring and the other is exocyclic, the absorption bands are found at lower wavelengths (around 235 mμ) than cyclic dienes. The absorption spectra of cyclic dienes have been thoroughly studied in the steroid and

Table 4.1. Absorption Spectra of Different Types of Conjugated Molecules

Compound	Chromophoric system	$\pi \to \pi^*$ band		$n \to \pi^*$ band	
		λ_{max}, mμ	ϵ_{max}	λ_{max}, mμ	ϵ_{max}
1:3-Butadiene	C=C—C=C	217	21,000	—	—
Vinylacetylene	C=C—C≡C	219	6,500	—	—
Crotonaldehyde	C=C—C=O	217	16,000	321	20
Biacetyl	O=C—C=O	—	—	435	18
Butylcrotonaldimine	C=C—C=N	220	23,000	—	—
1-Nitropropene	C=C—NO$_2$	229	9,500	—	—
Hexatriene	C=C—C=C—C=C	258	35,000	—	—
Octa-3,7-dien-5-yn-2ol	C=C—C=C—C=C	257	17,000	—	—
Sorbaldehyde	C=C—C=C—C=O	263	27,000	—	—
5-Nitro-2,4-pentadiene	C=C—C=C—C—NO$_2$	298	12,500	—	—

triterpenoid families and the data have been used most fruitfully for structural elucidation[2]. In general, the steroid and triterpenoid dienes containing the two ethylenic linkages in the same ring (usually in ring B) absorb at much longer wavelengths (around 260–283 mμ) than simple cyclic dienes. If the conjugation is distributed over more than one ring, the absorption band is found at lower wavelengths (235–248 mμ). The extinction coefficient of the band is considerably lower in homoannular dienes. This is because the homoannular dienes are necessarily in the *cis* form while the heteroannular dienes

Table 4.2. Ultra-violet Absorption Spectra of Dienes[3,4]

Type	Compound	λ_{max}, mμ	ϵ_{max}
Linear dienes	1:3-Butadiene	217	21,000
	Isoprene	220	23,000
	2:4-Hexadiene	227	23,000
Semicyclic dienes	β-Phellandrene	231	9,100
	Cyclohex-1-enylethylene	230	8,500
	Menthadiene	235	10,700
Cyclic dienes	Cyclopentadiene	238	3,400
	Cyclohexa-1:3-diene	256	8,000
	Cyclohepta-1:3-diene	248	7,500
Polycyclic dienes	L-Pimeric acid	273	7,100
	Ergosterol	280	13,500
	7-Dehydrocholesterol	280	11,400
	7-Dehydrholestene	280	12,700
	Cholesta-3:5-diene	235	23,000
	Cholestadienol-C	248	17,800
	Ergosterol-D	242	21,400
	Abietic acid	238	16,100

are in the *trans*-form[39]. The heteroannular and acyclic dienes indeed exhibit extinctions of the order of 12,000–25,000. (See Chapter 7 for a discussion cis–trans isomerism). The data on some typical dienes have been summarized in *Table 4.2*. The absorption spectra of conjugated dienes have been categorized by Booker, Evans and Gillam[3] (*Table 4.3*).

Woodward[4] analysed the data on the absorption spectra of dienes and found that alkyl substituents and exocyclic double bonds cause regular bathochromic wavelength displacements. By taking 1:3-butadiene as the reference (λ_{max} at 217 mμ), Woodward found that each alkyl substituent

Table 4.3. Absorption Spectra of Dienes[3]

	λ_{max} range in mμ
1. Acyclic dienes:	
(a) only acyclic substituents	217–228
(b) one cyclic substituent	235·5–236·5
(c) two cyclic substituents	246–248
2. Semicyclic dienes	230–242
3. Cyclohexadienes	256–265
4. Bicyclic dienes:	
two double bonds in different rings	236
5. Polycyclic dienes:	
(a) double bonds in the same ring	260–282
(b) double bonds in different rings	235–248

and each exocyclic double bond caused a bathochromic displacement of 5 mμ in substituted symmetrical and unsymmetrical dienes. This empirical rule, often known as Woodward's Rule, has been of value in the elucidation of organic structures. The validity of Woodward's rule is given in *Table 4.4* and *Chart 4.1*. Calculation of ultra-violet absorption maxima of steroid dienes[40] is shown in *Table 4.5*.

Chart 4.1. Calculations of Diene Absorption

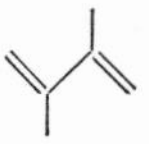

Reference = 217 mμ
Alkyl substituents = 5 × 2 = 10
calc. λ_{max} = 227 mμ (obs. 226 mμ)

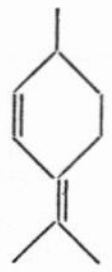

Reference = 217 mμ
Substituents = 20
exo. C=C = 5
calc. λ_{max} = 242 mμ (obs. 243 mμ)

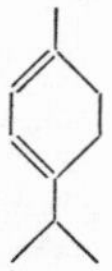

Reference = 253 mμ
Substituents = 15
calc. λ_{max} = 268 mμ (obs. 265 mμ)

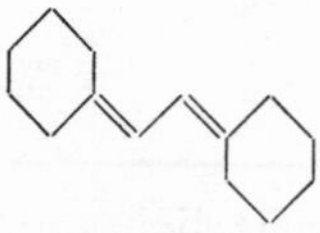

Reference = 217 mμ
Substituents = 20
exo. C=C = 10
calc. λ_{max} = 247 mμ (obs. 247 mμ)

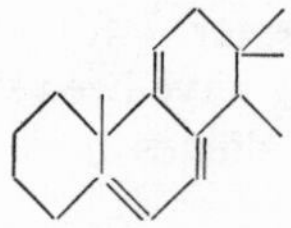

Reference = 253 mμ
Ring residues = 25
exo. C=C = 15
C=C external conj. = 30
calc. λ_{max} = 323 mμ (obs. 320 mμ)

Forbes and co-workers[64] have found that the ultra-violet absorption spectra of some conjugated dienes show deviations from Woodward's rules due to steric interactions as well as some special interactions occurring in the *cis*-conformation.

The absorption spectrum[42] of 1,2-dimethylenecyclohexane,

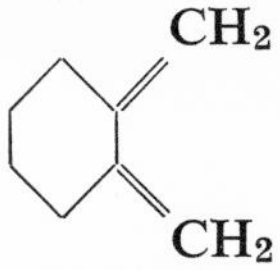

$$(\lambda_{max}220 \text{ m}\mu, \ \epsilon_{max}10,050)$$

Table 4.4. Validity of Woodward's Rule Related to the Absorption Spectra of Substituted Dienes[4]

Diene	No. of alkyl substituents	No. of exocyclic double bands	λ_{max}, mμ calculated	λ_{max}, mμ observed
1:3-Butadiene	0	0	—	217
2:3-Dimethylbutadiene	2	0	227	226
1:1'-Dicyclohexenyl	4	0	237	236
2'-Hydroxy-1:2-dicyclo-hexylidene ethane	4	2	247	248
Cholestadienol-B$_3$-acetate	4	2	247	246
Piperylene	1	0	222	223
Isoprene	1	0	222	220
Menthadiene	3	0	232	235
β-Phellandrene	2	1	232	232
Cholesta-3:5-diene	3	1	237	235
Testosterone enolacetate	4	1	242	240

Table 4.5. Calculation of Ultra-violet Absorption Maxima of Steroid Dienes[40]

	Hetereoannular dienes
Parent system	214 mμ
Increment for each	
alkyl substituent	5
exocyclic $>$C$=$	5
	λ_{max} = Total
	Homoannular dienes and polyenes
Parent homoannular diene system	253 mμ
Increment for each	
alkyl substituent	5
exocyclic $>$C$=$	5
C$=$C extending conjugation	30
	λ_{max} = Total

For ultra-violet absorption spectra of steroids, see DORFMAN, L., *Chem. Revs.* 1953, **53**, 47

The shifts caused by other auxochromic substituents are given below:

N (alkyl)$_2$	60 mμ
O (alkyl)	6
S (alkyl)	30
O Ac	0

cannot be accounted for by any of the rules. This may possibly be due to the non-planarity of the two double bonds. The 3,6-dimethyl derivative[43] shows further decrease in wavelength ($\lambda_{max} < 220$ mμ). The 1,2-dimethylenecyclopentane, on the other hand, shows the absorption maximum at 243 mμ which is nearly the same as the expected value ($217 + 2 \times 5 + 2 \times 5 + 5$ for 5-membered rings), if the contribution from the 5-membered ring is assumed to be 5 mμ. In bicyclo (3·1·1) heptyl system an increment of 15 mμ is to be added to get agreement with Woodward's rule. This may be due to the rigidity of the bicyclo system which raises the energy of the ground state[44]. In 2,3-dimethylene derivatives of (2·2·1) and (2·2·2) bicyclo systems, the increment of 15 mμ is much too large to give agreement with Woodward's rule[45].

Enynes and Diynes

When an acetylenic linkage is conjugated with an ethylenic linkage a fairly intense band is observed in the 219–230 mμ region. The intensity of this enyne band is generally less than that of the corresponding diene. Further, enynes show an inflection (around 230 mμ) to the long wavelength side of the peak. The simplest enyne is vinylacetylene which exhibits a band at 219 mμ ($\epsilon \sim 6{,}500$) compared to butadiene which shows absorption at 217 mμ ($\epsilon \sim 21{,}000$). Data on a number of enyne alcohols have been reported[5].

There have been some data[6] available on the absorption of molecules with two acetylenic linkages in conjugation (diyne). Diynes show at least three well-defined maxima around 230 mμ ($\epsilon \sim 350$), 240 mμ ($\epsilon \sim 400$) and 250 mμ ($\epsilon \sim 220$). Substitution seems to affect these bands to an appreciable extent. Data on some diynes ($RC{\equiv}C{-}C{\equiv}CR$) are shown below[41]:

R	λ_{max}, mμ*	ϵ_{max}
H	235	270
C_2H_5	239	340
$ClCH_2CH_2$	241	490
CH_3OCH_2	244	440
$(CH_3)_2NCH_2$	244	1,600
$ClCH_2$	253	2,100
ICH_2	280	7,400
C_6H_5	306	31,000

* Data on the most intense band with vibrational structure.

αβ-Unsaturated Carbonyl Compounds

It was mentioned in the preceding chapter that an isolated ethylenic linkage gives a high intensity ($\epsilon \sim 10{,}000$) $\pi \to \pi^*$ band near 190 mμ and that an isolated carbonyl group gives a low intensity ($\epsilon < 100$) $n \to \pi^*$ band (R-band) near 275 mμ. However, when a carbonyl group is conjugated with an ethylenic linkage as in an αβ-unsaturated carbonyl compound, both the bands undergo bathochromic shifts to the regions 220–260 mμ and 310–330 mμ respectively (*Figures 2.3 and 3.2*). αβ-unsaturated carbonyl derivatives are now readily distinguished by the presence of a high intensity $\pi \to \pi^*$ band ($\epsilon \sim 10{,}000$) between 220 and 260 mμ and a low intensity $n \to \pi^*$ band ($\epsilon < 100$) around 320 mμ. The $\pi \to \pi^*$ band has charge-transfer character as evidenced by substituent and solvent effects. Thus, a positively charged or an electronegative substituent on the adjacent β-carbon or transannular to the carbonyl group, causes a blue-shift of the $\pi \rightarrow \pi^*$ transition and a red-shift of the $n \rightarrow \pi^*$ transition. The intensity of the $n \rightarrow \pi^*$ band in these compounds is dependent on the intensity of the $\pi \rightarrow \pi^*$ transition. Mixing is generally possible between the two transitions and it increases the intensity of the $n \rightarrow \pi^*$ transition. The two bands are affected differently by solvents, the $\pi \rightarrow \pi^*$ band of the ethylenic linkage showing red-shifts in polar solvents and the $n \rightarrow \pi^*$ band of the carbonyl group showing blue-shifts in polar solvents. A typical example of solvent effects was given for mesityl oxide in Chapter 2.

Substituents markedly affect the position of the $\pi \rightarrow \pi^*$ bands (K-bands) in $\alpha\beta$-unsaturated carbonyl derivatives. Woodward[4] has studied the effect of alkyl substituents on $\alpha\beta$-unsaturated ketones in detail and has shown that

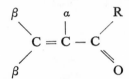

the absorption maxima for the different types of substituted $\alpha\beta$-unsaturated ketones may be generally predicted with fair certainty. It is possible to substitute an $\alpha\beta$-unsaturated ketone by alkyl or perhydroaromatic groups in five ways: monosubstituted, α or β; disubstituted, $\alpha\beta$ or $\beta\beta$, and trisubstituted, $\alpha\beta\beta$. The $\pi \rightarrow \pi^*$ band exhibits progressive bathochromic displacements with increase in substitution. In addition to the substituent effect, there is also a structural effect depending on whether the ethylenic linkage is exocyclic or not. Woodward's generalizations are given in *Table 4.6*. These empirical generalizations have been verified and tested extensively[7] (*Table 4.7*) and they have been very useful for identification of the $\alpha\beta$-unsaturated ketones and for the prediction of the number of alkyl substituents in a system.

Table 4.6. Generalizations Regarding the Spectra of $\alpha\beta$-unsaturated Aldehydes and Ketones

Ketones[4]	Mean λ_{max} in ethanol, mμ
Unsubstituted	215 ± 5
Monosubstituted (α or β) (no exocyclic ethylenic linkage)	225 ± 5
Disubstituted ($\alpha\beta$ or $\beta\beta$))	
(no exocyclic ethylenic linkage)	235 ± 5
(one exocyclic ethylenic linkage)	240 ± 5
Trisubstituted, $\alpha\beta\beta$	
(no exocyclic ethylenic linkage)	247 ± 5
(one exocyclic ethylenic linkage)	252 ± 5
Aldehydes[7]	
Monosubstituted (α or β)	220 ± 5
Disubstituted ($\alpha\beta$ or $\beta\beta$)	230 ± 5
Trisubstituted ($\alpha\beta\beta$)	242 ± 5

Evans and Gillam[7] have proposed empirical generalizations for the substituent effects on the $\pi \rightarrow \pi^*$ bands of $\alpha\beta$-unsaturated aldehydes (*Table 4.6*). Data on the absorption spectra of a few $\alpha\beta$-unsaturated aldehydes are summarized in *Table 4.7* and *Chart 4.2*. The $n \to \pi^*$ bands of the carbonyl group in $\alpha\beta$-unsaturated aldehydes and ketones are also affected by alkyl substituents. In general, the bands are shifted to lower wavelengths by alkyl substitution[46]. The empirical generalizations for ketones and aldehydes can only give very approximate positions of the λ_{max} and are not as accurate as Woodward's rule for dienes. There are some limitations and exceptions to these empirical generalizations. Evans and Gillam[7] have pointed out that small positional effects are also operative in the spectra of substituted $\alpha\beta$-unsaturated ketones. Substitution by methyl groups on the β-carbon apparently produces a larger bathochromic shift of the $\pi \to \pi^*$ band than substitution on the α-carbon. Gillam and West[8] have observed that five-membered ring compounds with both the ethylenic linkage and the carbonyl group in the ring, absorb at lower wavelengths than predicted by Woodward's rule[34-36]. For

Chart 4.2. Calculations of Enone Absorption

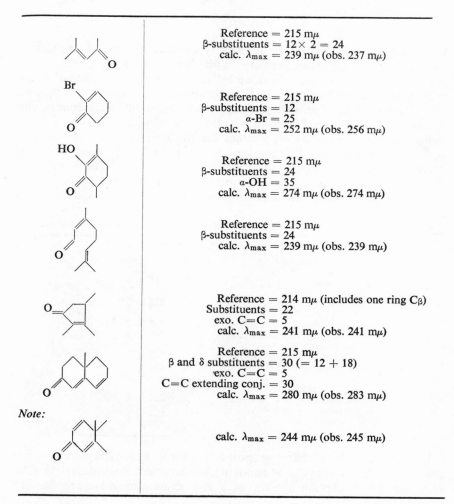

Reference = 215 mμ
β-substituents = 12 $\times$ 2 = 24
calc. λ_{max} = 239 mμ (obs. 237 mμ)

Reference = 215 mμ
β-substituents = 12
α-Br = 25
calc. λ_{max} = 252 mμ (obs. 256 mμ)

Reference = 215 mμ
β-substituents = 24
α-OH = 35
calc. λ_{max} = 274 mμ (obs. 274 mμ)

Reference = 215 mμ
β-substituents = 24
calc. λ_{max} = 239 mμ (obs. 239 mμ)

Reference = 214 mμ (includes one ring Cβ)
Substituents = 22
exo. C=C = 5
calc. λ_{max} = 241 mμ (obs. 241 mμ)

Reference = 215 mμ
β and δ substituents = 30 (= 12 + 18)
exo. C=C = 5
C=C extending conj. = 30
calc. λ_{max} = 280 mμ (obs. 283 mμ)

Note:

calc. λ_{max} = 244 mμ (obs. 245 mμ)

example, *iso*-thujone, dihydrojasmone and tetrahydropyrethrolone exhibit the $\pi \to \pi^*$ bands at 238 mμ, 237 mμ and 232 mμ respectively while Woodward's rule predicts the absorption maxima at 247 mμ for these compounds. In general, it seems to be necessary to add an increment to the observed wavelength to get agreement with the Woodward's rule in the case of $\alpha\beta$-unsaturated cyclopentanones. By assigning a base value of 214 mμ to the cyclopentenone chromophore (which includes the effect of the ring residue at C_β), good correlations can be obtained

(See *Chart 4.2* for an illustration.)

Schubert and Sweeney[9] have studied the effect of ring size and ring strain on the $\pi \to \pi^*$ bands of $\alpha\beta$-unsaturated carbonyl derivatives.

In cyclic α,β-unsaturated ketones[46,47], equatorial substituents in γ-position produce bathochromic shifts of 2 to 5 mμ of the $n \to \pi^*$ absorption band while the axial substituents produce much larger shifts (7–20 mμ). Differences in $\pi \to \pi^*$ band positions are seen in the *cisoid* (*S-cis*) and *transoid* (*S-trans*) conformers of $\alpha\beta$-unsaturated ketones (see Chapter 8).

Table 4.7. *Absorption Spectra of αβ-unsaturated Ketones and Aldehydes[7]: Validity of the Generalizations*

Compound	Nature of substitution	$\pi \to \pi^*$ band (K-band)			$n \to \pi^*$ band (R-band)	
		λ_{max} calc., mμ	λ_{max} obs., mμ	ϵ_{max}	λ_{max}, mμ	ϵ_{max}
Methylvinyl-ketone	none	215	219	3,600	324	24
2-Ethylhex-1-en-3-one	mono	225	221	6,450	320	26
Methyl-*iso*-propenyl-ketone	mono	225	218	8,300	319	27
Ethylidene-acetone	mono	225	224	9,750	314	38
Irone	mono	225	228	11,400	308	100
Mesityloxide	di	235	235	14,000	314	60
Cedrone	di	235	240	9,350	326	27
2:3:4:5-Tetra-hydroaceto-phenone	di	235	234	9,650	305	44
3:4-Dimethyl-pent-3-en-2-one	tri	247	249	>4,000	—	—
Acraldehyde	none	—	<210	—	328	13
Crotonaldehyde	mono	220	217	15,650	321	19
Tiglinaldehyde	di	230	228	>5,000	290	11
2-Ethylhex-2-en-1-al	di	230	229	10,650	313	27
Citral	di	230	238	13,500	324	65
β-Cyclocitral	tri	242	245	8,300	328	43

If a hydroxyl group is substituted in the α or β position in an $\alpha\beta$-unsaturated ketone, the $\pi \to \pi^*$ band is shifted to longer wavelengths ($\sim$270 mμ). Acetylation of the hydroxy group brings down the λ_{max} to that of an alkyl substituted derivative. For example[10]:

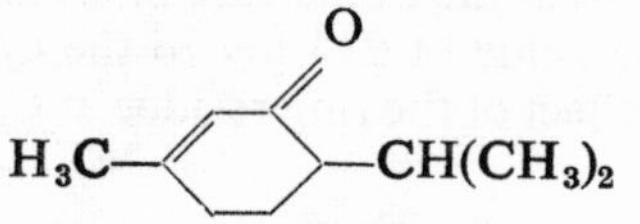

Piperitone
λ_{max} 235 mμ

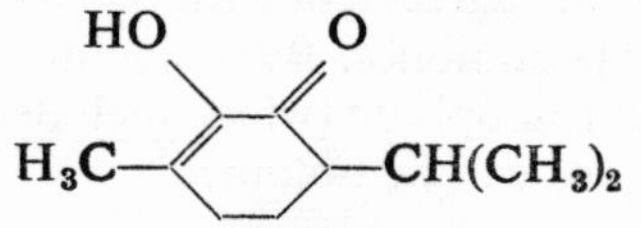

Diosphenol
274 mμ

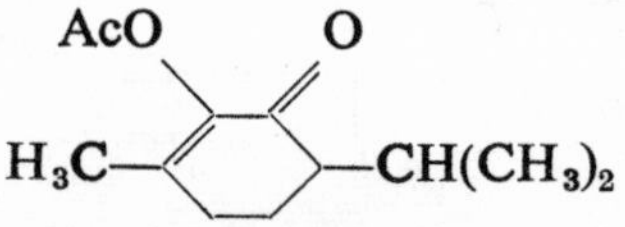

Diosphenolacetate
240 mμ

In *Table 4.8*, calculation of the ultra-violet absorption maxima of $\alpha\beta$-unsaturated enones and dienones of steroids[40] has been indicated. For acyclic dienones also these rules seem to be applicable.

Table 4.8. *Calculation of Absorption Maxima of Steroid Enones and Dienones*[40].

Parent enone	215 mμ
Increment for each substituent R, OCOCH$_3$, OCOC$_6$H$_5$, OR or Br	
α	10
β	12
γ	18
δ	18
Increment for an α—OH	35
Increment for exocyclic C=	5
Increment for C=C extending conjugation	30
Increment for C=O extending conjugation	0
	$\lambda_{max} =$ Total

* Measurements made in solvents other than methyl or ethyl alcohol should be corrected for by adding appropriate correction factors.

Nielsen[11] has correlated the ultra-violet absorption spectra and the structure of $\alpha\beta$-unsaturated acids and their derivatives. For alicyclic and acyclic types, each alkyl substituent at the olefinic double bond produces a bathochromic shift of 8–10 mμ. For alicyclic acids, an exocyclic double bond produces a bathochromic shift of 5 mμ. A 5 mμ shift is also produced by an endocyclic double bond in a five- or seven-membered ring. Other factors which shift the λ_{max} in these compounds have also been discussed. The correlations have been summarized below:

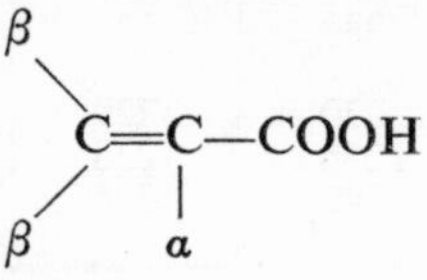

Parent chromophore + alkyl substituent:

α or β	208 mμ
$\alpha\beta$ or $\beta\beta$	217 mμ
$\alpha\beta\beta$	225 mμ

For each exocyclic C=C or C=C endocyclic to a 5- or 7-membered ring, add 5 mμ. Uncertainty in the above correlations is $\pm$ 5 mμ.

Derivatives of Carbonyl Compounds

Carbonyl compounds are usually characterized by the preparation of some of their derivatives. The more important derivatives are semicarbazones, thiosemicarbazones, oximes and 2:4 dinitrophenylhydrazones. The absorption spectra of these derivatives are appreciably different from those of the

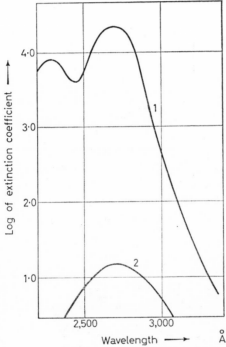

Figure 4.2. Absorption spectra of (2) methyl ethyl ketone and (1) its thiosemicarbazone.[7]

parent carbonyl compounds and may therefore be used for characterization and identification. The derivatives of $\alpha\beta$-unsaturated carbonyl compounds exhibit intense $\pi \rightarrow \pi^*$ bands (K-bands) which are highly characteristic of these systems and differ in position and intensity from the $\pi \rightarrow \pi^*$ bands exhibited by the derivatives of saturated carbonyl derivatives. The ultraviolet absorption spectra of methyl ethyl ketone and its thiosemicarbazone are compared[7] in *Figure 4.2*. In *Figure 4.3*, the absorption spectra of an $\alpha\beta$-unsaturated aldehyde, tiglinaldehyde, its semicarbazone and thiosemicarbazone are reproduced[7]. Approximate values of λ_{max} and ϵ_{max} for the various derivatives of saturated and $\alpha\beta$-unsaturated carbonyl compounds are summarized in *Table 4.9*.

45

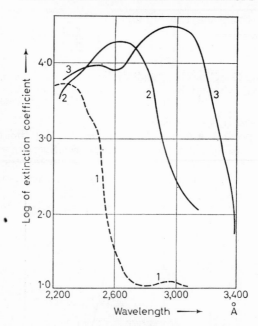

Figure 4.3. Absorption spectra of (1) tiglinaldehyde, (2) its semicarbazone and (3) thiosemicarbazone[7]

It may be seen from *Table 4.9* that the derivatives of $\alpha\beta$-unsaturated carbonyl compounds exhibit absorption bands at considerably longer wavelengths than the derivatives of simple saturated carbonyl derivatives.

Table 4.9. Absorption Spectra of Carbonyl Compounds and their Derivatives

| | Saturated | | $\alpha\beta$-Unsaturated | |
	λ_{max}, mμ	ϵ_{max}	λ_{max}, mμ	ϵ_{max}
Carbonyl compound	275	<100	220–260	10,000
			320	<100
Semicarbazone	225–230	11,000	265	25,000
Thiosemicarbazone	230	7,000	245	10,000
	280	20,000	300	30,000
Oxime	<220	—	235	15,000
2:4 Dinitrophenylhydrazone	360	20,000	380	25,000

Data on the ultra-violet absorption spectra of these derivatives have been compiled by Gillam and Stern[10]. In addition to giving confirmatory evidence for the presence of an isolated or conjugated carbonyl group in a molecule, the characteristic intense bands of these derivatives render it possible to observe the absorption bands with minute quantities of material. Oximes are not very useful for analytical or structural work since they absorb below 220 mμ in the case of saturated carbonyl compounds and absorb in the same region as the parent compound in the case of $\alpha\beta$-unsaturated carbonyl compounds. Thiosemicarbazones are probably best because there is least interference in the 300 mμ region and the position of the absorption maximum is nearly constant and does not vary with alkyl substitution. Also the band is very intense and small quantities of material may be examined. Dinitrophenylhydrazones are equally good although the position of the absorption maximum varies slightly with alkyl substitution.

Dicarbonyl Compounds

Glyoxal, $(HCO)_2$, and biacetyl, $(CH_3CO)_2$, exhibit only weak $n \rightarrow \pi^*$ bands around 450 mμ ($\epsilon \sim 20$). The bands show fine structure in non-polar solvents. Polar solvents shift the bands to lower wavelengths and diminish the structural character.

The $n \rightarrow \pi^*$ transition intensity is not much affected by conjugation of a carbonyl group with another carbonyl group. The $\pi \rightarrow \pi^*$ bands of α-diketones are generally found around 175 mμ compared to 230 mμ in $\alpha\beta$-unsaturated ketones. It happens that there is little mixing of the $n \rightarrow \pi^*$ and $\pi \rightarrow \pi^*$ transitions in α-diketones. In α-diketones, there are two lone-pair molecular orbitals and two π^* orbitals, formed by the antisymmetric and symmetric combinations of the n and π^* orbitals of each carbonyl group. There will be two $n \rightarrow \pi^*$ transitions in these compounds, of which the one between the symmetric states will strongly depend on the angle of twist about the intercarbonyl bond. Leonard and co-workers[12] have studied the spectra of some diaryl ketones and of a series of cyclic α-diketones

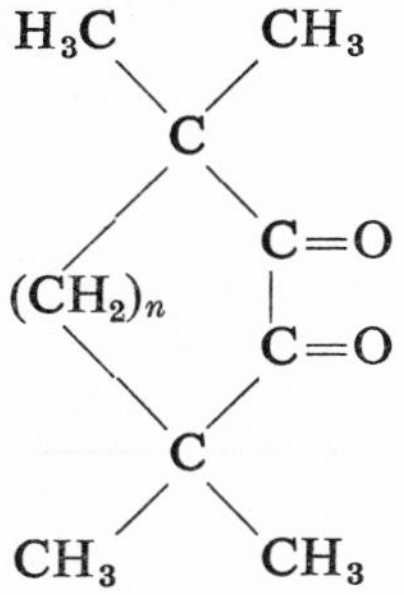

$$n = 1, 2, 3, 4 \text{ and } 14$$

where the angle between the planes of the carbonyl groups depends upon the size of the ring. When $n = 1$, the spectrum will be that of a *cis* co-planar dicarbonyl grouping due to the rigid size of the five-membered ring. With increase in n, the angle between the carbonyl groups increases from $0°$ until the ring is large enough to accommodate the carbonyl groups at $180°$. When n is large, the two carbonyl groups will be *trans* and co-planar. In *Table 4.10*, the λ_{max} and the estimated angles are given for several diketones[12]. These studies of Leonard and co-workers clearly illustrate the effect of co-planarity on resonance or p-orbital overlap between two conjugated double bonds. Resonance is greatest when the two carbonyl groups are co-planar (angle of 0 degrees and 180 degrees) and least when perpendicular to each other (also see Chapter 8).

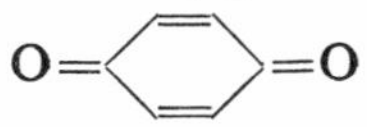

p-Benzoquinone, which may be considered as an $\alpha\beta$-unsaturated ketone, exhibits a high intensity band at 245 mμ possibly due to the $\pi \rightarrow \pi^*$ transition of the benzene system and a weak intensity band at 435 mμ due to the $n \to \pi^*$ transition of the carbonyl group[13]. It is the latter transition that is responsible for the colour of p-benzoquinone.

In cyclic α-diketones enolization is often encountered and the ultra-violet absorption will be similar to that of α,β-unsaturated ketones

Table 4.10. Intercarbonyl Angles and Absorption Maxima of Some Diketones*

Compound	Angle	λ_{max}, mμ	λ_{max}, mμ
Camphorquinone	0–10°	466 (31)	280 (23)
3,3,6,6-Tetramethyl- cyclohexadione-1,2	0–60°	380 (11)	298 (29)
3,3,7,7-Tetramethyl- cycloheptadione-1,2	90–110°	337 (34)	299 (35)
3,3,8,8-Tetramethyl- cyclooctadione-1,2	100–140°	343 (21)	296 (43)
2,2,5,5-Tetramethyl- hexadione-3,4	90–180°	365 (21)	285 (51)
3,3,18,18-Tetramethyl- cyclooctadecanedione-1,2	100–180°	384 (22)	237 (59)
Benzil	90°	370 (75)	—
Isoduryl phenyl diketone	90–180°	402	—
Isoduril	180°	490	—

* Values in parentheses are the ϵ_{max} values.

$\alpha\beta$-Unsaturated Compounds with Nitro and C=N groups

Simple compounds containing $\alpha\beta$-unsaturated nitro and C=N groups have been studied by Braude and co-workers[14,15]. Nitro olefins[14] show high intensity $\pi \to \pi^*$ bands (K-bands) in the region 220–250 mμ. The $n \to \pi^*$ bands of the nitro group in nitro olefins seem to get completely masked by the intense $\pi \to \pi^*$ bands.

Aliphatic compounds containing the $\alpha\beta$-unsaturated C=N group[15] exhibit high intensity absorption bands in the 205–220 mμ region, while the phenyl derivatives absorb in the 300–325 mμ region.

Conjugated Polyenes and Related Compounds

In connection with their studies on carotenoid pigments, Kuhn and Winterstein[16] found that the colour of diphenylpolyenes, Ph—(CH=CH)$_n$—Ph, deepened with increase in n. Extensive data on the electronic absorption spectra of several polyene systems were collected by Hausser, Kuhn and co-workers[17,19]. Conjugated polyene aldehydes and polyene acids were the first to be studied in detail. Absorption spectra of some conjugated polyene

Table 4.11. Absorption Spectra of Some Systems with Extended Conjugation

System	Solvent[a]	λ_{max}, mμ					$\epsilon_{max} \times 10^{-3}$				
	$n =$	1	2	3	4	6	1	2	3	4	6
$CH_3-(CH=CH)_n-COOH$[17]	A	204	254	294	327	—	11·7	24·8	36·5	48·7	—
$CH_3-(CH=CH)_n-CHO$[18]	A	220	271	315	353	393	14·8	24·5	37·1	40·7	64·6
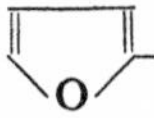 [furanyl]$-(CH=CH)_n-COOH$[19]	A	300	320	353	—	—	~21·7	~34·8	~39·1	—	—
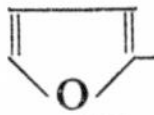 [furanyl]$-(CH=CH)_n-CHO$[18]	D	312	346	366	389	429	26·5	29·5	37·0	49·0	83·0
$Ph-(CH=CH)_n-Ph$[17]	B	306	334	358	384	420	24·4	40·0	75·0	86·0	114·0
$Ph-(CH=CH)_nCHO$[48]	A	285	323	355	382	425	25·0	43·0	54·0	51·0	—
$Ph-(CH=CH)_nCOPh$[48]	A	305	342	373	400	430	25·0	39·0	46·0	60·0	—
$H-(CH=CH)_n-H$[49]	C, H	167	217	268	304	364(b)	~10	21	34·6	—	138
$CH_3-(C\equiv C)_n-CH_3$[26]	A	178	—	207	234	284(c)	107	—	135	281	445

(a) A, Alcohol; B, Benzene; C, Cyclohexane; D, Dioxane; H, Hexane.
(b) $n = 10$, $\lambda_{max} = 447$ mμ.
(c) The low-intensity long-wavelength bands vary from 222 to 340 mμ (n 1 to 6) and ϵ_{max} varies from 160 to 1,000.

49

acids[19] have been reproduced in *Figure 4.4*. Data on some of the polyene systems have been collected in *Table 4.11*.

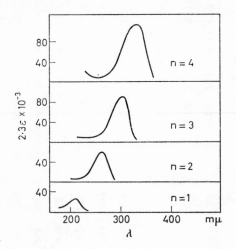

Figure 4.4. Absorption spectra of conjugated polyene acids[19], $CH_3(CH = CH)_n COOH$

Kuhn and Grundmann[20] have made empirical generalizations regarding the effects of substituents and other additional chromophores on the position of the absorption maxima of carotenoid systems. According to them, a terminal carboxylic or ester group produces the same bathochromic shift as an additional ethylenic linkage (20 mμ in carotenes). A phenyl group produces a shift one and a half times that of an ethylenic linkage. A methyl group and an alicyclic ethylenic linkage produce shifts one quarter and one half of that of an ethylenic linkage. These generalizations have been found to be precise in several polyenes of the carotenoid family[20].

In all the polyenes of the type mentioned above and also in polyene-azines of the type

$$R—(CH=CH)_n—CH = N—N=CH—(CH=CH)_m—R,$$

there is bond alteration and the greater resonance contribution is from the dipolar structures such as

$$R—\overset{\pm}{C}H—(CH=CH)_n—\overset{\pm}{C}H—R$$
$$R—\overset{+}{C}H—(CH=CH)_n—\overset{-}{N}—N=CH—(CH=CH)_m—R$$
$$R—\overset{-}{C}H—(CH=CH)_n—N=\overset{+}{N}=CH—(CH=CH)_m—R$$

The excited states are more stabilized by the dipolar structures than the ground states in these molecules and the difference between the energies of the excited and the ground states decreases (λ_{max} increases) with increase in

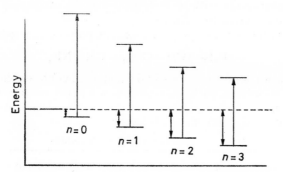

Figure 4.5. Ground and excited state energy levels in α,ω-diphenylpolyenes (From A. Maccol[50] by courtesy of The Chemical Society)

such resonance interaction (increase in n). (*Figure 4.5*). For such polyene systems, Lewis and Calvin[21] and Ferguson[20] have shown that the square of the λ_{max} varies linearly with the number of conjugated ethylenic bonds, n (*Figure 4.6*).

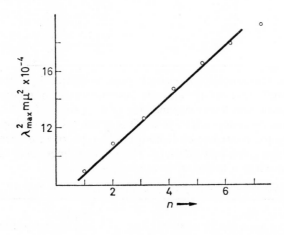

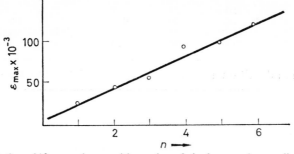

Figure 4.6. Relation of λ^2_{max} and ε_{max} with number of vinyl groups in α,ω-diphenylpolyenes

Braude[23] has proposed a general linear relation between the λ_{max} and the length of the conjugated chromophore. The molar extinction coefficient also seems

51

C

to vary proportionally with n[17,23] (*Figure 4.6*). In carotenoid pigments, the λ_{max} tends to converge to a limit[51].

There is another class of polyenes, such as polyene-azomethines

$$R_2N\text{---}(CH\text{=}CH)_n\text{---}CH\text{=}\overset{+}{N}R_2$$

where there is no bond alternation and resonance mainly stabilizes the ground states of the molecules. Such molecules show a linear relation of λ_{max} with n. Typical examples of such polyenes are the cyanine dyes[24]. Absorption data on a few of these dyes are shown below[52]:

$$Me_2^+N\text{=}CH(CH\text{=}CH)_nNMe_2$$

n	λ_{max}	$\varepsilon_{max}\times10^{-2}$	n	λ_{max}	$\varepsilon_{max}\times10^{-2}$
0	224	145	1	313	645
				228	10
2	416	1195	3	519	2070
	254	22		309	28
	229	26		267	28
				235	24
4	625	2950	6	848	2200
	364	48		470	129
	305	47		437	78
	242	48		385	102
	228	49		317	88
				302	87
				272	98

In these days, the longest wavelength peak is shifted by about 100 $m\mu$ for each additional vinyl group, and the increments are non-convergent.[24]

Polyphenyls show non-linear dependence of λ_{max} on n. The λ_{max} of *meta*-polyphenyls is nearly independent of n. This is because in *meta*-polyphenyls there is no resonance contribution from quinoid type of structures. Data on polyphenyls[25,53] are given in *Table 4.12*. The intensity increment in the *meta*-series is constant while it increases in the *pona*-series.

Table 4.12. Absorption Spectra of Meta- *and* Para-*polyphenyls*, $H(C_6H_4)_nH$[25, 53]

n	Para-λ_{max}, $m\mu$	$\varepsilon \times 10^{-3}$	n	Meta-λ_{max}, $m\mu$	$\epsilon \times 10^{-3}$
2	252	18·3	2	252	18·3
3	280	25	3	252	44·0
4	300	39	9–14	253	184–283
5	310	63	15	254	309
6	318	56	16	255	320

Absorption data[41] on a few cyclic polyenes $[(CH\text{=}CH)_n]$ are given below.

n	λ_{max}	ε_{max}
4	290	250
7	374; 314	5,700; 69,000
9	448; 408; 369	21,800; 7,500; 30,300
12	512; 363; 350	1,740; 201,000; 195,000
15	428; 329	144,000; 44,000

The data are difficult to interpret since there is no simple correspondence with linear polyenes or aromatics. It is interesting that $C_{18}H_{18}$ shows effects of bond alternation while $C_{30}H_{30}$ shows evidence of considerable bond fixation.

Polyacetylenes[26,27] exhibit a number of fine-structure bands (*Table 4.11*). Diacetylenes show medium intensity bands ($\epsilon \sim$ 100–350) in the 210–250 mμ region. Tri- and tetra- and higher acetylenes, however, exhibit very high intensity bands ($\epsilon >$ 100,000) at lower wavelengths (200–280 mμ) in addition to the medium intensity bands (240–390 mμ). Absorption spectra of diphenyl- and dimethyl[26] polyacetylenes have been reported[27] (see references 37 and 38 for naturally occurring acetylenic compounds).

Classical vibration theory has been satisfactorily applied when interpreting the absorption spectra of polyenes. Kuhn[54] has derived the expression,

$$\lambda^2 = \lambda_0^2 / \{1 - a \cos [\pi s/(n + 1)]\}$$

where λ_0 is the wavelength of absorption of the individual olefinic unit in the polyene or of benzene in the polyphenyl, n is the number of conjugated units, a is a constant which depends on the strength of the coupling and s is the order of the harmonic of vibration. Similarly, the oscillator strength of a polyene has been given the expression,

$$f = 8nf_0/\pi^2 s^2$$

where f_0 is the oscillator strength of the individual unit. Kuhn's expression nicely accounts for the convergence of wavelengths found in polyenes and polyphenyls. There are also other expressions[55] of the form $\lambda^2 = A - BC^n$ where A, B and C are constants, which are quite satisfactory.

There have been a number of quantum mechanical treatments of the absorption spectra of polyenes. Platt[56] has reviewed the valence-bond approach to the problem. The free electron model has been most successful in explaining the spectra of all molecules with extended conjugation[57–59]. Kuhn[59] has derived the expression,

$$\nu = \nu_L(1 - 1/N) + h(N + 1)/8mL^2$$

where N is the number of π-electrons in the linear conjugated molecule, ν_L the frequency of the convergence limit of the series and L the length of the conjugated system. The length of the conjugated system can be set at one or two bond distances from the terminal conjugated atom and the above equation can be written in the form

$$\nu(\text{cm}^{-1}) = \nu_L + (3 \times 10^5/r^2 - \nu_L)/N'$$

where r is the average bond distance in Å and N' (which is nearly the same as N) is the effective number of π bonds. This equation is obeyed by both the cyanines and polyenes (including polyphenyls and polyacetylenes) and the frequencies of the first absorption bands show linear relation with $1/N'$. In polyenes the linear relation converges to a finite frequency while in cyanines

53

the relation converges to zero. Merocyanines also follow this equation if N' is taken as $(N - 2)$. The free electron model gives the expression

$$f = 0.0134(N + 1)/s^3$$

for the oscillator strength and the calculated oscillator strengths agree well with the observed values.

In addition to the main absorption bands, polyenes and cyanines also show a number of weaker bands at lower wavelengths due to transitions involving quantum number changes greater than one.

Insulation of Chromophores

Compounds with two insulated chromophores, i.e. chromophores separated by one or more methylene groups or *meta*-oriented about a benzene ring, exhibit absorption in the same region as an isolated chromophore. From *Table 4.12* it can be seen that *meta*-polyphenyls containing 14 benzene rings absorb at nearly the same wavelength as biphenyl.

Ramart-Lucas and co-workers[28] have studied the electronic absorption spectra of a series of compounds of the type X—$(CH_2)_n$—Y where X and Y are chromophoric groups and n varies from zero to about twelve. When n is zero, X and Y are conjugated. The types of compounds studied were

$$Ph(CH_2)_n\text{—Y, where Y} = COOH, C\equiv N, CH=CH_2, CHCH_3CHO,$$

$$COCH_3, CH(COOH)_2 \text{ and Ph}$$

$$Ph\text{—O—}(CH_2)_n\text{—Y, where Y} = COOH \text{ and OPh}$$

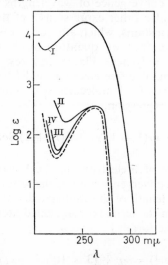

Figure 4.7. Absorption spectra of I, Ph Ph; II, PhCH$_2$Ph; III, Ph(CH$_2$)$_2$Ph; IV, Ph(CH$_2$)$_4$Ph; - - - - PhCH$_2$CH$_3$ in double concentration[28]

Spectra of three diphenyl derivatives of paraffins have been compared with those of biphenyl and ethylbenzene in *Figure 4.7*. The spectrum of Ph—$(CH_2)_n$—Ph when n is equal to two or greater, is nearly identical with the absorption of ethylbenzene, PhCH$_2$·CH$_3$, in double concentration. The two important generalizations resulting from the investigations of Ramart-Lucas are: (i) If two chromophores are not separated by methylene groups, the absorption maximum is shifted to longer wavelengths and the absorption intensity is increased, (ii) if more than one methylene group separate the two chromophores, the absorption spectrum is just a summation of the absorptions of the two chromophores. These generalizations are valid only when methylene groups separate the chromophores. If groups containing atoms like nitrogen, sulphur, etc. separate the chromophores, the absorption spectra of the systems change appreciably and the additivity rules will not hold good. This is because of the interaction of the unshared electrons on the hetero atoms.

Cumulated Systems

Systems containing chromophores directly next to one another are referred to as cumulated systems. The data on some simple cumulated systems are given below:

ethyl allene[29], $C{=}C{=}C$,	181, 188, 227	20,000, 4,000, 630
Diethyl ketene[30], $C{=}C{=}O$,	227, 375	360, 20
Diethyldicarbonamide[30], $N{=}C{=}N$,	230, 270	200, 25
Ketene[63], $x{=}C{=}O$,	220, 330	80, 12
Ethyl azide, $-\overset{-}{N}{-}\overset{+}{N}{\equiv}N$[32],	217, 287	150, 20*
Ethyl isothiocyanate, $N{=}C{=}S$[33],	249	2570
Carbon dioxide[60], $O{=}C{=}O$,	112, 133, 148	80,000, 600, 300
Carbon disulphide[61], $S{=}C{=}S$,	318	108
Butatriene[62], $C{=}C{=}C{=}C$,	240, 310	20,300, 250

* See discussion in Chapter 3

Compared to conjugated systems, the absorption intensity is very low in these compounds. Compounds containing extended cumulated systems exhibit high intensity absorption maxima at long wavelengths. The absorption spectra of tetraphenyl cumulenes and bisdiphenylenecumulenes have been studied by Kuhn and co-workers[31]. Just as in conjugated systems, here also the absorption band shifts towards longer wavelengths as the number of cumulated double bonds increases and converge to a unit. Butatriene[62], $H_2C{=}C{=}C{=}CH_2$, which has the same number of double bonds as 1,3,5-hexatriene shows considerably lower λ_{max}. The λ_{max} values for these two compounds are 240 (ϵ 29,300) and 256 mμ (ϵ 22,400) respectively.

REFERENCES

[1] BRAUDE, E. A., in *Determination of Organic Structures by Physical Methods*, Edited by Braude, E. A. and Nachod, F. C., Academic Press, New York, 1955, Chapter 4.

[2] FIESER, L. F. and FIESER, M., *Natural Products Related to Phenanthrene*, Reinhold, New York, 1949.

[3] BOOKER, H., EVANS, L. K. and GILLAM, A. E., *J. Chem. Soc.*, 1940, 1453.

[4] WOODWARD, R. B., *J. Amer. Chem. Soc.*, 1941, **63**, 1123; 1942, **64**, 72, 76.

[5] BRAUDE, E. A. and JONES, E. R. H., *J. Chem. Soc.*, 1946, 122 and the references listed there.

[6] ARMITAGE, J. *et al.*, *J. Chem. Soc.*, 1952, 1998, 2005.

[7] EVANS, L. K. and GILLAM, A. E., *J. Chem. Soc.*, 1941, 815; 1943, 565.

[8] GILLAM, A. E. and WEST, T. F., *J. Chem. Soc.*, 1941, 811; 1942, 483, 486.

[9] SCHUBERT, W. M. and SWEENEY, W. A., *J. Amer. Chem. Soc.*, 1955, **77**, 2297.

[10] GILLAM, A. E. and STERN, E. S., *Electronic Absorption Spectroscopy*, Edward Arnold, London, 1957.

[11] NIELSEN, A. T., *J. Org. Chem.*, 1957, **22**, 1539.

[12] LEONARD, N. J., *et al.*, *J. Amer. Chem. Soc.*, 1950, **72**, 484, 5388.

[13] BRAUDE, E. A., *J. Chem. Soc.*, 1945, 490.

[14] BRAUDE, E. A., JONES, E. R. H. and ROSE, G. G., *J. Chem. Soc.*, 1947, 1104.

[15] BARANY, H. C., BRAUDE, E. A. and PIANKA, M., *J. Chem. Soc.*, 1949, 1898.

[16] KUHN, R. and WINTERSTEIN, A., *Helv. Chim. Acta.*, 1928, **11**, 87, 116, 123, 144, 427; 1929, **12**, 493, 899

[17] HAUSSER, K. W., KHUN, R. and co-workers, *Z. phys. Chem.*, 1935, **B29**, 363, 371, 378, 384, 391, 417.

[18] BLOUT, E. R. and FIELDS, M., *J. Amer. Chem. Soc.*, 1948, **70**, 189.

[19] HAUSSER, K. W. and SMAKULA, A., *Angew. Chem.*, 1935, **47**, 657; 1935, **48**, 152.

[20] KUHN, R. and GRUNDMANN, C., *Ber. dtsch. chem. Ges.*, 1937, **70**, 1318; 1938, **71**, 442.

[21] LEWIS, G. N. and CALVIN, M., *Chem. Rev.*, 1939, **25**, 273.

[22] FERGUSON, L. N., *Chem. Rev.*, 1948, **43**, 408.

[23] BRAUDE, E. A., in *Chemistry of Carbon Compounds*, 1, Edited by Rodd, E. H., Elsevier, Amsterdam, 1951.

[24] BROOKER, L. G. S., *Rev. Mod. Phys.*, 1942, **14**, 275.

[25] GILLAM, A. E. and HEY, D. H., *J. Chem. Soc.*, 1939, 1170.

[26] COOK, C., JONES, E. H. R. and WHITING, M., *J. Chem. Soc.*, 1952, 2883 and the references listed there.

[27] BOHLMAN, F., *Angew. Chem.*, 1953, **65**, 385 and the references listed there.

[28] RAMART-LUCAS, *Bull. Soc. Chim.*, 1932, **51**, 289, 965.

[29] BURR, G. O. and MILLER, E. S., *Chem. Rev.*, 1941, **29**, 419.

[30] LARDY, G. C., *J. Chim. Phys.*, 1924, **21**, 353.

[31] KUHN, R. and ZAHN, H., *Chem. Ber.*, 1951, **84**, 566.

[32] LIEBER, E., RAO, C. N. R., CHAO, T. S. and WAHL, W. H., *J. Sci. Industr. Res. (India)*, 1957, **16B**, 95.

[33] RAO, C. N. R., RAMACHANDRAN, J. and SOMASEKHARA S., *Curr. Sci. (India)*, 1958, **27**, 474.

[34] FRANK, R. L., ARMSTRONG, R., KWIATEK, J. and PRICE, H. A., *J. Amer. Chem. Soc.*, 1948, **70**, 1379.

[35] FRENCH, H. S. and WILEY, L., *J. Amer. Chem. Soc.*, 1949, **71**, 3702.

[36] DEV, S., *J. Indian Chem. Soc.*, 1955, **32**, 259; 1957, **34**, 171.

[37] SÖRENSEN, N. A., *Proc. Chem. Soc.*, 1961, 98.

[38] BOHLMANN, F. and MANNHARDT, H. J., *Fortschr. Chem. org. Naturstoffe*, Ed. by ZECHMEISTER, L., Springer-Verlag, Vienna, 1957, **14**, 1.

[39] KOCH, H. D., *Chem. & Ind. (London)*, 1942, 273.

[40] FIESER, L. F., FIESER, M. and RAJAGOPALAN, S., *J. Org. Chem.*, 1948, **13**, 800.

[41] MASON, S. F., *Quart. Res. (London)*, 1961, **15**, 287.

[42] BAILEY, W. J. and LAWSON, W. B., *J. Amer. Chem. Soc.*, 1957, **79**, 1444.

[43] BAILEY, W. J. and HUDSON, R. L., *J. Amer. Chem. Soc.*, 1956, **78**, 2806.

[44] MOORE, R. N. and FISHER, G. S., *J. Amer. Chem. Soc.*, 1956 **78**, 4362.
[45] BAILEY, W. J. and co-workers, *J. Amer. Chem. Soc.*, 1955, **77**, 1606; 1953, **75**, 4780
[46] COOKSON, R. C. and DANDEGAONKER, S. H., *J. Chem. Soc.*, 1955, 1651.
[47] COOKSON, R. C. and co-workers, *J. Chem. Soc.*, 1955, 352; 1956, 3675.
[48] THOMAS, J. F. and BRANCH, G., *J. Amer. Chem. Soc.*, 1953, **75**, 4793.
[49] SONDHEIMER, F., BEN-EFRAIM, D. A. and WOLOVSKY, R. *J. Amer. Chem. Soc.*, 1961, **83**, 1675.
[50] MACCOLL. A., *Quart. Revs. (London)*, 1947, **1**, 16.
[51] KARRER, P. and EUGSTER, C. H., *Helv. chim. Acta*, 1951, **34**, 1805.
[52] MALHOTRA, S. S. and WHITING, M. C., *J. Chem. Soc.*, 1960, 3812.
[53] WENZEL, A., *J. Chem. Soc.*, 1953, **21**, 403.
[54] KUHN, R., *Helv. chim. Acta*, 1948, **31**, 1780.
[55] HIRAYAMA, K., *J. Amer. Chem. Soc.*, 1955, **77**, 373, 379, 383.
[56] PLATT, J. R., *J. Chem. Phys.*, 1956, **25**, 80.
[57] BAYLISS, N. S., *Quart. Revs.*, 1952, **6**, 319.
[58] SIMPSON, W. T., *J. Chem. Phys.*, 1948, **16**, 1124; 1949, **17**, 1218.
[59] KUHN, R., *Fortschr. Chem. org. Naturstoffe*, 1958, **16**, 169; 1959, **17**, 404.
[60] WATANABE, K., INN, E. C. Y. and ZELIKOFF, N., *J. Chem. Phys.*, 1953, **21**, 1648.
[61] DORAN, W. and GILLAM, A. E., *J. Soc. Chem. Ind.*, 1928, **47**, 259.
[62] SCHUBERT, W. M., LIDDICOET, T. H. and LAHKA. W. A., *J. Amer. Chem. Soc.*, 1952, **74**, 569.
[63] KNOX, K., NORRISH, R. G. W. and PORTER, G., *J. Chem. Soc.*, 1952, 1477.
[64] FORBES, W. F., SHILTON, R. and BALASUBRAMANIAN, A., *J. Org. Chem.*, 1964, **29**, 3527.

CHAPTER 5

AROMATIC MOLECULES

AROMATIC hydrocarbons show three main types of absorption bands which designated as the α, p and β bands by Clar[42], were based on the band intensities. The extinction coefficients, the α, p and β bands are of the order of 10^2, 10^4 and 10^5 respectively and the wavelengths are generally in the order $\alpha > p > \beta$. In some hydrocarbons α bands are not observed or the order is changed. In certain large aromatics, another intense band (β') is found at lower wavelengths next to the β band. A weak band (τ) due to triplet absorption is also found at longer wavelengths in aromatics. The α, β, p and τ bands of a few aromatic hydrocarbons are shown in *Table 5.1*. It is found that the α and β bands form a pair and the p and τ another pair. These pairs of bands show similar wavelength shifts with linear (acene series) or angular (phene series) annellation. In the phene series, the ratio of the β and α frequencies (ν_β/ν_α) and the ν_τ/ν_p are nearly constant (~ 1.35 and 0.6 respectively). In addition to these bands, weak R bands ($n \rightarrow \pi^*$) are seen in substituted aromatics containing chromophoric groups.

Table 5.1. Absorption Bands ($\lambda_{\max}$ mμ) of a few Aromatic Hydrocarbons[43]

Hydrocarbon	β	p	α	τ
Benzene	183	207	264	340
Naphthalene	221	289	315	470
Anthracene	255	379	—	670
Tetracene	274	471	—	976
Pentacene	310	576	428	1300
Phenanthrene	255	295	345	463
Chrysene	267	319	360	505
Picene	287	329	376	—
1,2-Benzanthracene	290	359	385	606
Coronene	305	342	410	515

Both the free-electron model[44] and the molecular orbital[45] approaches have been applied to the study of the absorption spectra of aromatic hydrocarbons. In the molecular orbital method the transition from the highest occupied level, ψ_m, to the next higher level, ψ_{m+1}, is considered to be responsible for the p-band. The degenerate transitions ψ_{m-1} to ψ_{m+1} and ψ_m to ψ_{m+2} are responsible for the forbidden α and allowed β bands respectively. The molecular orbital treatment clearly shows how the α and β bands arise from the same set of levels and explains the trends in these bands with linear and angular annellation. The τ and p bands show similar shifts with annellation since the τ band is the triplet corresponding to the singlet p-band. Unlike the free electron model which does not explain the spectra of peri-condensed aromatics, the molecular orbital method satisfactorily explains both the cata- (phenes and acenes) as well as peri-condensed aromatic hydrocarbons.

Benzene

Benzene exhibits two intense absorption bands at about 180 mμ ($\epsilon_{max} \sim$ 47,000) and 200 mμ ($\epsilon_{max} \sim 7000$) and a weak absorption band around 260 mμ ($\epsilon_{max} \sim 220$)[1]. All the three bands are associated with the π electron system of benzene. The two intense bands may be ascribed to transitions to dipolar excited states, while the weak 260 mμ band is ascribed as the forbidden transition to a homopolar excited state. Studies on crystalline hexamethylbenzene with polarized ultra-violet radiation have clearly indicated that the electric vectors associated with the three bands lie in the plane of the benzene ring[1-4]. Different nomenclatures have been used to describe the three bands of benzene (*Table 5.2*). We will not use any of these terminologies but denote the bands by their position, as the 180, 200 and 260 mμ bands.

Table 5.2. Nomenclature of Benzene Bands

180 mμ band	200 mμ band	260 mμ band	Ref.
$A_{1g} \rightarrow E_{1u}$	$A_{1g} \rightarrow B_{1u}$	$A_{1g} \rightarrow B_{2u}$	5
E_1	E_2	B	6
—	K	B	7
A	B	C	8, 9
Primary (second)	Primary (first)	Secondary	10
—	Principal	—	11
β	p	a	42

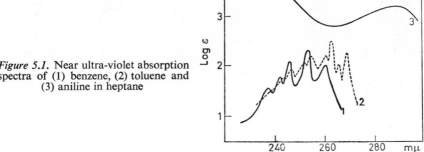

Figure 5.1. Near ultra-violet absorption spectra of (1) benzene, (2) toluene and (3) aniline in heptane

The low intensity a band centred around 260 mμ exhibits a completely resolved vibrational structure (*Figure 5.1*) and the mechanism of this absorption is explained in terms of the distortion of the benzene ring due to a bending vibration which allows the a-band to borrow intensity from the β-band. The well-defined absorption maxima of the 260 mμ band in solution spectra are as follows:

Solvent	Absorption maxima, $m\mu$
Heptane	234, 239, 244, 249, 255, 261, 269
Alcohol	— 238, 243, 248, 255, 261, 268

The 260 $m\mu$ band possessing the fine structure is often referred to as 'benzenoid absorption'.

Substituted Benzenes

All the three bands of benzene are affected markedly by substitution. The 200 $m\mu$ and 260 $m\mu$ bands in substituted benzenes are of greater interest since both of them occur in the wavelength range normally accessible with most spectrophotometers. With substitution, both the bands are shifted to longer wavelengths. Substitution is supposed to perturb the benzene ring both by resonance and inductive effects[10, 12-14]. A substituent with positive inductive effect lowers the ionization energy of the substituted benzene, while one with negative inductive effect increases it. The resonance effect lowers the ionization energy of the molecule. The variation in ionization energy is seen in terms of wavelength shifts. Both the resonance and the inductive effects intensify the bands. Resonance effects apparently cause greater changes in the spectra than inductive effects[10,13]. In *Table 5.3*, the 200 and 260 $m\mu$ bands of several monosubstituted benzene derivatives have been listed.

Table 5.3. Near Ultra-violet Absorption Spectra of Some Monosubstituted Benzene Derivatives[10,15] (RPh)

R	200 $m\mu$ band (K or E or primary band)		260 $m\mu$ band (B or secondary band)		Solvent
	λ_{max}, $m\mu$	ϵ_{max}	λ_{max}, $m\mu$	ϵ_{max}	
H	203·5	7,400	254	204	2% methanol in water
CH$_3$	206·5	7,000	261	225	,,
Cl	209·5	7,400	263·5	190	,,
Br	210	7,900	261	192	,,
OH	210·5	6,200	270	1,450	,,
OCH$_3$	217	6,400	269	1,480	,,
CN	224	13,000	271	1,000	,,
COOH	230	11,600	273	970	,,
NH$_2$	230	8,600	280	1,430	,,
NO$_2$	268·5	7,800	—	—	,,
CH=CH$_2$	244	12,000	282	450	Alcohol
C≡CH	236	12,500	278	650	Heptane
Ph	246	20,000	—	—	,,
COCH$_3$*	240	13,000	278	1,100	,,
N=NPh* (trans)	319	19,500	—	—	Chloroform

* In addition, these compounds exhibit weak bands (R-bands) due to $n \rightarrow \pi^*$ transitions of the chromophores at longer wavelengths: acetophenone at 320 $m\mu$ and azobenzene at 445 $m\mu$.

Matsen, Robertson and Chouke[16] have found that alkyl substitution intensifies and also shifts the 260 $m\mu$ band of benzene to longer wavelengths (*Figure 5.1*). Of all the alkyl groups, the methyl group causes the greatest intensification and wavelength shift. The effect decreases as the hydrogens of the methyl groups are replaced. This has been attributed to the predominant C—H hyperconjugation controlling the energy of absorption, since the 260 $m\mu$ band is affected mainly by the resonance effects of substituents, unlike the 200 $m\mu$ band which seems to be affected both by inductive and resonance effects.

Compound (a)	λ_{max}, $m\mu$, O—O band (b)
Benzene	262·5
Toluene	266·8
Ethylbenzene	266·4
iso-Propylbenzene	265·9
tert-Butylbenzene	265·5

(a) In vapour state.
(b) From vibrationless ground state to vibrationless excited state.

Several objections have been raised for this interpretation[17]. Unlike in the 260 $m\mu$ band, no definite trend has been found in the position of the 200 $m\mu$ bands in alkyl benzenes or p-alkyl substituted benzenes. In many cases, the observed wavelengths are actually found to be in the reverse order (i.e., in the inductive order) to that predicted by C—H hyperconjugation. At this point it may be stated that the evidence for hyperconjugation from the absorption spectra of alkyl substituted benzene derivatives is not definitive.

Substitution with unsaturated groups has a more profound effect on the absorption bands than with alkyl groups (e.g. styrene and phenylacetylene, see Table 5.3). The effect of the ethynyl group is less than that of a vinyl group. Cyclopropyl group shifts the 260 $m\mu$ band to 271 $m\mu$ and also intensifies it, thus lending evidence of its unsaturation properties[13].

Substitution of benzene with polar groups containing unshared electrons (auxochromes like OH or NH_2), shifts the absorption bands to longer wavelengths and also intensifies them. The spectra of phenol and aniline in heptane solution are reproduced in Figures 5.1 and 5.2. The vibrational structure of the 260 $m\mu$ band is not seen in the aniline spectrum. In general, the fine structure of the 260 $m\mu$ band disappears in polar solvents when the

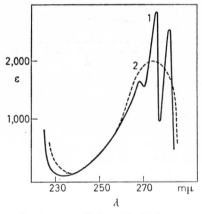

Figure 5.2. Absorption spectra of phenol in (1) heptane and (2) ethano

substituents are polar groups. In Figure 5.2, the absorption curves of phenol in heptane and alcohol are shown. The effect of auxochromes on the benzene bands is explained in terms of the interaction of the unshared electrons with the benzene nucleus. Braude calls this interaction $\pi - p$ conjugation[18]. Bowden and Braude[18] have studied the spectra of a number of benzene derivatives containing groups XR_n where X = C, Si, Sn, Pb, N, P, Sb, Bi,

61

Se, Te, F, Cl, Br and I, and R = H or alkyl groups, and have found that the spectra bear no simple relation to basicities, ionization potentials and other parameters. Recently, Rao and co-workers[19] studied the absorption spectra of several polyphenyl derivatives of the elements of groups IVb and Vb. In the case of the Vb elements, the spectra of derivatives in which the atoms possess and do not possess unshared p-electrons (i.e. derivatives of the atoms in their 'trivalent' and 'pentavalent' states respectively) have been studied. The unshared p-electrons on the central atoms of the triphenyl derivatives of the Vb elements interact strongly with the π-orbitals of the benzene rings and the vibrational structure of the 260 mμ band of benzene is completely absent.

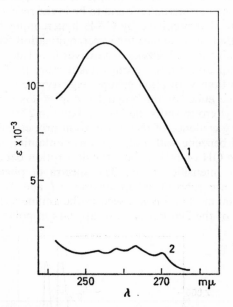

Figure 5.3. Absorption spectra of (1) Sb(Ph)$_3$ and (2) Sb(Ph)$_3$Cl$_2$ in ethanol[19]

When the central atoms do not possess unshared electrons as in the case of the derivatives of the IVb and the pentavalent Vb elements, the 260 mμ bands exhibit the vibrational structure similar to benzene. The absorption spectra of triphenylstibine and tetraphenylstiboniumdichloride are reproduced in *Figure 5.3.* The position of the 260 mμ band does not vary with the number of phenyl groups in the phenyl-substituted paraffins and the phenyl derivatives of the pentavalent Vb elements and the intensity seems to be directly proportional to the number of phenyl groups. In contrast to this behaviour, the phenyl derivatives of the trivalent Vb elements show progressive bathochromic shifts in the 260 mμ band with the increase in the number of phenyl groups. For example, aniline, diphenylamine and triphenylamine exhibit the bands at 280, 285 and 297 mμ respectively. Such a variation in a series of compounds is a measure of the resonance interaction of the phenyl groups with the central atom[13]. Evidence has also been presented for the expansion of valence shells in phosphorus and silicon derivatives[19].

When the substituent on the benzene nucleus is a chromophore like the carbonyl group, the absorption bands are shifted towards the red just as in the case of vinyl substituion. A weak band due to the $n \to \pi^*$ transition of the chromophore (R-band) is also observed at longer wavelengths (e.g. aceto-phenone, azobenzene, see *Table 5.3*). The $n \to \pi^*$ bands of carbonyl compounds are completely submerged by the 260 mμ benzene band if the spectra are

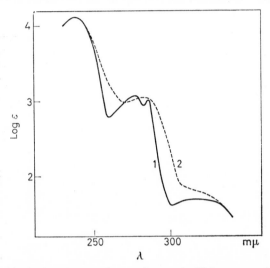

Figure 5.4. Absorption spectra of acetophenone in (1) heptane and (2) methanol

taken in polar solvents. The absorption curves of acetophenone in heptane and alcohol are given in *Figure 5.4*. Nitro group in nitrobenzene does not show the $n \to \pi^*$ band. It is probably marked by the stamp absorption due to the benzene nucleus occurring in the same region. The intense bands of nitro- and carbonyl-substituted benzene derivatives in the near ultra-violet region have been interpreted as due to intramolecular charge-transfer where the —NO$_2$ or C—O groups act as acceptor islands[46].

Correlations of Substituent Effects

The 260 mμ band is due to a forbidden transition and a change in the symmetry of the benzene molecule by substitution causes an increase in the intensity and a shift in the wavelength of absorption. Sklar[12] has treated the effect of substitution on the intensity of the 260 mμ band quantitatively by the use of molecular orbital theory and finds good agreement with experiment. Matsen and co-workers[13] have computed the wavelength shifts and intensity changes of this band in a number of substituted benzenes relative to benzene. Based on the experimentally measured intensities of the 260 mμ bands in substituted benzenes, Platt[14] has deduced a table of 'spectroscopic moments' which have been employed to correlate and predict intensity changes and wavelength shifts in a large number of benzene derivatives (*Table 5.5*). These additivity rules do not hold good for groups like —NH$_2$ or —NO$_2$ which interact strongly with the ring.

Effects of substitution on the 200 mμ band of benzene have been studied in great detail by Doub and Vandenbelt[10]. They find that the ratio of the wavelengths of the 260 mμ band (primary band) and the 200 mμ band (secondary band) is about 1·25 for most monosubstituted benzenes. The 200 mμ band is capable of displacement to the edge of the visible region. If substituent groups are divided into electron contributing (*ortho-para* directing) and electron attracting (*meta*-directing) types and arranged in the order of increasing wavelengths of the 200 mμ band, two series are found[10].

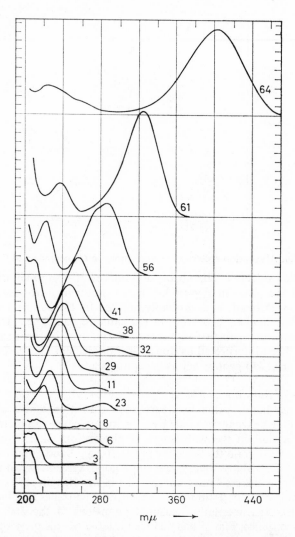

Figure 5.5. Absorption spectra of several monosubstituted and *para*-disubstituted benzenes[10]. 1, benzene; 3, toluene; 6, phenol; 8, benzensulphonamide; 23, *p*-chlorophenol; 11, benzoic acid; 29, *p*-toluicacid anion; 32, *p*-chloroaniline; 38, *p*-hydroxybenzoic acid (1st) anion; 41, *p*-hydroxybenzoic acid; 56, *p*-hydroxybenzaldehyde; 61, *p*-hydroxyacetophenone anion; 64, *p*-nitrophenol anion (Each unit on the ordinate axis represents an ϵ of 2000)

Electron contributing: $CH_3 < Cl < Br < OH < OCH_3 < NH_2 < O^-$

Electron
attracting: $NH_3^+ < SO_2NH_2 < CO_2^- = CN < CO_2H < COCH_3 < CHO < NO_2$

The effect of various combinations of these groups in p-disubstituted benzenes on the λ_{max} of the 200 mμ band is very interesting[10,20]. If both the substituent groups on the benzene ring are electron donating or electron withdrawing in nature, the observed displacement is similar to the displacement in the most displaced monosubstituted benzene. However, when the two substituents are of complementary types ($o - p$ directing *versus* m-directing) a very large bathochromic displacement of the 200 mμ band occurs. This is well illustrated in p-dinitrobenzene with a λ_{max} of 266 mμ and p-nitroaniline with a λ_{max} of 381 mμ, noting that nitrobenzene and aniline absorb at 269 and 230 mμ respectively. Similar examples may be visualized from the data in *Table 5.4*. Complementary disubstitution seems to have the greatest effect in the *para*-position[10,20]. For example, p-nitrophenol exhibits the 200 mμ band at 318 mμ, while the m- and o-derivatives absorb at 274 and 279 mμ respectively. This indicates the importance of polar resonance forms in determining the shifts of the 200 mμ band of benzene[10,20]. The absorption curves for a few monosubstituted and p-disubstituted benzene derivatives have been given in *Figure 5.5*. The absorption data of several p-, m- and o-disubstituted benzene derivatives have been summarized in *Table 5.4*.

$$O_2N = \hspace{-0.5em}\langle \; \rangle \hspace{-0.5em} = \overset{+}{N}H_2 \qquad\qquad O_2N = \hspace{-0.5em}\langle \; \rangle \hspace{-0.5em} = \overset{+}{O}H$$

Doub and Vandenbelt[10] have developed an empirical semi-quantitative relationship for the displacement of complementarily *para*-disubstituted benzene derivatives. In these derivatives, the observed wavelength shift of the 200 mμ band is found to be proportional to the product of the shifts in the corresponding monosubstituted benzenes. Doub and Vandenbelt[10] and Rao[20] have proposed that the displacing effect of a substituent group on the 200 mμ band of benzene is associated with the directional displacement of electrons to or from the benzene ring, depending on the electron attracting or contributing character of the group. The nature of the electronic interaction responsible for the displacement of the 200 mμ band has been associated mainly with resonance rather than inductive effects. Rao[20,21,47] has correlated the position of 200 mμ band in monosubstituted and p-disubstituted benzene derivatives with the Hammett reactivity constants and resonance parameters of groups. For *para*-complementary disubstituted benzenes, the relation with σ-constants is of the form,

$$\lambda = \lambda_0 + \rho\sigma$$

Typical curves for a few series of benzene derivatives are shown in *Figure 5.6*. A similar equation with the Taft resonance parameters is not very satisfactory[47]. A generalized correlation of the type

$$\lambda = \lambda_0 + |\sigma' - \sigma''|\,\rho$$

has also been proposed for complementarily disubstituted benzenes where σ' and σ'' are the substituent constants of the two substituents. These correlations have be found to be useful in estimating the reactivity

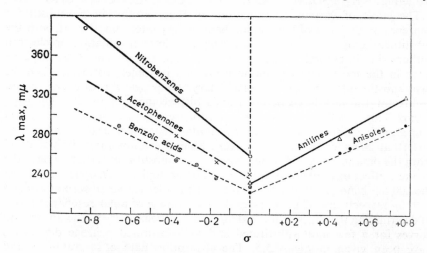

Figure 5.6. Correlation of the absorption maxima of *para*-complementarily disubstituted benzene derivatives with Hammett σ constants

constants and resonance parameters of groups[19,22,23,24]. Exner, Horak and Pliva have found a relationship between the infra-red and ultra-violet absorption frequencies in some benzoic acid derivatives which they propose to employ for evaluation of substituent constants.

The ultra-violet absorption maxima of *p*-halogen substituted benzene derivatives are found to be in the order I > Br > Cl > F[9,20]. This is exactly in the reverse order to the normally accepted trend of the resonance parameters of the halogens, F > Cl > Br > I. Schubert and co-workers[11] have studied the 200 mμ band in *p*-halonitrobenzenes, acetophenones, phenols, anisoles and anilines in different solvents and have interpreted the results in terms of the polarizability of the halogen substituent and the solvent orientation and solvent polarization effects. Baliah and Uma[26] have pointed out the importance of the expansion of valency shells of chlorine, bromine and iodine in determining the λ_{max}. Rao and co-workers[47] have evaluated the substituent constants (σ and σ^+) for halogens in *para*-disubstituted benzene, where the other substituents are electron-withdrawing or electron-donating. They find that the halogens become increasingly electron-donating (in the order F,Cl,Br,I) when the other para-substituent is electron-withdrawing in nature and *vice versa*. The effective σ values of para-F,Cl,Br,I are found to be -0.05, -0.11, -0.14 and -0.25 respectively in the first case and 0.03, 0.11, 0.11 and 0.15 respectively in the second case. These derived σ-values satisfactorily correlate the ultra-violet absorption data for *p*-halogen substituted benzene derivatives.

There has been considerable discussion on the nature of interaction of alkyl groups in benzene derivatives. The eletronic absorption spectra of alkyl substituted benzene derivatives have been interpreted in terms of hyperconjugation. Schubert and co-workers[17,48] have pointed out the importance of polarizability and the relief of strain on excitation in the case of the p-neopentyl group in explaining the absorption spectra of p-alkylnitrobenzenes. Employing the data of Schubert and co-workers on p-alkylnitrobenzenes and acetophenones, the σ constants for CH_3, C_2H_5, i-C_3H_7 and t-C_4H_9 groups have been derived[47] making use of the λ_{max}—σ correlations for complementarily disubstituted benzenes, and the values are quite close to the normally accepted values of σ for these groups. Studies on the $n \rightarrow \pi^*$ transitions of p-alkylacetophenones indicate the Baker–Nathan order in the λ_{max} values[15].

In the correlations of λ_{max} of *para*-complementarily disubstituted benzenes with σ constants, an interesting trend is found in ρ values. The sign and magnitude of the slope, ρ, varies systematically with the electrical property of the invariant group of the series.

Series (R—C_6H_4—X)	X	σ of X	ρ
Nitrobenzenes	p-NO_2	0·78	$-159\cdot4$
Acetophenones	p-$COCH_3$	0·50	$-118\cdot2$
Benzoic acids	p-$COOH$	0·45	$-93\cdot7$
Anisoles	p-OCH_3	$-0\cdot27$	$89\cdot5$
Anilines	p-NH_2	$-0\cdot66$	$109\cdot9$

The ρ values vary nearly linearly with σ of X.

Absorption spectra of trisubstituted benzenes have been studied by Doub and Vandenbelt[49] who have interpreted the spectra in terms of the disubstituted components. The spectrum of the trisubstituted derivative shows the most displaced bands of the constituent disubstituted compounds. The shapes and intensities of the bands also remain about the same.

It has already been pointed out earlier that solvent effects on the spectra could be quite marked in the case of benzene derivatives with polar groups like OH or with chromophoric substituents like $COCH_3$. In some cases the vibrational structure of the band is affected (*Figure 5.2*), while in others bands may get shifted (*Figure 5.4*). The band shifts in polar solvents are marked in the case of $n \rightarrow \pi^*$ transitions, but $\pi \rightarrow \pi^*$ transitions of substituted aromatics are also shifted considerably in certain cases. Thus, nitrobenzene exhibits its $\pi \rightarrow \pi^*$ transition maximum at 266, 260, 252 and 239 mμ in water, ethanol, heptane and vapour phase respectively[50]. In such cases, the excited state is likely to be stabilized by solvation. Appreciable variations in λ_{max} may also arise in some cases due to solute-solvent hydrogen bonding, the proton-donating ability of the solvent determining the magnitude of the shift. For example, the λ_{max} of benzoic acid and acetophenone in water are 230 and 246 mμ respectively, while in ethanol they are found to be 228 and 243 mμ. In the case of molecules which are highly associated (e.g. benzoic acid), change of solvent will cause wavelength and intensity variations due to the change in the magnitude and nature of association. Benzoic acid which is mostly dimeric in heptane solution essentially becomes monomeric in an ether[51]. There will, however, be hydrogen bonding between benzoic acid and ether.

Table 5.4. Absorption Spectra of Disubstituted Benzene Derivatives[10] (R_1—C_6H_4—R_2)

R_1	R_2	para-Derivatives Observed band		meta-Derivatives 200 mμ band		260 mμ band		ortho-Derivatives 200 mμ band		260 mμ band	
		λ_{max}, mμ	ϵ_{max}	λ_{max}, mμ	ϵ_{max}	λ_{max}, mμ	ϵ_{max}	λ_{max}, mμ	ϵ_{max}	λ_{max}, mμ	ϵ_{max}
CH_3	CN	237	17,200*	229·5	11,000	276	1,280	228·5	11,100	276·5	1,440
Cl	COOH	241	16,300	231·5	9,100	283	1,080	229	5,900	280	870
Cl	NO_2	280	10,300	264	7,100	313	1,300	260	4,000	310	1,400
NO_2	CH_3	285	9,250	273	7,300	315	1,300	266	5,300	325	1,300
NO_2	OH	317·5	10,000	273·5	6,000	333	1,960	278·5	6,600	351	3,200
NO_2	NH_2	381	13,500	280	4,800	358	1,450	282·5	5,400	412	4,500
NO_2	COOH	264·5	12,400	—	—	—	—	—	—	—	—
NH_2	NO_2	266	14,500	241·5	16,300	305	1,100	—	—	327	1,940
NH_2	COOH	284	14,000	250	2,400	310	650	248	3,900	—	—
NH_2	$COCH_3$	311·5	17,100	—	—	—	—	—	—	—	—
OH	CN	270	19,800	236·5	8,200	308	2,400	—	—	—	—
OH	CHO	283·5	16,000	254·5	10,100	314	2,580	256	12,600	324	3,400
OH	COOH	255	13,900	236·5	7,500	296	2,500	237	9,000	302·5	3,600
OH	$COCH_3$	275	14,300	250·5	9,100	308	2,300	252·5	10,900	324	3,300

* There is another band at 268 mμ (ϵ_{max} = 750)

Forbes and co-workers[9] have extensively studied the ultra-violet absorption spectra of several series of disubstituted benzene derivatives: acetophenones, benzoic acids, benzaldehydes, phenylbenzoates, acetanilides, nitrobenzenes, anilines, fluorobenzenes, chlorobenzenes, phenols and anisoles. They have collected valuable data and interpreted them in terms of the resonance and steric interactions of substituents. Considerable absorption data have been reported for alkyl phenyl sulphides and diphenyl sulphides[52,53], for phenyl alkyl sulphones and diphenyl sulphones[27,52,54,55] as well as phenyl alkyl sulphoxides and diphenyl sulphoxides[27,54,55-57]. The absorption spectra of substituted phenylazides[28] and phenyl isothiocyanates[29] have been discussed by Rao and colleagues.

Goodman and Shull[30] have recently summarized the empirical regularities in the ultra-violet absorption spectra of substituted benzenes as follows: Conjugative substitution: (1) A red shift of the 200 $m\mu$ and 260 $m\mu$ bands is produced. (2) The 180 $m\mu$ band shifts slightly to the blue or remains insensitive to substitution. (3) The 200 $m\mu$ band undergoes the greatest red shifts. (4) The long wavelength band is intensified, but the sum of the 180 $m\mu$ band intensities remains insensitive to substitution. (5) For certain very strongly conjugative substituents like $-NH_2$, the correspondence to benzene breaks down. Inductive substitution: (6) The 200 $m\mu$ and 260 $m\mu$ bands are only slightly shifted; the 180 $m\mu$ band undergoes stronger shifts to the blue. (7) The long wavelength band is greatly intensified; in general, more than in the case of conjugative substitution. Mixed conjugative and inductive substitution: (8) While the rules for mixed effects are less clear-cut, the conjugative effect, in general, seems to control the shifts of the long wavelength (260 $m\mu$) band.

Table 5.5. *Comparison of* λ_{max} *and Spectroscopic Moments with Orientation in Substitution*

Group	% *meta* in nitration	λ_{max}, $m\mu$[10] (200 $m\mu$ benzene band)	Spectroscopic moment[14]
OH	2	210	34
Cl	0·2	209·5	6
Br	0·2	210	4
CH$_3$	4	206·5	7
CH$_2$Cl	16	—	−3
CHCl$_2$	34	—	−11
COCH$_3$	55	245·5	—
COOH	80	230	−28
CN	81	224	−19
NO$_2$	93	268·5	—

Resonance and induction have a marked effect on orientation in aromatic substitution. One would therefore expect some correlation between orientation in substitution and the electronic absorption spectra of benzene derivatives. In *Table 5.5* the position of the 200 $m\mu$ benzene band[10] and the spectroscopic moments[14] have been compared with the percentage of the *meta* isomer produced in nitration. A fair parallelism is apparent in the three columns.

Stevenson and McConnell[31] have surveyed the ultra-violet absorption spectra of monoaromatic hydrocarbons of a wide range of structure and substitution and have enunciated general criteria that the spectrum of a substance or a mixture of substances must satisfy in order that it may be classified as a spectroscopically pure monoaromatic hydrocarbon. They have described and discussed the basis for the formulation of these criteria of spectroscopic purity and have exemplified the mode of application.

Condensed-Ring Benzenoid Hydrocarbons

All the condensed ring aromatic hydrocarbons absorb at longer wavelengths than benzene and the absorption bands of these molecules are also associated with the π electron systems. There are two series of condensed ring hydrocarbons: the linear series having planes of symmetry along their

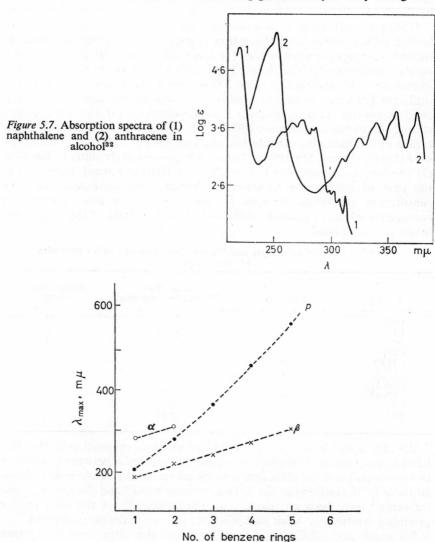

Figure 5.7. Absorption spectra of (1) naphthalene and (2) anthracene in alcohol[32]

Figure 5.8. α, p and β bands in the acene series[58] (From G. M. Badger by courtesy of Cambridge University Press)

70

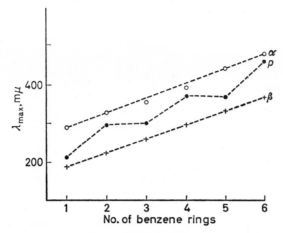

Figure 5.9. α, *p* and β bands in the phene series[58] (From G. M. Badger by courtesy of Cambridge University Press)

short and long axes (e.g. naphthalene, anthracene), and the angular series with no well-defined axes (e.g. phenanthrene, chrysene). Some absorption data of the condensed-ring systems are given in *Table 5.1*. The variations of the α, *p* and β bands of the acenes and phenes with the number of benzene rings are shown in *Figure 5.8* and *Figure 5.9*.

The absorption bands of the condensed ring hydrocarbons of the linear series exhibit pronounced vibrational structure. In *Figure 5.7* the spectra of naphthalene and anthracene have been reproduced[32]. There is a progressive displacement of the absorption maxima to longer wavelengths with the increasing number of fused benzene rings. While naphthalene and anthracene are colourless, naphthacene and pentacene are yellow and blue respectively. The λ_{max} of the long wavelength bands in these four compounds are found to be at 314, 380, 480 and 580 mμ. The extinction coefficients also increase in the same order (log ϵ, 2·50, 3·90, 4·05 and 4·10 respectively). The effects of various substituents on the ultra-violet absorption spectrum of anthracene have been studied by Jones[33] and the band shifts have been correlated with the type and position of the substituents.

Mayneord and Roe[32] have studied the absorption spectra of several angular condensed ring hydrocarbons. The absorption spectra of these compounds are more complex than those of the members of the linear series. Many of the compounds of the angular series have carcinogenic action and they can be detected in minute quantities spectrophotometrically by virtue of their high intensity absorption bands.

Non-Benzenoid Aromatics: Non-alternant hydrocarbons

Non-alternant hydrocarbons may be discussed under two classes: one with $(4n + 2)$ conjugated atoms where *n* is an integer and the other with $4n$ conjugated atoms. The former class exhibits the α, *p* and β bands similar to alternant hydrocarbons while the latter class of compounds show spectra similar to those of the vinyl derivatives of the corresponding hydrocarbon with

71

$(4n - 2)$ conjugated atoms[43]. The absorption data of a few non-alternant hydrocarbons are given below

	λ_{max}, mμ	ϵ_{max}
Azulene	270; 347; 656	47,000; 4000; 300
Acenaphthylene	265; 324; 338	2000; 9700; 4000
Fulvene	242; 373	14,000; 280
Pleiadiene	250; 350; 550	25,000; 6300; 100
Fluoranthene	235; 286; 340	39,800; 31600; 7940

The characteristic ultra-violet spectrum of benzene results from its circular and planar array of six π-orbitals. By analogy, conjugated molecules like cyclobutadiene and cyclooctatetraene should exhibit similar characteristics. However, one would expect these molecules to be less 'aromatic', because the CCC angles differ from the 120° angle of benzene. It has not been possible to prepare cyclobutadiene, while cyclooctatetraene is a 'puckered' ring without aromatic properties. Five and seven membered rings cannot form conjugated systems. On the other hand, the carbanions and carbonium ions of the five and seven membered rings would be completely conjugated. Thus, the tropylium ion (cycloheptatrienylium carbonium ion) exhibits absorption characteristics (λ_{max} 275 mμ, $\epsilon_{max} \sim 4470$) of a monoaromatic system[34]. The absorption data of several tropylium salts have been tabulated by Nozoe[34]. Similarly, the metal sandwich compounds of the highly acidic cyclopentadiene, like ferrocene, $(C_5H_5)_2Fe$, nickelocene $(C_5H_5)_2Ni$, and their cations exhibit aromatic character[35]. Ferrocene shows two absorption bands at 326 mμ ($\epsilon \sim 50$) and 440 mμ ($\epsilon \sim 87$) and its blue cation at 253 mμ ($\epsilon \sim 13,000$) and 619 mμ ($\epsilon \sim 400$).

Tropolones behave like aromatic molecules because of the possible

tautomerism and resonance. The ultra-violet spectra of troponoid derivatives resemble benzenoid absorption curves in appearance. They exhibit a high intensity band in the 220–270 mμ region (ϵ 10^4–10^5) and a band in the 290–400 mμ region (ϵ 10^3–10^4)[34]. The former band corresponds to the conjugation band and is unchanged by alkyl substitution. Substitution with halogen, hydroxyl or carbonyl group, however, results in bathochromic shifts. The second band varies with the structure of the troponoid. The shapes of the troponoid absorption curves change markedly with the solvent and pH of the solution. The absorption data of some troponoids have been summarized by Nozoe[34]. Absorption spectra of natural products containing tropolone units have also been reported[36].

Another important series of non-benzenoid aromatic molecules are the azulenes. Azulenes are blue or violet in colour and exhibit a series of absorption bands in the ultra-violet and visible regions (230–700 mμ)[37]. The bands

72

in the visible region are of low intensity ($\epsilon \sim 100$–350) and are displaced by alkyl substitution, the nature and the magnitude of the shift depending on the position. These bands are of greater value in the identification of azulenes. The wavelength shifts of the visible absorption bands in polyalkyl azulenes

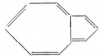

are found to be additive. Alkyl substitution causes bathochromic displacement of the high intensity bands ($\epsilon \sim 1000$–50,000) in the ultra-violet region. Inductive effects of alkyl groups are of greater importance in determining these shifts. Steric hindrance to resonance also causes bathochromic shifts of the absorption bands[38]. The absorption spectra of azulenes have been excellently discussed by Heilbronner[39].

The two best known series of inorganic aromatic molecules are the phosphonitrilic halides and borazoles. Recently, the ultra-violet absorption spectra of phosphonitrilic chlorides[40] $(PNCl_2)_n$, and some borazole derivatives[41], $B_3N_3R_6$, have been reported. In the series of $(PNCl_2)_n$ with n from 3–13, the absorption wavelength remains constant. In concentrated sulphuric acid the spectrum of the trimer is unchanged indicating that the lone-pair electrons on the nitrogen are not involved. It is possible that the chlorine lone-pair is responsible for the absorption[43].

Phosphonitrilic
chloride trimer

Borazole

REFERENCES

[1] PLATT, J. R. and KLEVENS, H. B., *Chem. Rev.*, 1947, **41**, 301; *J. Chem. Phys.*, 1948, **16**, 832; 1949, **17**, 470, 481.

[2] COULSON, C. A., *Proc. Phys. Soc.*, 1948, **60**, 257.

[3] NAKAMOTO, K., *J. Amer. Chem. Soc.*, 1952, **74**, 390.

[4] CRAIG, D. P. and LYONS, L. E., *Nature*, 1952, **169**, 1102.

[5] MATSEN, F. A. in *Chemical Applications of Spectroscopy*, Edited by West, W., Interscience, New York, 1956, Chapter V.

[6] BRAUDE, E. A., *Rep. Progr. Chem.*, 1945, **42**, 105.

[7] BURAWOY, A. and co-workers, *Tetrahedron*, 1958, **2**, 122, 403; 1959, **5**, 340.

[8] MOSER, C. M. and KOHLENBERG, A. I., *J. Chem. Soc.*, 1951, 804.

[9] FORBES, W. F. and co-workers, *Canad. J. Chem.*, 1955, **33**, 1145, 1829; 1956, **34**, 1340, 1447; 1957, **35**, 488, 1049; 1958, **36**, 1350, 1362, 1371; 1959, **37**, 1294, 1305, 1977; 1960, **38**, 1104.

[10] DOUB, L. and VANDENBELT, J. M., *J. Amer. Chem. Soc.*, 1947, **69**, 2714; 1949, **71**, 2414.

[11] SCHUBERT, W. M. and co-workers, *J. Amer. Chem. Soc.*, 1957, **79**, 910; 1959, **81**, 2695; 1960, **82**, 1353, 1357.

[12] SKLAR, A. L., *J. Chem. Phys.*, 1937, **7**, 339, 353; 1942, **10**, 135.

[13] MATSEN, F. A. and co-workers, *J. Amer. Chem. Soc.*, 1950, **72**, 5243, 5248, 5250, 5252, 5256, 5260.

[14] PLATT, J. R., *J. Chem. Phys.*, 1951, **19**, 263.

[15] Data from the laboratory of Inst. of Sci., Bangalore, India.

[16] MATSEN, F. A., ROBERTSON, W. W. and CHUOKE, R. L., *Chem. Revs.*, 1947, **41**, 273.

[17] SCHUBERT, W. M. and SWEENEY, W. A., *J. Org. Chem.*, 1956, **21**, 119 and the references listed there.

[18] BOWDEN, K. and BRAUDE, E. A., *J. Chem. Soc.*, 1952, 1068.

[19] RAO, C. N. R., RAMACHANDRAN, J. and BALASUBRAMANIAN, A., *Canad. J. Chem.*, 1961, **39**, 171.

[20] RAO, C. N. R., *J. Sci. Ind. Research (India)*, 1958, **17B**, 56, Curr. Sci. (India), 1957, **26**, 276.

[21] RAO, C. N. R., *Chem. & Ind. (London)*, 1956, 666; 1957, 1239.

[22] RAO, C. N. R., *J. Sci. Industr. Research (India)*, 1958, **17B**, 89.

[23] LIEBER, E., RAO, C. N. R., RAMACHANDRAN, J., and PILLAI, C. N., *Canad. J. Chem.*, 1959, **37**, 563.

[24] BLOOR, J. E. and COPLEY, D. B., *Chem. & Ind.*, 1960, 526.

[25] EXNER, O., HORAK, M. and PLIVA, J., *Chem. & Ind.*, 1958, 1174.

[26] BALIAH, V. and UMA, M., *Naturwiss.*, 1958, **45**, 512.

[27] BALIAH, V. and co-workers, *J. Indian Chem. Soc.*, 1957, **34**, 364; 1958, **35**, 31, 151; 1960, **37**, 321.

[28] RAO, C. N. R., RAJKUMAR, T. V. and RAMACHANDRAN, J., *J. Sci. Industr. Research (India)*, 1958, **17B**, 504.

[29] RAO, C. N. R., RAMACHANDRAN, J. and SOMESEKHARA, S., *Curr. Sci. (India)*, 1958, **27**, 474.

[30] GOODMAN, L. and SHULL, H., *J. Chem. Phys.*, 1957, **27**, 1388.

[31] STEVENSON, D. P. and McCONELL, H. M., *Spectrochim. Acta*, 1958, **12**, 262.

[32] MAYNEORD, W. V. and ROE, E. M. F., *Proc. Roy. Soc. (London)*, 1935, **A152**, 299.

[33] JONES, R. N., *Chem. Rev.*, 1947, **41**, 353.

[34] NOZOE, T., in *Non-Benzenoid Aromatic Compounds*, Edited by Ginsburg, D., Interscience, New York, 1959, Chapter VII.

[35] FISCHER, E. O. and FRITZ, H. P., in *Advances in Inorganic Chemistry and Radiochemistry*, Edited by Emeleus, H. J. and Sharpe, A. G., Academic Press, New York, 1959, Vol. I, p. 81.

[36] AUTIN-ERDTMAN, G., *Acta. Chem. Scand.*, 1950, **4**, 1031.

[37] GORDON, M., *Chem. Rev.*, 1952, **50**, 185 and the references listed there.

[38] HEILBRONNER, E. and GERDIL, R., *Helv. Chim. Acta*, 1956, **39**, 997.

[39] HEILBRONNER, E., in *Non-Benzenoid Aromatic Compounds*, Edited by Ginsburg, D., Interscience, New York, 1959, Chapter V.

[40] LUND, L. G., PADDOCK, N. L., PROCTOR, J. E. and SEARLE, H. T., *J. Chem. Soc.*, 1960, 2542.

[41] RECTOR, C. W., SCHAEFFER, G. W. and PLATT, J. R., *J. Chem. Phys.*, 1949, **17**, 460.

[42] CLAR, E., *Aromatische Kohlenwasserstoffe*, Springer-Verlag, Berlin, 1952.

[43] MASON, S. F., *Quart. Revs. (London)*, 1961, **15**, 287

[44] PLATT, J. R., *J. Chem. Phys.*, 1949, **17**, 484; 1954, **22**, 1448.

[45] DEWAR, M. J. S. and LONQUET-HIGGINS, H. C., *Proc. Phys. Soc. (London)*, 1954, **67A**, 1795.

[46] NAGAKURA, S., *J. Chem. Phys.*, 1955, **23**, 1441.

[47] RAO, C. N. R. and co-workers, *Proc. 10th Intern. Conf. Spectroscopy*, Maryland, 1962, Spartan Press, Washington, 1963.

[48] SCHUBERT, W. M. and ROBINS, J., *J. Amer. Chem. Soc.*, 1958, **80**, 559.

[49] DOUB, L. and VANDENBELT, J. M., *J. Amer. Chem. Soc.*, 1955, **77**, 4435.

[50] UNGANADE, H. E., *J. Amer. Chem. Soc.*, 1953, **75**, 432.

[51] FORBES, W. F. and co-workers, *Canad. J. Chem.*, 1958, **36**, 180; 1959, **37**, 334; 1960, **38**, 728.

[52] FEHNEL, E. A. and CARMACK, M., *J. Amer. Chem. Soc.*, 1949, **71**, 84, 231, 2889.

[53] MANGINI, A., *J. Chim. Phys.*, 1959, 240.

[54] SZMANT, H. H. and MCINTOSH, J. J., *J. Amer. Chem. Soc.*, 1951, **73**, 4356.

[55] MANGINI, A. and co-workers, *J. Chem. Soc.*, 1957, 1386; *Gazz. chim. Ital.*, 1954, **84**, 73.

[56] OAE, S. and ZAULT, C., *J. Amer. Chem. Soc.*, 1960, **82**, 5359.

[57] BORDWELL, F. G. and BOULTON, P. J., *J. Amer. Chem. Soc.*, 1957, **79**, 717.

[58] BADGER, G. M., *The Structure and Reactions of Aromatic Compounds*, Cambridge University Press, 1954.

CHAPTER 6

HETEROCYCLIC COMPOUNDS

SATURATED five- and six-membered oxygen heterocyclic compounds (e.g. tetrahydrofuran, tetrahydropyran and dioxane) absorb below 200 mμ similar to acyclic ethers. These low wavelength absorption bands are probably due to $n \rightarrow \sigma^*$ transitions. Ethylene oxide, which is a three-membered ring, absorbs below 175 mμ. Saturated rings containing nitrogen (e.g. pyrrolidine, piperidine and piperazine) also exhibit spectra similar to those of the corresponding acyclic compounds. Absorption data on a few saturated heterocyclic compounds are given below

Compound	Region of absorption, mμ
Ethyleneoxide	144,157
Tetrahydrofuran	162–180; 180–200
Tetrahydropyran	165–174; 174–184
Dioxan	165–192
Pyrrolidine	162–187; 187–250
Piperidine	176–250
Piperazine	175–213

It is only the unsaturated heterocyclic compounds that absorb in the near ultra-violet region.

Five-Membered Unsaturated Heterocyclic Compounds

The three well-known unsaturated five-membered heterocyclic compounds are furan, I, thiophene, II, and pyrrole, III, which may be considered as analogues of cyclopentadiene, IV.

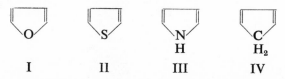

O	S	N / H	C / H$_2$
I	II	III	IV

These compounds exhibit a very intense band below 220 mμ due to the diene absorption and a low intensity band at longer wavelengths. The long wavelength band is most intense in the case of thiophene, possibly because of the interaction of the low-lying *d*-orbitals. Some of the other unsaturated five-membered heterocycles for which the absorption spectra have been reported are pyrazole, V, imidazole, VI, 1,2,3-triazole, VII, tetrazole, VIII, and isothiazole, IX, and isoxazole, X. Absorption data of the five-membered unsaturated heterocyclic compounds are summarized in *Table 6.1*.

76

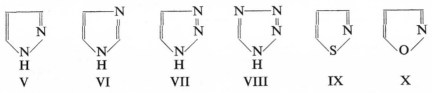

V	VI	VII	VIII	IX	X

Unlike tetrazole, triazole exhibits an intense absorption band in the near ultra-violet region[1,2], perhaps due to the presence of the $C=C$ in the latter, which gives a $\pi \to \pi^*$ band at longer wavelengths than either $C=N$ or $N=N$. The low intensity band of imidazole at 250 mμ may be due to the $n \to \pi^*$ transition of the $C=N$ group. Pyrazole and imidazole[43] show intense bands at 210 and 207 mμ, while both isoxazole and isothiazole absorb around 210 mμ. Tetrazole[3] has been found to give rise to a very weak band ($\epsilon < 5$) around 260 mμ, which may be due to the $n \to \pi^*$ transition of the $N=N$ or $C=N$ group. The $n \to \pi^*$ transition band due to $N=N$ in triazole has not been identified.

Substitution of these five-membered unsaturated heterocycles by auxochromic or chromophoric groups shifts the absorption bands to longer wavelengths and also intensifies them. Conjugation of furan with exocyclic double bonds was mentioned in the discussion of polyenes (Chapter 4). The absorption spectra of substituted furans[8-11], pyrroles[11,12,44,45] thiophenes[13,14], triazoles[15], tetrazoles[2], pentazoles[41], pyrazoles[43], imidazoles[43], isoxazoles[43], isothiazoles[43] and thiatriazoles[16] and benzthiazoles[46,47] have been reported. Particular mention should be made of the absorption spectrum of furfural ($\lambda_{max} = 278$ mμ, ϵ_{max} 15,000, in water) which has been employed for the microdetermination of pentose sugars[10]. Pyrrole pigments are biochemically the

Table 6.1. *Absorption Spectra of Five-membered Heterocycles*

	λ_{max}, mμ	ϵ_{max}	λ_{max}, mμ	ϵ_{max}	Solvent
Cyclopentadiene[4]	200[a]	10,000	238·5	3,400	Hexane
Furan[5,7]	~200	10,000	250[a]	1	Hexane
Thiophene[5,7,43]	204-260	—	235	4,500	Hexane or Vapour
Pyrrole[5]	210[a]	15,000	350	300	Hexane
Imidazole[7]	210	5,000	250	60	Alcohol
1,2,3-Triazole[1]	210	3,980	—	—	Alcohol
Thiazole[6,7]	—	—	240	4,000	Alcohol
Indole[5]	215	25,000	265[a]	6,300	Hexane
Carbazole[5]	242	24,000	291	19,000	Hexane
Selenophene[44]	170-210	—	245,267	—	Vapour

(a) Approximate centre of the group of bands.

most important coloured substances. Chlorophylls (causing green colour in plants) and haemin (causing red colour of blood) contain pyrrole rings. These pigments will be discussed in Chapter 12. (See reference 42 for coumarins.)

Six-Membered Heterocyclic Aromatic Compounds

When a CH group in an aromatic hydrocarbon is replaced by $=N$, there is very little change in the spectrum, except for a slight intensification of the

Table 6.2. Absorption Spectra of a few Hetero-aromatics

	λ_{max}, mμ [a]	ϵ_{max}	λ_{max}, mμ	ϵ_{max}	Solvent
Benzene	255	250	—	—	Hexane
Pyridine[17]	256	1,860	281*	—	Cyclohexane
Pyrimidine[17]	244	3,160	267[a]	316	Water
Pyrazine[17]	258	5,620	313[a]	794	Cyclohexane
Pyridazine[17]	250	1,120	341	282	Cyclohexane
Sym-triazine[19]	222	146	272	881	Cyclohexane
Naphthalene	275	5,600	311[a]	320	Alcohol
Quinoline[24]	275	4,500	311[a]	6,300	Hexane
Phthalazine[18]	212	59,500	296[a]	795	Cyclohexane
	259	4,100	357[a]*	54	
Quinoxaline[18]	232	32,080	345[a]*	554	Cyclohexane
	304	4,830			
Anthracene	252	160,000	380[a]	6,500	Alcohol
Acridine[25]	252	170,000	347[a]	8,000	Alcohol
Phenazine[25]	250	120,000	370[a]	15,000	Alcohol

(a) Approximate centre of fine structure bands. * Shoulder.

long wavelength band (forbidden $\pi \rightarrow \pi^*$ band or B-band). Thus, the absorption spectra of benzene and pyridine, XI, naphthalene and quinoline, XII, and anthracene and acridine, XIII, are similar (*Table 6.2*). The absorption curves of a few hetero-aromatic compounds are compared with the curve for benzene, in *Figure 6.1*. In the case of the heterocycles, in addition to the bands due to $\pi \rightarrow \pi^*$ transitions, weak bands with vibrational structure (R-bands) due to $n \rightarrow \pi^*$ transitions are observed at longer wavelengths. In polar solvents, the $n \rightarrow \pi^*$ bands are shifted to lower wavelengths with loss

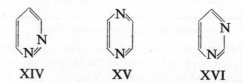

XI   XII   XIII

of fine structure (see *Figure 2.2* for the spectrum of pyrazine in different solvents). If the $n \rightarrow \pi^*$ bands are very close to the $\pi \rightarrow \pi^*$ bands (e.g. pyridine), the former bands completely submerge with the latter in polar solvents.

When two CH groups of benzene are replaced by nitrogen atoms in the ortho-, para- and meta- positions to form, pyridazine, XIV, pyrazine, XV, and pyrimidine, XVI, the position of the $\pi \rightarrow \pi^*$ bands are not greatly affected compared with pyridine (*Figure 6.1*).

XIV   XV   XVI

However, the $n \rightarrow \pi^*$ bands are shifted to much longer wavelengths in the case of pyridazine and pyrazine[17]. The $\pi \rightarrow \pi^*$ bands are not greatly affected in di-aza-naphthalenes[18] compared to naphthalene and quinoline. Further substitution of CH groups by nitrogen atoms, as in triazenes[19] and tri-aza-naphthalenes[20], often displaces the lower wavelength $\pi \to \pi^*$ bands to still shorter wavelengths. The absorption spectra of *sym*- and *asym*-triazene

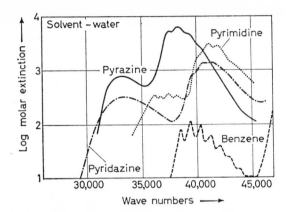

Figure 6.1. Absorption spectra of pyridine, pyridazine, pyrimidine and benzene in water solutions[17]

derivatives have been studied by Hirt and co-workers[21,22]. The $n \to \pi^*$ band of *sym*-tetrazine, XVII, has been found[23] to be in the visible region (542 mμ),

XVII

while the $\pi \to \pi^*$ band is found around 250 mμ. Mason[23] has recently investigated the $n \to \pi^*$ and $\pi \to \pi^*$ transitions in a number of monocyclic azines and their derivatives in great detail.

The effect of substituents on the absorption spectrum of pyridine has been investigated and the data of several pyridine derivatives are given in *Tables 6.3* and *6.4*. In acidic solution, the vibrational fine structure of the $\pi \to \pi^*$ band (B-band) of pyridine is diminished, but the intensity of the band is enhanced. This is due to the introduction of a formal positive charge at the nitrogen atom (protonation). Salt formation also causes a decrease in the fine structure and an increase in the intensity of the $\pi \to \pi^*$ band[17]. Brown and co-workers[26,27] determined the dissociation constants of the conjugate acids of a number of substituted pyridines by a study of their absorption spectra in alkaline (of the free base) and acidic (of the protonated form) solutions (see Chapter 7 for details regarding the determination of acid dissociation constants by spectrophotometry). The absorption spectrum of pyridine seems to be affected more by the position than by the nature of the alkyl substituent[26]. A 2- or 3-alkyl substituent increases the absorption wavelength and intensity of the $\pi \to \pi^*$ band, while a 4-alkyl substituent decreases both. The absorption band is shifted to longer wavelengths by halogen substituents[27] in 2- or 3-position, their effectiveness varying in the order $I > Br > Cl > F$ (just as in benzene derivatives, see Chapter 5).

Table 6.3. Absorption Spectra of Pyridine Derivatives[26-28, 48] $(R-C_5H_4N)$

R	Alkaline solution[a]		Acidic solution	
	λ_{max}, mμ	ϵ_{max}	λ_{max}, mμ	ϵ_{max}
H	257	2,750	256	5,300
2-CH$_3$	262	3,560	262·5	6,600
3-CH$_3$	263	3,110	262·5	5,500
4-CH$_3$	255	2,100	252·5	4,500
2-C$_2$H$_5$	261·5	3,800	263	7,550
2-i-C$_3$H$_7$	262	3,700	263	7,150
2-F	257	3,350	260	5,900
2-Cl	263	3,650	269	7,200
2-Br	265	3,750	272	7,600
2-I	272	4,000	290	8,300
2-OH	230	10,000	225	7,000
	295	6,300	295	5,700
3-SH	255	7,800	268	13,500
	310	3,200	313	2,600

(a) Only the prominent fine structure band is given.

Table 6.4. Absorption Data[24, 26, 42, 48] of Pyridine Derivatives $(RC_6H_4N)^*$

R	2R		3R		4R	
	λ_{max}	ϵ_{max}	λ_{max}	ϵ_{max}	λ_{max}	ϵ_{max}
CN	265	2,730	265	2,230	271	2,840
Cl	265	2,920	268	2,400	—	—
CH$_3$	262	2,420	258	2,260	—	—
OCH$_3$	269	3,230	276	2,960	235	2,000
NH$_2$	290	3,800	294	3,500	—	—
SCH$_3$	292	4,200	294	2,500	263	

* All data in non-polar solvents except the OCH$_3$ derivative. The data on the OCH$_3$ derivative are in water. Data or only long wavelength bands listed.

A hydroxy group in 2- or 3-position causes a bathochromic shift of the $\pi \to \pi^*$ band of pyridine. Keto-enol and thione-thiol tautomerism is possible in these hydroxy and mercapto derivatives (see Chapter 7 for a discussion of tautomerism). The spectrum of 2-hydroxypyridine[28] varies little when the solvent is alkaline or acidic, indicating that the keto form (2-pyridone) predominates in this compound. However, 3-hydroxypyridine[29] shows consider-

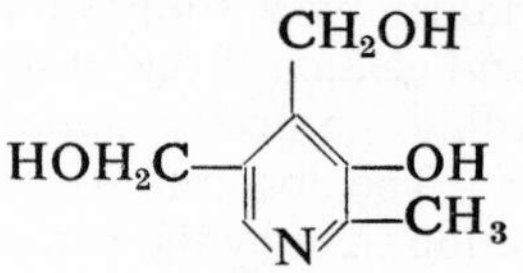

CH$_2$OH

HOH$_2$C———OH
———CH$_3$
N

XVIII

80

able variation in its spectrum from alkaline to acidic medium. Vitamin B$_6$ (pyridoxine, XVIII) which is a derivative of 3-hydroxypyridine also shows similar variations with the pH of the solvent (*Table 6.5*).

Table 6.5. Absorption Spectra of 3-Hydroxypyridine and Pyridoxine

	Alkaline solution		Neutral solution		Acidic solution	
	λ_{max}, mμ	ϵ_{max}	λ_{max}, mμ	ϵ_{max}	λ_{max}, mμ	ϵ_{max}
3-Hydroxypyridine[29]	234	10,200	246	4,700	222	3,300
	298	4,500	313	3,000	283	5,900
Pyridoxine[29]	245	6,300	254	3,900	232	2,100
	210	6,800	324	7,200	291	8,600

Pyridine-N-oxide[30] exhibits intense bands at 254 mμ (ϵ 12,000) and 203 mμ (ϵ 17,000). The 254 mμ band probably arises from the resonance interaction of the ring with the co-ordinated oxygen atom. While *p*-alkyl substitution causes a slight bathochromic shift, *m*-alkyl substitution does not affect the spectrum of pyridine-N-oxide.

Generally, intensity changes are more prominent than wavelength changes due to substituent effects on the $\pi \rightarrow \pi^*$ transitions of aromatic heterocyclic compounds. In pyridines substituted with SR, OR or NR$_2$ groups, the spectra of the differently charged species are quite different. The possible different species are:

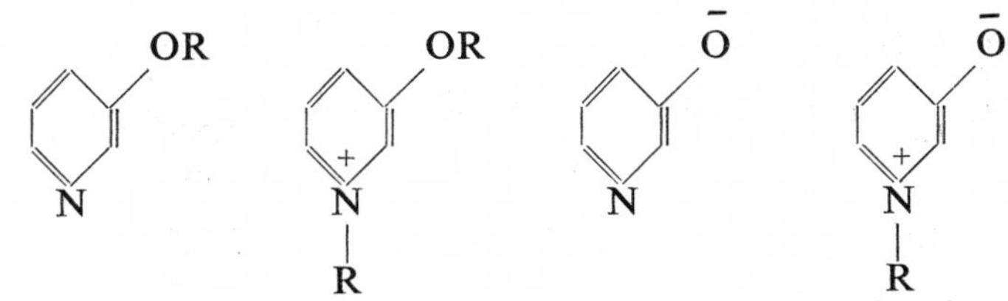

| Neutral | Cation | Anion | Zwitterion |

The absorption wavelength of these species are in the order zwitterion > anion > cation > neutral[23]. The effect of position of substitution is generally 3 > 2 > 4 and for a charged species, SR > NR$_2$ > OR[23].

The spectra of isomeric mono-chloro and mono-methyl quinolines have been investigated and substituent effects have been correlated with the molecular dimensions of the substituted quinoline molecules[31].

Dewar and co-workers[49] have been investigating the electronic absorption spectra of boron containing heteroaromatic compounds.

Pyrimidines and Purines

Pyrimidine, XVI, is a heterocycle of great biochemical interest since its skeleton occurs in nucleic acids. The absorption curve of pyrimidine has been compared with that of pyridine in *Figure 6.1*. The absorption spectra of

81

several pyrimidine derivatives have been reported in the literature[32-34] and some of the data are summarized in *Table 6.6*. Chlorine or alkyl substitution shifts the $\pi \rightarrow \pi^*$ band of pyrimidine to longer wavelengths accompanied by intensification and loss of fine structure. In pyrimidines substituted by OH, SH or NH_2 groups, tautomerism is possible and the spectra change markedly with the pH of the solvent[32]. The 4-hydroxy and 4-mercapto derivatives exist predominantly in the form of the corresponding ketones (pyrimidones) or thioketones respectively. Similarly, 2-hydroxy and 2-mercapto derivatives

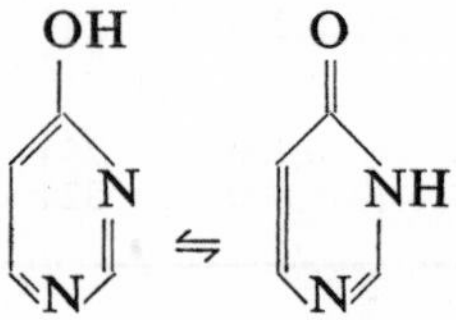

exist mostly as cyclic amides and thioamides. Although amino-imino tauto-merism is possible in the amino-pyrimidines, they seem to exist mostly in the amino-form in aqueous solution[33]. Keto-enol tautomerism in uracil, XIX, barbituric acid XX, and alloxan XXI, has been investigated by a study of their absorption spectra[32,34]. The prominent tautomeric forms of these three compounds seem to be:

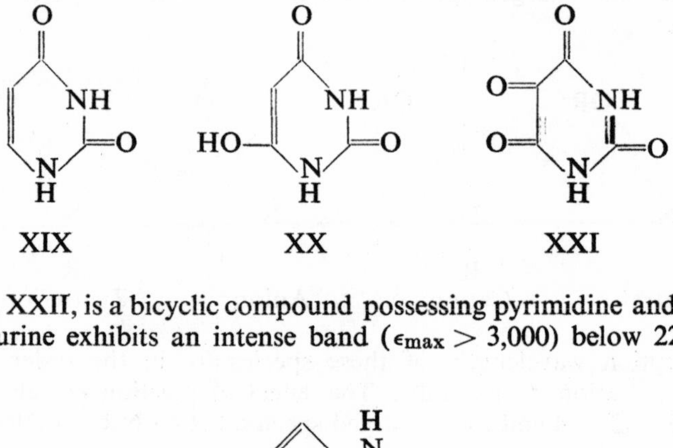

XIX   XX   XXI

Purine, XXII, is a bicyclic compound possessing pyrimidine and imidazole nuclei. Purine exhibits an intense band ($\epsilon_{max} > 3,000$) below 220 mμ and

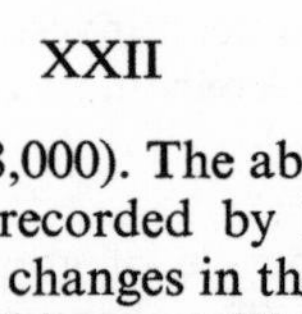

XXII

another band at 263 mμ (ϵ_{max} 8,000). The absorption spectra of a number of purine derivatives have been recorded by Mason[35]. The spectra of these derivatives are very sensitive to changes in the pH of the medium (*Table 6.7*). Purines are of great biochemical interest. The purine skeleton is found in the nucleoproteins of the living cells. On continued alkaline hydrolysis, nucleic

82

Table 6.6. Absorption Spectra of a few Pyrimidine Derivatives[32-34]

Compound	Alkaline solution		Neutral solution		Acid solution	
	λ_{max}, mμ	ϵ_{max}	λ_{max}, mμ	ϵ_{max}	λ_{max}, mμ	ϵ_{max}
Pyrimidine	—	—	243	3,000	—	—
4-Methyl	—	—	244	3,400	244	5,000
2:4-Dichloro	—	—	259	4,700	—	—
4-Methoxy	—	—	247	3,400	288	7,700
4-Hydroxy	227	11,000	223	7,500	224	9,750
	263	3,500	260	3,700	251	3,000
2-Hydroxy-4-methyl	220	11,500	213	11,000	305	7,100
	290	5,800	296	6,000	—	—
2-Mercapto-4-methyl	269	17,000	215	10,000	221	8,000
	—	—	277	19,000	281	27,500
	—	—	338	3,250	366	1,500
2-Methylthio-4-methyl	210	4,000	210	4,000	215	6,300
	250	14,000	250	14,000	253	14,000
	—	—	—	—	304	4,500
2-Amino	—	—	224	13,500	221	15,000
	—	—	292	3,000	302	4,000
Uracil	—	—	261	6,300	—	—
6-Methyluracil	277	9,000	—	—	261	10,000
Barbituric Acid	—	—	257	25,000	—	—

acids give purines, sugar residues and phosphoric acid. Uric acid is another important purine derivative (trihydroxypurine). Caffeine is a purine alkaloid. By a comparison of the absorption spectra of nucleosides from natural sources with those of the synthetic substituted purines, it has been shown that the sugar unit is attached at the 9-position of the purine nucleus[37].

All the naturally occurring purines show intense absorption in the 250–290 mμ region[36,37] (Table 6.7) and ordinary spectrophotometric methods fail to

Table 6.7. Absorption Spectra of a few Purine Derivatives[35-37]

Compound	Alkaline solution		Neutral solution		Acid solution	
	λ_{max}, mμ	ϵ_{max}	λ_{max}, mμ	ϵ_{max}	λ_{max}, mμ	ϵ_{max}
Purine	219	8,300	<220	>3,000	<220	>12,000
	271	7,600	263	8,000	260	6,000
6-Methyl	271	8,500	261	8,400	265	7,600
8-Methyl	274	8,500	266	10,250	264	8,300
2-Hydroxy	265	4,000	238	2,900	264	2,300
	312	6,750	315	4,900	322	6,500
2-Methoxy	283	7,600	246	2,600	284	6,750
	—	—	283	8,100	—	—
2-Amino	276*	4,100	236	5,000	235	6,500
	303	5,750	305	6,000	325	4,200
6-Hydroxy	262	11,000	249	10,500	248	10,500
8-Hydroxy	284	12,600	235	3,250	280	10,500
	—	—	277	11,000	—	—
Xanthine	—	—	269	11,200	—	—
Guanine	—	—	249	9,100	—	—
	—	—	273	7,500	—	—
Adenine	—	—	261	9,200	—	—
Uric acid	—	—	238	9,800	—	—
	—	—	293	12,200	—	—
Caffeine	—	—	278	10,900	—	—
Theophylline	—	—	274	9,100	—	—

* Inflection

83

D

identify and quantitatively estimate individual purines. In order to determine the amount of any individual purine present in the natural mixture, the technique of 'preferential spectrophotometry' has been employed[38]. The total absorption intensity is measured at a wavelength and the particular purine is then destroyed by a specific enzyme. The decrease in the absorption intensity is taken as a measure of the purine destroyed.

In the opinion of the author, there is need for systematic investigations of the spectroscopy of heterocyclic systems, particularly with regard to substituent and solvent effects.

Meso-ionic Compounds

Baker and Ollis[39] have defined a meso-ionic compound as a five- or possibly six-membered heterocyclic compound which cannot be satisfactorily represented by any one co-valent or polar structure and possesses a sextet of electrons in association with all the atoms comprising the ring. The ring bears a fractional positive charge balanced by a negative charge on a co-valently attached atom or group of atoms. Sydnones, which are considered to be meso-ionic, contain no other conjugated system, but show a well-defined absorption maximum around 292 mμ. This is explained by the suggestion that the sydnone ring possesses aromatic character and is a hybrid of a large number of contributing forms. Henry, Finnegan and Lieber[40] have found that 1,3-dialkyl-5-imino-tetrazoles exhibit characteristic absorption between 254 and 258 mμ, while the substituted tetrazoles containing no other conjugated system show only end absorption[2]. On this basis, the meso-ionic structure XXIII was proposed for 1,3-dialkyl-5-iminotetrazoles. It is difficult

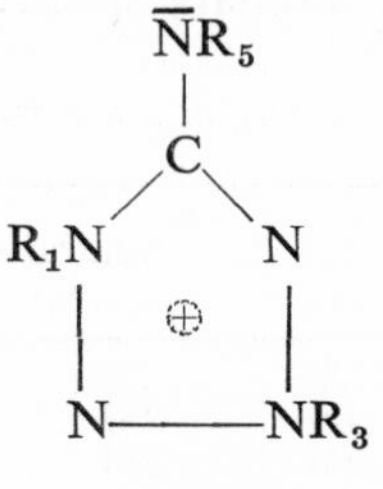

$$\overline{N}R_5$$

XXIII

to represent such structures and the attempted exclusion of structures which can be represented satisfactorily by any one co-valent or polar structure might exclude compounds which may indeed be meso-ionic. As pointed out

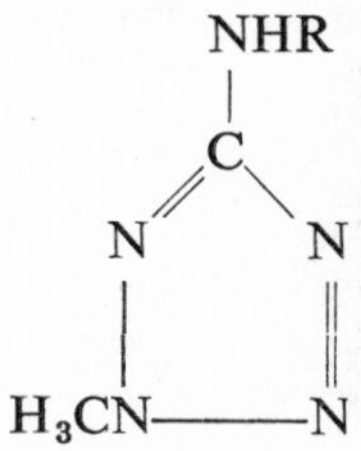

XXIV

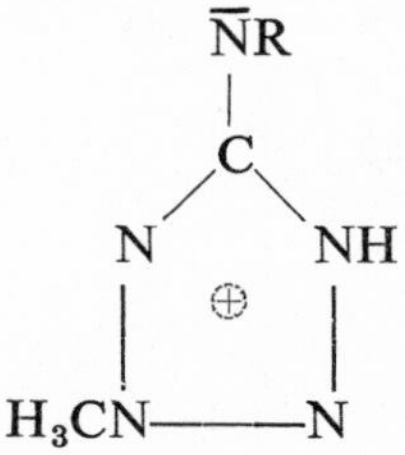

XXV

by Baker and Ollis[39], the ambiguity here is the word *satisfactory*. Thus, 2-methyl-5-alkylamino tetrazoles which had been considered to possess the tetrazole ring with normal co-valent bonds, XXIV, actually exist in the meso-ionic form, XXV. The ultra-violet absorption spectra of these derivatives are very similar to those of 1,3-dialkyl-5-iminotetrazoles. Ultra-violet absorption spectra of 5-substituted amino-1,2,3,4-thiatriazoles could not decide whether they were meso-ionic or not[14]. It may be concluded that ultra-violet absorption data alone cannot prove that a particular compound is meso-ionic, but can only serve as additional evidence.

REFERENCES

[1] HARTZEL, L. W. and BENSON, F. R., *J. Amer. Chem. Soc.*, 1954, **76**, 667.

[2] LIEBER, E., RAO, C. N. R. and PILLAI, C. N., *Curr. Sci. (India)*, 1957, **26**, 167.

[3] RAO, C. N. R. and co-workers, Unpublished Data.

[4] PICKETT, L. W., HOEFLICH, N. J. and LIU, T., *J. Amer. Chem. Soc.*, 1941, **63**, 1073.

[5] MENCZEL, S., *Z. phys. Chem.*, 1927, **125**, 161.

[6] RUEHLE, A. E., *J. Amer. Chem. Soc.*, 1935, **57**, 1887.

[7] BRAUDE, E. A., *Ann. Repts. on Progr. Chem.*, 1945, **42**, 105.

[8] HAUSSER, K. W. and SMAKULA, A., *Angew. Chem.*, 1935, **47**, 657.

[9] WILLARD, J. R. and HAMILTON, C. S., *J. Amer. Chem. Soc.*, 1951, **73**, 4805 and references listed there.

[10] DUNSTAN, S. and GILLAM, A. E., *J. Chem. Soc.*, 1949, S140.

[11] ANDRISAND, R. and PAPPALARDO, G., *Gazz. chim. Ital.*, 1955, **85**, 1430.

[12] COOKSON, G. H., *J. Chem. Soc.*, 1953, 2789.

[13] GRONOWITZ, S., *Arkiv. Kemi.*, 1958, **13**, 1239.

[14] ANDRISANO, R. and PAPPALLARDO, G., *Spectrochim. Acta*, 1958, **12**, 350.

[15] LIEBER, E., RAO, C. N. R., CHAO, T. S. and RUBINSTEIN, H., *Can. J. Chem.*, 1958, **36**, 1441.

[16] LIEBER, E., RAMACHANDRAN, J., RAO, C. N. R. and PILLAI, C. N., *Canad. J. Chem.*, 1959, **37**, 563.

[17] HALVERSON, F. and HIRT, R. C., *J. Chem. Phys.*, 1951, **19**, 711.

[18] HIRT, R. C., KING, F. T. and CAVAGNOL, J. C., *J. Chem. Phys.*, 1956, **25**, 574.

[19] HIRT, R. C., HALVERSON, F. and SCHMITT, R. G., *J. Chem. Phys.*, 1954, **22**, 1148.

[20] LEESE, C. L. and RYDON, H. N., *J. Chem. Soc.*, 1955, 303.

[21] HIRT, R. C. and SALLEY, D. J., *J. Chem. Phys.*, 1953, **21**, 1181.

[22] HIRT, R. C. and SCHMITT, R. G., *J. Chem. Phys.*, 1955, **23**, 600.

[23] MASON, S. F., *J. Chem. Soc.*, 1959, 1240, 1247, 1253, 1263, 1269; 1960, 218, 1282.

[24] MORTON, R. A. and deGOUVEIA, A. J. A., *J. Chem. Soc.*, 1934, 916.

[25] RADULESCU, D. and OSTROGOVICH, G., *Ber. dtsch. chem. Ges.*, 1931, **64**, 2233.

[26] BROWN, H. C. and MIHM, X. R., *J. Amer. Chem. Soc.*, 1955, **77**, 1723.

[27] BROWN, H. C. and McDANIEL, D. H., *J. Amer. Chem. Soc.*, 1955, **77**, 3752.

[28] EWING, G. W. and STECK, E. A., *J. Amer. Chem. Soc.*, 1946, **68**, 2181.

[29] METZLER, E. E. and SNELL, E. E., *J. Amer. Chem. Soc.*, 1955, **77**, 2431.

[30] JAFFE, H. H., *J. Amer. Chem. Soc.*, 1955, **77**, 4451.

[31] KNIGHT, S. B., WALLICK, R. H. and BALCH, C., *J. Amer. Chem. Soc.*, 1955, **77**, 2577 and references listed there.

[32] MARSHALL, J. R. and WALKER, J., *J. Chem. Soc.*, 1951, 1004.

[33] BROWN, D. J., HOERGER, E. and MASON, S. F., *J. Chem. Soc.*, 1955, 4035.

[34] AUSTIN, J. E., *J. Amer. Chem. Soc.*, 1934, **56**, 2141.

[35] MASON, S. F., *J. Chem. Soc.*, 1954, 2071.

[36] STIMPSON, M. M. and REUTER, M. A., *J. Amer. Chem. Soc.*, 1943, **65**, 153.
[37] GULLAND, J. M. and HOLIDAY, E. R., *J. Chem. Soc.*, 1936, 765.
[38] KALCKAR, H. M. and SHAFRAN, M., *J. Biol. Chem.*, 1947, 167, 429.
[39] BAKER, W. and OLLIS, W. D., *Quart. Rev. Chem. Soc.*, *Lond.* 1957, **11**, 15.
[40] HENRY, R. A., FINNEGAN, W. G. and LIEBER, E., *J. Amer. Chem. Soc.*, 1954, **76**, 2894.
[41] UGI, I., PERLINGER, H. and BEHRINGER, L., *Chem. Ber.*, 1958, **91**, 2324.
[42] ANDON, R. L. J. and others, *Trans. Faraday. Soc.*, 1954, **50**, 1918.
[43] LEANDRI, G. and others, *Gazz. chim. Ital.*, 1955, **85**, 769.
[44] MILAZZO, G. and others, *Gazz. chim. Ital.*, 1952, **82**. 576; 1953, **83**, 782.
[45] MILAZZO, G., *Gazz. chim. Ital.*, 1953, **83**, 787.

[46] SURESH, K. S., RANMCHANDRAN, J. and RAO, C. N. R., *J. Sci. Indwtr. Res.* (*India*), 1961, **20B**, 20.
[47] EDISBURY, J. R., HUNTER, R. F. and SCOTT, A. D., *J. Chem. Soc.*, 1948, 1497.
[48] ALBERT, A. and BARLIN, G. B., *J. Chem. Soc.*, 1959, 2384.
[49] DEWAR, M. J. S. and POESCHE, W. H., *J. Amer. Chem. Soc.*, 1963, **85**, 2253.

Chapter 7

APPLICATIONS

The literature is full of instances where ultra-violet and visible spectroscopy have been employed as tools for identification, specification of purity or assignment of structures to compounds. Only a few typical examples will be considered here.

Control of Purification

Ultra-violet and visible spectrophotometry can be effectively used for the control of purification and specification of purity of compounds. If a compound is transparent in the near ultra-violet and the visible regions, the purification is continued until the absorbancy is reduced to a minimum ($\epsilon < 1$). Traces of impurities present in 'pure' transparent organic compounds can be readily detected and estimated, provided the impurities themselves have fairly intense absorption bands. Before a liquid is used as a spectroscopic solvent, it should be tested for spectrophotometric purity. For example, commercial absolute alcohol usually contains benzene as impurity. The absence of benzene in the alcohol should be confirmed spectrophotometrically by using sufficiently large cells (4 or 10 cm cells), before using the alcohol as a solvent. The presence of carbon disulphide in carbon tetrachloride may be detected by the presence of the disulphide absorption band at 318 mμ. The detection of the characteristic benzenoid absorption in the spectra of many organic compounds (e.g. diethyl ether, cyclohexene) showed that the bands attributed to these compounds earlier were only due to the contamination by benzene[1].

If a compound exhibits absorption bands in the near ultra-violet or visible region, the purification should be continued until the molar absorption coefficient attains a constant maximum value. This is similar to carrying out a crystallization of a compound to a constant maximum melting point. It was found spectrophotometrically that polynuclear aromatic hydrocarbons which were considered to be pure earlier, actually contained considerable amounts of impurities (e.g. impurity of anthracene up to 10% in phenanthrene)[2]. The spectrophotometric control of purification is particularly important in biochemistry, where the various stages of concentration of a biologically active compound may be followed by the increasing absorption intensity. Specification of purity of compounds may be made by quoting the absorption intensity at a particular wavelength. The absorption data can be taken as truly characteristic of a compound only when its purity has been ascertained by attainment of constant maximum absorption intensity after repeated fractional purifications. Already, the absorption data are being quoted for the purity specifications of several therapeutic solutions (e.g. vitamins A, C and D).

Identification and Assignment of Structure

The identity of a synthetic product is often established by comparison of its absorption curve with that of the natural product or another standard sample. The absorption curves of synthetic and natural vitamin A_2 are shown in *Figure 7.1*. The identification of coloured substances is easier since colour can almost always be correlated with the presence of certain types of chromophoric groups. Thus, visible absorption spectra are employed for the detection and identification of the natural pigments (e.g. carotenoids, anthocyanins and porphyrins), dyes and other colouring matters. The absorption spectra of these colouring principles will be discussed separately in Chapter 12.

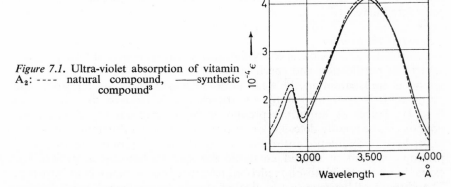

Figure 7.1. Ultra-violet absorption of vitamin A_2: - - - - natural compound, ———synthetic compound[3]

Absorption spectroscopy is of greater value for the detection and identification of colourless organic compounds. Before attempting to interpret the spectra, one should naturally have sufficient information on the compound with regard to the elements present, qualitative tests for functional groups, etc. Compounds which do not exhibit absorption ($\epsilon < 1$) in the 220–800 mμ region may be aliphatic or alicyclic hydrocarbons or their simple derivatives (chlorides, alcohols, ethers or carboxylic acids, etc.) or even simple olefinic compounds. If compounds show sufficiently intense bands in the 220–250 mμ region, they may contain two unsaturated linkages in conjugation. They may also be benzene derivatives. Simple benzene derivatives like toluene show the benzenoid band with vibrational structure around 260 mμ. A high intensity band in the 250–330 mμ region may indicate more than two unsaturated linkages in conjugation. Polycyclic dienes with both ethylenic linkages in the same ring, give bands around 280 mμ. Low intensity bands ($\epsilon < 1000$) in the region 250–350 mμ may indicate $n \rightarrow \pi^*$ bands (R-bands) of chromophoric groups. A conjugated carbonyl group usually gives a medium intensity band between 250 and 300 mμ. If the systems are very complex as in many aromatics (particularly the condensed ring hydrocarbons), heterocycles, enzymes and steroids, the absorption curves will have several maxima, probably with characteristic shape or fine structure. Solvent effects on spectra may often be employed to confirm the assignment of bands. Absorption intensities may also be used for purposes of identification. However, the compounds should be absolutely pure to be able to rely on the absorption intensities. There is a wide range of intensities in organic compounds (ϵ 1–500,000) and once the

88

nature of the compound is known, the absorption intensities may be used as additional evidence for identification or assignment of structure.

Quite often, the absorption data of the derivatives or degradation products of a compound of 'unknown' structure have led to the ultimate structure determination of the parent compound. Recently, the degradation product of vitamin B_{12}, 5:6-dimethylbenziminazole, was identified by its ultra-violet absorption spectrum[4]. The structure of vitamin B_1 (thiamine) was elucidated by comparison of the spectra of its sodium sulphite fission products with the spectra of model compounds[5]. The crude structure of vitamin K_1 was found[6] by the use of spectral data. The absorption spectrum of vitamin K_1 has the following bands: λ_{max}, 249 mμ (ϵ 19,000), 260 mμ (ϵ 18,000) and 325 mμ (ϵ 2,400). The bands around 250 and 330 mμ are characteristic of a naphthaquinone. On reductive acetylation, only one band was seen at 230 mμ, characteristic of a hydronaphthaquinone. Comparison of the vitamin K_1 spectrum with the spectra of several model compounds indicated that the positions of the absorption maxima were similar to those of 2,3-dialkyl-1,4-naphthaquinone. The structure of vitamin K_1 was later found to be I.

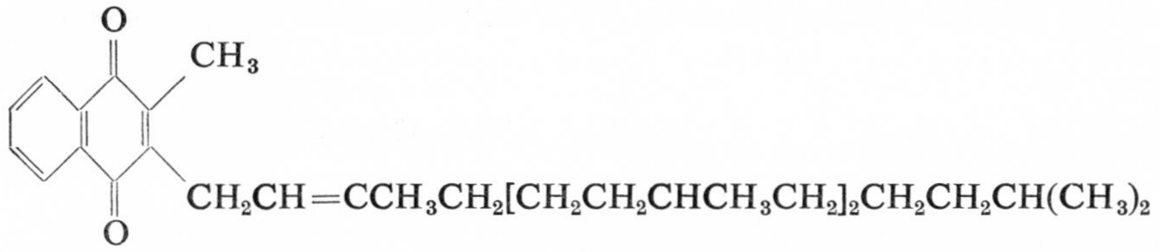
O
CH3
CH2CH=CCH3CH2[CH2CH2CHCH3CH2]2CH2CH2CH(CH3)2
O

I

Vitamin A gives a blue colour with antimony trichloride in chloroform. This blue solution showed two well-defined maxima around 585 and 620 mμ and another weak band around 695 mμ. With liver oil from fresh-water fish, the 695 mμ was prominent and the 620 mμ band was not observed. This indicated the presence of two different species of vitamin A, A_1 and A_2 (II and III)[5]. The near ultra-violet absorption spectra of vitamins A_1 and A_2 are also different. The longer wavelength band of A_2 is probably due to an additional double bond in the conjugated system, III. The 287 mμ band of vitamin A_2 has been ascribed to the diene 'partial chromophore'[93].

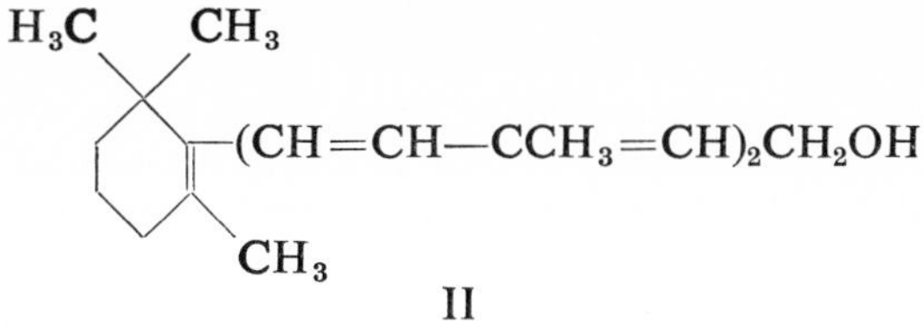
H3C
CH3
(CH=CH—CCH3=CH)2CH2OH
CH3

II

λ_{max} 326 mμ, ϵ 51,000

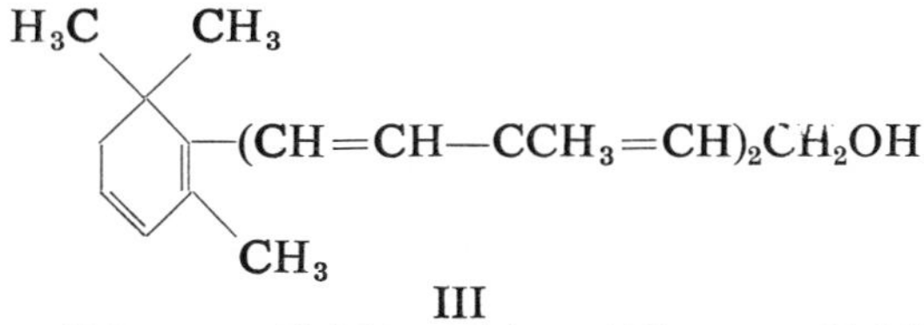
H3C
CH3
(CH=CH—CCH3=CH)2CH2OH
CH3

III

λ_{max} 287 mμ, ϵ 22,000 and λ_{max} 351 mμ, ϵ 41,000

The spectrophotometric analysis of vitamin A has now replaced the tedious biological method of assay. Other important examples where ultra-violet spectroscopy has replaced the biological methods of assay are vitamin D (four peaks around 280 mμ) and vitamin K.

The structures of the insect pigments, erythroaphins, were found to contain perylene-quinone units by comparison of the ultra-violet-visible spectra[99]. The structure of hypericin was found to contain the dimethylmesonaphthadianthrene skeleton by comparison of the synthetic specimen with the product of reductive acetylation of hypericin[100]. The structure of the glucoside, plumieride, was solved by the study of the ultra-violet absorption spectra of the products of various transformations of the glucoside[102].

Electronic absorption spectroscopy did not provide any direct evidence for the characterization of penicillins, since they show little absorption in the near ultra-violet or visible regions which can be associated with chromophoric groups. However, ultra-violet absorption spectra were useful in solving the structures of some of the degradation products[7]. On reaction with alcohols, penicillins give α-esters of penicilloates, IV, which are quantitatively converted to penamaldates, V, in the presence of alcoholic mercuric

$$\underset{\text{IV}}{\begin{array}{c} \overset{O}{\overset{\parallel}{R-C}} \quad \overset{O}{\overset{\parallel}{C-R^1}} \quad HN\text{---}CH\text{---}COOH \\ HN\text{---}CH\text{------}HC \quad C\text{---}(CH_3)_2 \\ S \end{array}}$$

$$\underset{\text{V}}{\begin{array}{c} \overset{O}{\overset{\parallel}{R-C}} \quad \overset{O}{\overset{\parallel}{C-R^1}} \\ HN\text{---}CH\text{---}CH\text{=}N\text{---}CH\text{---}COOH \\ C \\ HS \quad (CH_3)_2 \end{array}}$$

chloride solutions. The penamaldates, being Schiff bases, absorb strongly at 283 mμ ($\epsilon \sim 18{,}000$). If mercuric ion is added to alcoholic solutions of pencilloates, the 283 mμ band develops rapidly. Benzylpenicillin undergoes a very slow change in its spectrum with the addition of mercuric ion, while N-acetylated penicilloates do not show any change. Acylation apparently stabilizes the thiazolidine ring towards mercuric ion. In benzylpenicillin, the rupture of the C—S bond does not take place until the N—C=O group has

$$\underset{\text{VI}}{\begin{array}{c} \overset{O}{\overset{\parallel}{R-C}}\text{---}NH\text{---}CH\text{---}HC \quad \overset{S}{\overset{}{C}}\text{---}(CH_3)_2 \\ O\text{=}C\text{---}N\text{------}CH\text{---}COOH \end{array}}$$

90

$$
\begin{array}{ccccc}
& N & & S & \\
R-C & CH & HC & C-(CH_3)_2 \\
| & & | & | & \\
O & C=O & HN & CH-COOH
\end{array}
$$

VII

been cleaved by slow alcoholysis. Such a behaviour could only be understood in terms of the β-lactam structure, VI, and not the oxazolone structure, VII, for penicillin. The product obtained by the Raney nickel desulphurization of sodium benzylpenicillinate gives many of the benzylpenicillin reactions. This indicated that the carboxylic group of benzylpenicillin still remained after the desulphurization. A crystalline N-nitroso-derivative of the methyl ester of the desulphurization product was prepared and its absorption spectrum showed absorption maxima at 425, 405 and 248 mμ, characteristic of N-nitrosoamides. The N-nitrosoamide structure becomes possible only if penicillin has the β-lactam structure.

Although the correct structural formula had been intuitively proposed earlier, the structure of strychnine was founded on a firm basis only when Woodward, Brehm and Nelson[8] discovered that strychnone obtained from the oxidation of Ψ-strychnine gave ultra-violet absorption maxima resembling those of N-acylindoles. Strychnine, on the other hand, gives bands similar to N-acyldihydroindoles. Woodward and McLamore[9] recently established the structure of another alkaloid, semperivirine, on the basis of its ultra-violet absorption spectrum. The presence of the indole nucleus in indole alkaloids is deduced by the presence of absorption bands in the regions 225 (ϵ 25,000) and 280 mμ (ϵ 6,000). Alloyohimbine and ajmalicine are two typical alkaloids belonging to this family and showing absorption in these regions. The spectra of oxindoles are similar to those of substituted acetanilides[101]. (For absorption data on alkaloids see references 94 and 95.)

The structure of the antibiotic terramycin was established by comparing the absorption spectrum of decarboxyterracinoic acid obtained by alkaline degradation and subsequent decarboxylation of terramycin, with the spectra of 5- and 7-hydroxindanones. The comparison clearly indicated the relation of the structure of terramycin to that of 5-hydroxyindanone[10]. The structures of the antibiotic mycomycin, VIII, and its isomer, isomycomycin, IX, were differentiated by absorption data[11]. The ultra-violet absorption spectrum of isomycomycin was similar to that of a triacetylenic system in conjugation with a diene, X.

$$CH{\equiv}C-C{\equiv}C-CH{=}C{=}CH-CH{=}CH-CH{=}CH-CH_2COOH$$

VIII, λ_{max}, 256 (ϵ 35,000), 267 (ϵ 61,000) and 281 mμ (ϵ 67,000)

$$CH_3-C{\equiv}C-C{\equiv}C-C{\equiv}C-CH{=}CH-CH{=}CH-CH_2COOH$$

IX, λ_{max}, 246 (ϵ 24,000), 258 (ϵ 58,000), 267 (ϵ 110,000), 288 (ϵ 14,000), 306 (ϵ 27,000), 324 (ϵ 41,000) and 347 mμ (ϵ 34,000)

$$CH_3-CH{=}CH-C{\equiv}C-C{\equiv}C-C{\equiv}C-CH{=}CHCH_3$$

X, λ_{max}, 245 (ϵ 25,000), 259 (ϵ 43,000), 269 (ϵ 76,000), 289 (ϵ 11,000), 306 (ϵ 18,000), 325 (ϵ 26,000) and 348 mμ (ϵ 20,000).

Absorption data can be used more effectively in molecular structure studies if the chemistry of the system is known in detail. Typical examples would be determination of the relative positions of functional groups in a molecule, differentiation of conjugated and unconjugated arrangements of unsaturated groups. The application of absorption spectra in the structure elucidation of dienes and $\alpha\beta$-unsaturated carbonyl compounds was already discussed in Chapter 4. The empirical relations proposed by Gillam and co-workers[12,14] and Woodward[13] between the structure and the location of the ultra-violet absorption maxima have been very useful in confirming the structures of several conjugated systems. The ultra-violet absorption data are of particular importance in the fields of steroids and terpenes[15]. A few typical examples of the application of absorption spectroscopy for the determination of structures of some conjugated systems will now be discussed.

Abietic and levopimaric acids are two isomeric diterpenoid acids and exhibit absorption bands at 238 mμ (ϵ 16,100) and 273 mμ (ϵ 7,100) respectively. As pointed out earlier in Chapter 4, the diene absorption band appears in the 235–248 mμ range if two conjugated ethylenic linkages are in two different rings and in the 260–283 mμ region if two ethylenic linkages are in the same ring[12]. On this basis, abietic acid was assigned the structure XI while levopimaric acid was assigned the structure XII[16]. The structures of

XI   XII

α- and β-phellandrenes, XIII and XIV, were similarly assigned from the positions of the absorption maxima[12]. The absorption spectra of α- and

XIII, λ_{max} 263 mμ (ϵ 2,500)   XIV, λ_{max} 231 mμ (ϵ 9,000)

β-ionones, XV and XVI, are markedly different. β-Ionone has a longer

XV, λ_{max} 228 mμ (ϵ 14,000)   XVI, λ_{max} 296 mμ (ϵ 11,000)

conjugated system than the α-isomer and would be expected to absorb at a longer wavelength. Further, α-ionone shows a low intensity carbonyl band around 305 mμ which is not observed in the case of the β-isomer. The sesquiterpene ketone, α-cyperone, was assigned the structure of a trisubstituted $\alpha\beta$-unsaturated ketone on the basis of its absorption spectrum (λ_{max} 251 mμ, $\epsilon \sim 10,000$; 312 mμ, $\epsilon \sim 100$). Woodward's rules[13] predict the absorption maximum for this trisubstituted $\alpha\beta$-unsaturated ketone at 252 mμ. In the study of morphine alkaloids[103], the β- and ϕ-dihydrothebaines were distinguished by the homoannular diene absorption (λ_{max} 284 mμ, ϵ_{max} 11,000) of the β-compound (λ_{max} calc. $253 + 3 \times 15 + 15$ for OMe $= 283$ mμ). The ϕ compound absorbs at 282 mμ (ϵ_{max} 200) characteristic of the dialkylcatechol.

An empirical method of calculating the position of the long wavelength absorption maximum of any steroid diene has been proposed by Fieser, Fieser and Rajagopalan[17]. The method was described in *Table 4.5*. This method has been employed for the differentiation of two diosterols[15].

Absorption data on isolated double bonds in steroids are summarized in *Table 7.1*.

Table 7.1. Absorption data on Isolated Double Bonds in Steroids[104]

	λ_{max}, mμ	ϵ_{max}	ϵ_{210}	ϵ_{215}	ϵ_{220}
Δ^2 or Δ^6 (Disubstituted)	203	600–1,300	~400	100	—
Δ^4, Δ^5, Δ^7 or Δ^{14} (Trisubstituted)	203–207	3,400–4,200	1,000–4,000	700–2,900	100–1,500
$\Delta^{8,9}$, $\Delta^{8,14}$ or $\Delta^{9,10}$ (Tetrasubstituted)	205–207·5	4,600–10,400	4,400–10,1000	3,900–8,000	1900–5,700
$\Delta^{7,22}$ (Two isolated double bonds)	204·5	5,400	4,900	3,500	1,700

Barrelene, C_8H_8, which is a highly symmetrical ring hydrocarbon with three double bonds, shows two bands at 208 (log ϵ 3·05) and 239 mμ (log ϵ 2·48). The long wavelength absorption in this compound indicates some orbital overlap between the 'isolated' double bonds[127]. Bicyclo [2·2·0] hexa-2,5-diene (Dewar benzene), on the other hand, shows only end absorption above 215 mμ, typical of isolated ethylenic bonds[128].

The absorption spectra of cross-conjugated dienes can be interpreted by resolving the system into linear conjugated units and calculating the λ_{max} based on the linear unit absorbing at the longest wavelength. Thus, the cross-conjugated triene[105] shown below should be considered as made up of the homoannular diene C and the double bond in ring B should be ignored

The calculated value will then be $253 + (5 \times 5) + (2 \times 5) = 288$ mμ (obs.

285 mμ ϵ 9,100). The λ_{max} of cross-conjugated dienones and enediones can also be interpreted, based on model compounds. The die–ones shown below show a considerable difference in λ_{max} as expected.

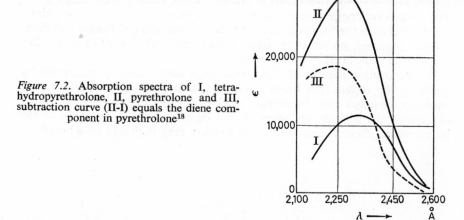

240 mμ 276 mμ

Gillam and West[18] established the structure of pyrethrolone, XVII, the hydrolysis product of pyrethrin, by comparing its absorption spectrum with that of tetrahydropyrethrolone, XVIII. Pyrethrolone was known to contain a five-membered ring, three ethylenic double bonds and a keto group, but their relative positions were not known. The absorption maxima of both pyrethrolone and tetrahydropyrethrolone were found to be about the same but the absorption intensity was much lower in the latter compound. The

XVII, λ_{max} 227 mμ (ϵ 26,700)   XVIII, λ_{max} 232 mμ (ϵ 11,600)

positions of the two bands indicate that both the compounds contain an $\alpha\beta$-unsaturated ketone grouping. The difference spectrum of the two compounds showed an intense peak ($\epsilon \sim$ 15,000) around 223 mμ (*Figure 7.2*).

Figure 7.2. Absorption spectra of I, tetra-hydropyrethrolone, II, pyrethrolone and III, subtraction curve (II–I) equals the diene component in pyrethrolone[18]

This indicated that the two ethylenic linkages in the side chain of pyrethrolone were in conjugation. Similar results were obtained[18] by the curve subtraction method with the absorption curves of the semicarbazones of pyrethrolone and tetrahydropyrethrolone. The structure of the metabolite, geodin, was settled by the subtraction spectrum of geodin minus dihydrogriseofulvin which showed a λ_{max} at 241 mμ (ϵ_{max} 14,000) corresponding to a dienone[106], which is cross-conjugated. The presence of an $\alpha\beta$-unsaturated carbonyl or a cross-conjugated dienone in zerumbone[113] was inferred from ultra-violet absorption spectra which showed bands at 248 (ϵ 8,480) and 325 mμ (ϵ 250) and a shoulder at 233 mμ (ϵ 8000). Woodward and Singh[19] proposed the structure of patulin as XIX, with the C=C—C=C—C=O unit, only because of the fact that it absorbs at 276 mμ (ϵ 17,000). Woodward and Yates[107] have employed ultra-violet spectroscopy as one of the tools in identifying the various isolated and unsaturated carbonyl fractions in α, β and γ-metasantonins.

$$O\text{---}C\text{=}O$$
$$|$$
$$CH$$

$$O\text{---}OH$$

XIX

The extent of alkylation in conjugated systems can be estimated by the empirical rules of Woodward[13]. For example, the two isomeric carbinols, XX and XXI, obtained by the acid-catalysed rearrangement of isobutenyl-vinylcarbinol, may be differentiated[20]. While XX is a monoalkylated diene,

$(H_3C)_2\text{---}C\text{---}CH\text{=}CH\text{---}CH\text{=}CH_2$
$\qquad\quad |$
$\qquad\quad OH$

λ_{max} 223 mμ (ϵ 26,000)

XX

$(H_3C)_2C\text{=}CH\text{---}CH\text{=}CH\text{---}CH_2OH$

λ_{max} 236 mμ (ϵ 19,000)

XXI

XXI is a trialkylated diene. The application of Woodward's rules in the case of α-cyperone has already been mentioned.

Studies on secoketone[108] (λ_{max} 318, ϵ_{max} 280) have shown that there is considerable spatial interaction between the carbonyl groups. The oxidation product of pinacone acetate[109] was found to be a α-diketone with characteristic absorption at 402 mμ (ϵ_{max} 52). The anomalous ultra-violet and infra-red spectra of germacrone, balchanolide and other ten-membered ring compounds have been explained on the basis of the special geometry of these molecules[114].

cis–trans *Isomerism*

Since geometrical isomers differ in the spatial arrangement of groups about a plane, the absorption spectra of the isomers will be different. The *trans*-isomer is normally more elongated than the *cis*-isomer and consequently both the λ_{max} and ϵ_{max} of the former should be greater. If steric effects of substituents are also operative, deviations from coplanarity in the case of the *cis*-isomers would also affect the absorption spectra (see Chapter 8). The long wavelength bands (K- or conjugation bands) for the *cis*- and *trans*- forms of some simple molecules are listed in *Table 7.2*. It appears that one makes the generalization that the positions as well as the intensities of of the long wavelength bands of the *trans*-isomers are always greater than those of the corresponding *cis*-isomers. (*Figure 7.3*).

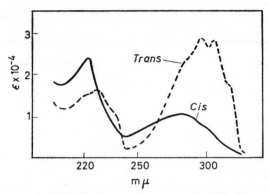

Figure 7.3. Absorption spectra of *cis*-and *trans*-stilbenes

Table 7.2. $\pi - \pi^*$ Absorption Bands of a few Simple Geometrical Isomers[21, 129]

	cis-form		*trans*-form	
	λ_{max}, mμ	ϵ_{max}	λ_{max}, mμ	ϵ_{max}
PhHC = CHPh	280	13,500	295	27,000
PhHC = CHCOOH	264	9,500	273	20,000
Ph N = NPh	285	15,000	319	20,000

Comparison of the absorption intensities of polycyclic dienes with both the ethylenic linkages in the same ring (and consequently of *cis*-configuration) with the corresponding dienes having the two linkages in two different rings (*trans*-configuration), shows that the dienes with the *trans*-configuration always exhibit higher intensities[22] (*Table 7.3*). Absorption intensities may thus be used for structure elucidation of polycyclic dienes in addition to the positions of the absorption maxima[12].

Table 7.3. Absorption Intensities of some Polycyclic Dienes[22]

Double bonds in the same ring (*cis*-configuration) $\lambda_{max} \sim 280$ mμ		Double bonds in two different rings (*trans*-configuration) $\lambda_{max} \sim 240$ mμ	
	ϵ_{max}		ϵ_{max}
Ergosterol	11,800	Ergosterol-D	21,000
7-Dehydrocholesterol	11,400	Dehydroergosterol	19,000
Cholesta-2:4-diene	7,000	Cholesta-4:6-diene	28,000
Levopimaric acid	7,100	Abietic acid	16,100

While only two geometrical isomers exist in simple unsaturated molecules, a number of *cis–trans* isomers can exist in polyenes (e.g. carotenoids[96]). Normally, the all-*trans*-isomer is preponderant in carotenoids. Isomerization of the all-*trans*-carotenoids by acid- or iodine-catalysis yield the so-called *neo*-carotenoids. The *neo*-carotenoids are believed to possess one *cis*-ethylenic bond in the central position of the conjugated chain[96]. The *neo*-carotenoids exhibit not only a weaker long wavelength band ($\sim$ 470 mμ) than the all *trans*-isomers, but also a new peak in the 320–380 mμ region. This peak is ascribed to the *cis*-ethylenic bond[23]. However, the poly-*cis*-carotenoids exhibit less intense peaks in this region than the *neo*-carotenoids. As an illustration, the absorption curves of all-*trans*, poly-*cis*- and *neo*-lycopenes are reproduced[23] in *Figure 7.4*. From theoretical considerations, it has been shown that the *cis*-peak is most intense in isomers with one centrally located ethylenic linkage in the *cis*-configuration.

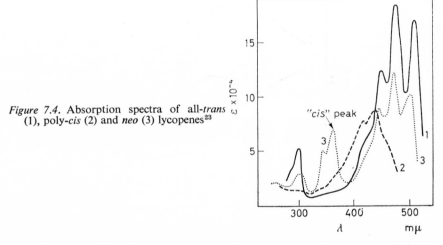

Figure 7.4. Absorption spectra of all-*trans* (1), poly-*cis* (2) and *neo* (3) lycopenes[23]

Optical Isomerism

The absorption spectra of optically active (d or l), racemic and inactive isomers are generally found to be similar. Optical isomerism has no effect on λ_{max} or ϵ_{max}[24]. However, when a compound has more than one asymmetric carbon atom, the optical isomers may not exactly have the same absorption properties[25,26]. Very recently, the technique of optical rotatory dispersion has been used effectively for structural investigations of optical isomers (see Chapter 12).

Tautomerism

Whenever two or more readily interconvertible isomers of a substance are in (dynamic) equilibrium, there will generally be migration of double bonds. The most often encountered tautomerism is between the keto and the enol forms of an oxygen-containing compound. Ethyl acetoacetate is probably one of the earliest known cases of keto-enol tautomerism. While the keto-form, XXII, shows a low intensity ($\epsilon \sim 20$) band around 275 mμ characteristic of an isolated keto-carbonyl group, the enol form, XXIII, shows a high intensity band ($\epsilon \sim 18{,}000$) around 245 mμ due to the conjugated double bond. The absorption curves of ethyl acetoacetate in different solvents have

$$H_3CCCH_2COOC_2H_5 \atop \| \atop O$$

$$H_3C \ C = CHCOOC_2H_5 \atop | \atop OH$$

XXII

XXIII

been reproduced[27] in *Figure 7.5*. The proportion of the enol-form seems to be greatest in hexane and least in water. The percentage of the enol form is nearly equal to 100 ϵ_m/ϵ_e where ϵ_m is the observed extinction coefficient at

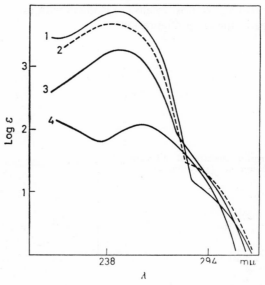

Figure 7.5. Absorption curves of ethylacetoacetate in different solvents[27]: 1, hexane; 2, ether; 3, alcohol; 4, water

245 mμ in a particular solvent and ϵ_e that of the pure enol-form[27]. Acetyl-acetone, XXIV, enolizes to the form XXV, and the latter absorbs strongly ($\epsilon \sim 12{,}000$) around 270 mμ in hexane. The enol-form is stabilized through chelation* and also by resonance. The absorption data and percentage of the

$$O \quad O \atop \| \quad \| \atop CH_3-CCH_2C-CH_3$$

XXIV

XXV

* Aromatic compounds with an *o*-OH group often absorb at longer wavelengths than the *m*- and *p*-OH derivatives. These bathochromic shifts have been ascribed to chelation[97].

Table 7.4. *Keto-enol Equilibria of Ethyl Acetoacetate and Acetylacetone*[27]

Solvent	Ethyl acetoacetate			Acetylacetone		
	λ_{max}, mμ	ϵ_{max}	% Enol	λ_{max}, mμ	ϵ_{max}	% Enol
Hexane	244	8,100	51	269	12,100	96
Ether	244	5,100	32	—	—	—
Alcohol	246	1,900	12	273	10,500	84
Water	255	120	—	277	1,900	15

enol-forms of ethyl acetoacetate and acetylacetone in different solvents are given in *Table 7.4.*

The keto-enol tautomerism of benzoylacetone, XXVI, and its derivatives has been studied in detail[28]. The absorption curves of benzoylacetone in

$$\overset{\text{O}}{\underset{\|}{}} \quad \overset{\text{O}}{\underset{\|}{}}$$
$$C_6H_5C-CH_2C-CH_3$$

XXVI

ether and water are shown in *Figure 7.6.* Both the bands at 247 and 310 mμ are composite bands. However, the intensity of the 310 mμ band may be taken as directly proportional to the enol content of the system (assuming that the diketo-form, XXVI, has negligible absorption, $\epsilon \sim 100$ or less). The enol-form is more prominent in ether solution ($\sim 99\%$) than in water.

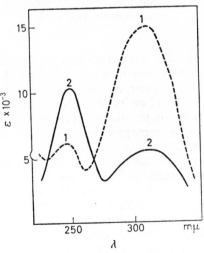

Figure 7.6. Absorption curves of benzoylacetone in (1) ether and (2) water[28]

Thione-thiol tautomerism has been investigated in several compounds. One of the best known examples is the tautomerism in 2-mercaptobenzo-thiazole, XXVII, which has been investigated in detail[29-31]. The spectrum

99

of the compound in alcohol is similar to that of the N-methyl derivative and not to that of the S-methyl derivative, thus indicating that the thione-form is predominant. The thione-thiol tautomerism in derivatives of mercapto-thiazoles[32] and mercaptotetrazoles[33] has been investigated.

$$\text{(structure)} \quad \text{C—SH} \rightleftharpoons \text{(structure)} \quad \text{C}=\text{S}$$

XXVII

The keto-enol and thione-thiol tautomerisms in pyridine and pyrimidine derivatives were already discussed in Chapter 6. Azo-hydrazo tautomerism, $CH—N=N \rightleftharpoons C=N—NH$, has been studied by Burawoy and Thompson[34]. Another type of tautomerism has been identified in the case of carbohydrates. The proportions of the ring and open structures of carbohydrates have been determined by measuring the intensity of the 280 mμ carbonyl band. Pacsu and Hiller[35] have shown that D-glucose exists almost completely in the ring form in neutral solution and to the extent of 0·1 per cent in the open chain form in acid solution.

Recently, Rao and co-workers have [111] studied the effect of solvents on keto-enol equilibria and found that polar and proton-donor solvents, which can stabilize the carbonyl group by dipolar association or hydrogen bonding, decrease the magnitude of enolization. The anomalous ultra-violet absorption of 1,2-dicyano-esters has been interpreted in terms of keto-enol equilibria, hydrogen bonding and unusual solvent effects[112].

Quantitative Analysis

For the past two decades, ultra-violet and visible spectrophotometry have been widely used for the quantitative determination of substances. The only criterion for developing a spectrophotometric method of analysis of a compound is that the compound or its derivative should obey Beer's law in the range of concentrations to be studied. The accuracy of the method will depend on the slope of the linear plot of optical density against concentration. The greater the slope, the higher is the accuracy. Any variety of examples may be given where spectrophotometry has been used for the routine quantitative analysis of substances in small amounts: benzene in cyclohexane; carbon disulphide in carbon tetrachloride; ergosterol content of sterols from natural sources[36]; vitamin A content in fish liver oils[37,39] and chlorophylls[38]. In some cases, special techniques or methods of analysis of absorption curves have been employed. Ergosterol was detected in cod liver oil by recording the absorption spectrum of a thin film of the oil between two quartz plates[40]. A method has been developed for the evaluation of 'irrelevant absorption' in samples of vitamin A, in order to correct the absorption intensity in the 324 mμ region, for the contribution by inactive material[39,41,98]. This method is used in the determination of a substance present in a mixture with other relatively transparent substances.

The procedure of Morton and Stubbs[115] to correct for background absorption has been useful in obtaining the true extinction of a compound at the λ_{max}. The procedure involves choosing three wavelengths λ', λ'' and λ''' where λ'' is the λ_{max} and λ' and λ''' are the 'fixation points' at which the extinction

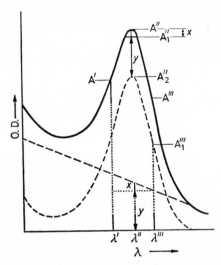

Figure 7.7. Procedure of Morton and Stubbs for correcting for background absorption (From R. A. Morton and A. L. Stubbs[115] by courtesy of W. Heffer & Sons Ltd.)

coefficients ϵ' and ϵ''' are equal. The ϵ'' value is equal to ϵ_{max}. The background absorption may be taken as linear between λ''' and λ' if $\lambda''' - \lambda'$ is not very large. The procedure as applied to Vitamin A in cod liver oil is given below, and the procedure can be understood by referring to *Figure 7.7.*

$$\lambda' = 313 \text{ m}\mu, \text{ A}' = 0\cdot640$$
$$\lambda'' = 328 \text{ m}\mu, \text{ A}'' = 0\cdot712$$
$$\lambda''' = 338\cdot5 \text{ m}\mu, \text{ A}''' = 0\cdot620$$
$$\lambda''' - \lambda'' = 10\cdot5 \text{ m}\mu$$
$$\lambda''' - \lambda' = 25\cdot5 \text{ m}\mu$$
$$C_1 = \frac{\lambda''' - \lambda''}{\lambda''' - \lambda'} = \frac{10\cdot5}{25\cdot5} = 0\cdot412$$
$$x = C_1(\text{A}' - \text{A}''') = 0\cdot412 \, (0\cdot640 - 0\cdot620)$$
$$= 0\cdot008$$
$$\text{A}_1'' = \text{A}'' - x = 0\cdot712 - 0\cdot008 = 0\cdot704$$

λ' and λ''' were chosen so that $\epsilon' = \epsilon''' = \frac{6}{7} \epsilon''$.

$$C_2 = \epsilon''/\epsilon''' = 7/6 = 1\cdot167$$
$$y = \frac{C_2\text{A}''' - \text{A}_1''}{C_2 - 1} = \frac{(1\cdot167 \times 0\cdot620) - 0\cdot704}{(1\cdot167 - 1)}$$
$$\text{and A}_2'' = \text{A}_1'' - y = 0\cdot704 - 0\cdot116 = 0\cdot588$$

101

Therefore, the background contribution to A'' at λ'' is 17 per cent.

From the above illustration it is clear that background correction can be considerable at the λ_{max}. It is important to note that A' and A''' must be measured carefully since the correction x can be quite small. Further, A' and A''' values are dependent on the errors due to the choice of λ' and λ''' and calibration of the instrument. Astwood, Greer and Ettlinger[116] have used a procedure similar to that of Morton and Stubbs[115] for background correction. Correction for background absorption due to scattering is necessary in the case of samples such as macromolecules which show scattering. Englander and Epstein[117] have discussed such corrections due to scattering by macromolecular solutes. Morton and Stubbs[118] have also discussed a general case where λ', λ'', λ''' and ϵ', ϵ'' and ϵ''' do not belong to the same band.

Most elements (chiefly metallic) may be determined quantitatively by using spectrophotometry and the method generally depends on the formation of reaction products or complexes which absorb in the ultra-violet or visible region. There are so many spectrophotometric applications in analytical work that a review will not be attempted in this book. Several reviews have appeared on the subject[42-44]. The applications of spectrophotometry in biological and pharmaceutical analysis have also been reviewed[45-47].

Mixture Analysis

A mixture of substances with widely separated absorption maxima may be readily analysed using the Beer's law plot for each component independently. A mixture of substances absorbing in the same wavelength region can be analysed from the observed absorption of the mixture at a number of suitable wavelengths, provided the components absorb independently and the extinction coefficient of each pure component is known. The measured optical density at any wavelength is given by the equation

$$D = \log I_0/I = (\epsilon_1 c_1 + \epsilon_2 c_2 + \ldots)l$$

where ϵ's are the extinction coefficients of the various components at a given wavelength and c's are the corresponding concentrations and l is the length of the cell. If n components are in the mixture, density measurements will have to be made at n different wavelengths and n simultaneous equations of the above-mentioned form will have to be solved. This method is very easily employed for mixtures of two components absorbing in the same wavelength region.

Another analytical method[48], based on the ratio of the observed optical densities at two wavelengths, has been used for binary mixtures. The two wavelengths are selected so that a straight line plot is obtained between the ratio of the optical densities and the relative concentration of each component. The method is as follows.

$$D' = \epsilon_1' c_1 + \epsilon_2' c_2 \text{ at } \lambda'$$

and

$$D'' = \epsilon_1'' c_1 + \epsilon_2'' c_2 \text{ at } \lambda''$$

Therefore

$$D'/D'' = (\epsilon_1' c_1 + \epsilon_2' c_2)/(\epsilon_1'' c_1 + \epsilon_2'' c_2)$$

If λ'' is so chosen that it is the point of intersection of the two absorption curves (isobestic point), then $\epsilon_1'' = \epsilon_2'' = \epsilon''$ and the above equation reduces to

$$D'/D'' = (\epsilon_1' c_1 + \epsilon_2' c_2)/(\epsilon'' c_1 + \epsilon'' c_2)$$

The denominator being a constant, a plot of the observed optical density ratio against the molar fraction of each component will be a straight line. This method has also been extended to mixtures of three substances. A further simplified form of the ratio method has been suggested[49]. If the optical densities of standard solutions of two substances at concentrations c_1 and c_2 are at wavelengths D_1 and D_2 respectively, then the observed optical density of a solution containing the two components at concentrations x_1 and x_2 will be

$$D_{obs} = x_1 D_1/c_1 + x_2 D_2/c_2$$

or

$$D_{obs}/D_1 = x_1/c_1 + x_2 D_2/c_2 D_1$$

A plot of D_{obs}/D_1 against D_2/D_1 will be a straight line with a slope of x_2/c_2 and an intercept of x_1/c_1.

In the literature, one finds procedures for the spectrophotometric analysis of a variety of bi-component or multicomponent systems. Typical examples would be analysis of a- and b- forms of chlorophyll[50], tyrosine and tryptophane in proteins[51], mixtures of hydrocarbons containing up to six components[52], styrene and polystyrene[53], mixtures of linoleic, linolenic and elaeostearic acids[54], vitamin A in butter[55], etc.

Determination of Molecular Weight

If a compound forms a derivative with a reagent which has a characteristic absorption band of high intensity at a wavelength where the compound does not absorb, then the extinction coefficient of the derivative is usually the same as that of the reagent. While the extinction coefficient, ϵ, of the absorption band remains constant in all the derivatives, the optical density, D, will depend on the molecular weight of the compound. The molecular weight of the compound, M, is readily calculated from the absorption data.

$$M = \epsilon w l/D$$

or

$$M = 10\ \epsilon/E_{1cm}^{1\%}$$

where w is the weight of the compound in grammes per litre and l is the cell thickness. A good example for the spectrophotometric determination of molecular weight would be the amine picrates[56]. Picric acid and the amine picrates absorb at 380 mμ with a ϵ value of 13,400. The spectrophotometric method gives molecular weights of amines with an accuracy of $\pm 2\%$. The molecular weights of sugars have been determined (within $\pm 2\%$) from the absorption spectra of the osazones[57]. Osazones show three absorption maxima at 256 mμ (ϵ 20,000), 310 mμ (ϵ 10,000) and 397 mμ (ϵ 20,000) and the extinction coefficients of the maxima are independent of the sugar component. The molecular weights of aldehydes and ketones may be determined from the absorption data of their 2,4-dinitrophenylhydrazones[58-60] (for saturated compounds, λ_{max} 360 mμ, $\epsilon \sim 22,000$). The molecular weights of saturated alcohols may be obtained from the absorption data of the β-2,4-dinitrophenyl-propionyl esters (λ_{max} 242 mμ, ϵ 14,400)[61].

Dissociation Constants of Acids and Bases

Determination of the dissociation constants of acids and bases is one of the important methods in the elucidation of the structures of organic molecules[62] and the spectrophotometric method offers an accurate method for the determination of the dissociation constants. The absorption spectra of organic compounds with acidic or basic functional groups are usually dependent on the pH of the medium. That is, the shape and intensity of the absorption curve vary with the hydrogen ion concentration. The spectrophotometric determination of the dissociation constant of an acid or a base is based on such changes in the absorption spectrum with the pH of the medium. Detailed discussions and derivations of the equations employed in the calculations have been given in the literature[63,64]. A typical formulation will be discussed here.

The dissociation of an acid HB in water may be written as

$$HB + H_2O \rightleftharpoons H_3O^+ + B^-$$

where B^- is the conjugate base. Applying the law of mass action to this equilibrium

$$K_a = a_{H_3O^+} \cdot a_{B^-} / a_{HB}$$

By substituting concentrations for activities in dilute solution

$$K_a = c_{H_3O^+} \cdot c_{B^-} / c_{HB}$$

Taking the negative logarithm on both sides

$$-\log K_a = -\log c_{H_3O^+} -\log (c_{B^-} / c_{HB})$$

$$pK_a = pH + \log (c_{HB}/c_{B^-})$$

If the pH of the solution and the concentrations of HB and B^- are measured, pK_a can be readily calculated. Spectrophotometry is employed in determining the ratio (c_{HB}/c_{B^-}). Since the conjugate acid and base forms of a substance will be in equilibrium, the relative concentration of each form will depend on the pH of the solution. For moderately weak acids or bases, the pH of the solution may be adjusted so as to make one of the forms predominant. For example, the spectrum of an acid HB in alkaline solution will correspond to the absorption of the anion (D_{B^-}) and in acid solution, to that of the undissociated acid (D_{HB}). At intermediate pH values, however, both forms will be present and the observed absorption (D) will be a linear combination of those of the two forms (provided Beer's law holds). Since the optical densities (D_{B^-} and D_{HB}) of the two forms (for a fixed concentration of the solute) are known, the relative concentrations of the two forms at any intermediate pH may be calculated. A similar spectrophotometric procedure may be applied to bases. The acidity function, H_0, which is a measure of the proton-donating tendency of a medium towards a neutral base, has also been determined by spectrophotometry[65].

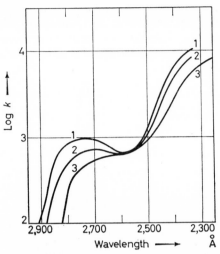

Figure 7.8. Absorption curves of benzoic acid[63] in 1, $0·1N\,H_2SO_4$, 2, buffer and 3, $0·1N$ NaOH

Let us now consider a specific example, that of benzoic acid, as worked out by Flexser, Hammett and Dingwall[63]. The absorption curves of benzoic acid in different media ($0·1N$ H_2SO_4, $0·1N$ NaOH and in a buffer of $0·1M$ sodium acetate in $0·35M$ acetic acid) are shown in *Figure 7.8*. The absorption data at different wavelengths are given in *Table 7.5*. The pK_a of benzoic acid was calculated using the equation

$$pK_a = (pH)_{Buffer} + \log c_{HB}/c_{B^-}$$
$$= pK_{HAc} + \log c_{Ac^-}/c_{HAc} + \log (D - D_{B^-})/(D_{HB} - D)$$

The pK_a of acetic acid at 25°C was taken as 4·76 and pK_a values of benzoic acid were calculated[63] from the absorption data at different wavelengths (*Table 7.5*).

Table 7.5. *The Acid Strength of Benzoic Acid*[63]

| Wavelength, mμ | Extinction coefficients (K) in | | | pK |
	$0·1N$ H_2SO_4	$0·1N$ NaOH	Buffer	
285·7	450	50	225	4·11
279·1	840	300	540	4·13
272·7	950	475	680	4·10
266·7	820	575	680	4·09
250·0	1350	900	1050	3·92
244·9	3050	1400	2350	4·35
240·0	6450	2300	4500	4·27
235·3	9200	4800	7200	4·30
			Average	4·16 ± 0·11

Flexser, Hammett and Dingwall[63] have determined the dissociation constants of several weak acids and bases by this method. Brown and McDaniel[66] have used a similar procedure for the determination of base strengths of pyridine derivatives.

An alternative method for determining dissociation constants involves plotting the observed optical density at a particular wavelength against the pH of the solution and obtaining the midpoint, where pH = pK (i.e. $c_{HB} = c_{B^-}$), graphically. This type of titration is tedious since it involves measurement of pH and optical density of a number of samples.

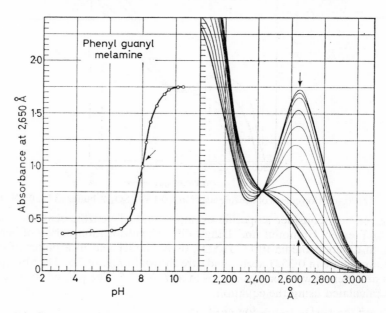

Figure 7.9. Cary trace of the titration of phenylguanylmelamine and plot of absorbance *versus* pH[67]

King and Hirt[67] have recently described an apparatus called a 'Spectortitrimeter' which provides a fast and accurate method for the spectrophotometric determination of dissociation constants. The apparatus consists of a titration flask, a glass and tygon pump, a 5 mm quartz absorption cell having inlet and outlet tubes, a pH meter, a constant temperature bath and a recording spectrophotometer. A typical set of absorption curves obtained with a 'Spectro-titrimeter' in conjunction with a Cary recording spectrophotometer is shown in *Figure 7.9.* A plot of absorbance *versus* pH is shown to the left side in the figure and the point where pH = pK is indicated by arrows.

Study of Chemical Reactions

If the absorption spectra of the reactants and products are considerably different,. spectrophotometry may be employed to follow the changes in the concentration of either the products or the reactants during a reaction (provided Beer's law is obeyed over the concentration range). The spectro-

106

photometric method of determining reaction rates is advantageous particularly in the study of fast reactions and those in very dilute solutions. Further, only minute quantities of the material would be required. The spectrophotometric method has been rendered more advantageous and much simpler after the advent of the recording spectrophotometers. Useful accessories like time-drive attachments, repetitive scanning attachments and thermostated cell-holders are commercially available for the Cary and Beckman instruments.

There are many instances reported in the literature where spectrophotometry has been employed for the determination of reaction rates or for the identification of labile intermediates in the reactions. Isomerization reactions are particularly well-suited for spectrophotometric studies: anionotropic rearrangements of substituted alcohols[68], $R_1CH(OH)CH = CHR_2 \rightarrow R_1CH = CHCH(OH)R_2$, photochemical transformation of ergosterol to vitamin D_2[69,70], alkali-catalysed isomerization of arachidonic acid[71], photochemical changes in thioctic acid[72] etc.

Let us now consider a specific case in detail where spectrophotometry has been used for rate studies. Fagley, Sutter and Oglukian[73] have studied the thermal decomposition of *ortho*-nitrophenylazide to benzofuraxan and nitrogen. o-Nitrophenylazide exhibits two absorption maxima at 240 mμ and 320 mμ and a prominent shoulder at 255 mμ, in cyclohexanol. Benzofuraxan

shows only one absorption maximum at 360 mμ. The 255 mμ shoulder of the azide and 360 mμ band of benzofuraxan gave satisfactory Beer's law plots over a wide range of concentrations. The decrease in the concentration of the azide and the increase in the concentration of benzofuraxan with time, were followed by measuring the optical densities of the 255 mμ shoulder and the 360 mμ band respectively. The first-order rate constants thus computed agreed well with the constants obtained by the gasometric method.

Several special techniques have been employed for the spectrophotometric study of the rates of rapid chemical and biochemical reactions[74-76]. Chance and collaborators[77] have studied very fast steady-state kinetics (< 1 minute) of enzyme reactions by spectrophotometry and thus made valuable contributions in biochemistry.

Other Physicochemical Studies

Spectrophotometry has been a useful tool in several types of physicochemical studies: heats of formation of molecular addition compounds and complexes in solution[78], determination of empirical formulae and successive formation constants of complexes in solution[44,79-84], hydration equilibria of carbonyl compounds[85], association constants between weak acids and bases in organic solvents[86], protein-dye interactions[87], chlorophyll-protein

107

complex[88], vitamin A aldehyde-protein complex[89] and association of cyanine-dyes[90,91].

Frequently, two compounds or two species of a compound existing in equilibrium exhibit overlapping absorption bands. Their absorption curves intersect at a fixed wavelength. This point of intersection will not be affected by changes in the pH of the medium or other changes affecting the equilibrium. That is, at this fixed wavelength, the extinctions of the two species are equal. Such a point is referred to as the 'isobestic point' (or iso-absorptive point). The presence of molecular and ionic forms of an acid or a base or the presence of tautomeric forms of a compound usually results in isobestic points (see *Figures 7.8* and *7.9*). The experimental realization of an isobestic point is taken as a criterion for the existence of two species in equilibrium. Isobestic points have been useful in the determination of substances in binary mixtures[48] and in the spectrophotometric determination of pH by indicators[92].

It is appropriate to summarize the methods employed for the determination of the stoichiometry of complexes and the equilibrium constants for the formation of complexes by spectrophotometry of solutions containing the components involved in complex formation. Complexes between donors and acceptors (charge-transfer or hydrogen bonded systems) and complexes between metal ions and ligands are generally investigated by spectrophotometry. Analytical expressions for the evaluation of the equilibrium constants have been derived by several workers[119-122]. One of the simpler expressions is that of Benesi and Hildebrand[119] commonly used in charge-transfer equilibria (for the interaction of donor with iodine) is given as:

$$[I]l/A = 1/[D] \cdot 1/K\epsilon + 1/\epsilon$$

where [I] and [D] are the concentrations of iodine and the donor, A is the absorbance of the complex, l, the path length of the cell, ϵ, the molar extinction coefficient of the complex and K, the equilibrium constant. A modification of the above equation in cases where the [D] and [I] are comparable has the form:

$$[I][D]/A = \{[I] + [D] - A/\epsilon\} 1/\epsilon + 1/K\epsilon$$

A more general procedure[122] ('absolute method') which does not make any assumptions regarding [D] and [I] has also been given:

$$K^{-1} = \{[D][I] \cdot (\epsilon - \epsilon_I)/(A - A^0)\} - [D] - [I] + (A - A^0)/(\epsilon - \epsilon_I)$$

where A^0 is the absorbance of the initial concentration of iodine and ϵ_I, the molar extinction coefficient of iodine. The evaluation of equilibrium constants becomes more difficult if successive equilibria are involved. Spectrophotometric methods have also been employed with success in such cases[84,124].

The stoichiometry of complexes are generally determined by the molar ratio method or the method of continuous variation. In the molar ratio method, the concentration of one reactant is fixed and the concentration of the other is increased. A plot of absorbance against the concentration of the varying component shows a break at the concentration at which the stoichiometry of the complex is established. In the method of continuous variation of Job[125], the sum of the molar concentrations of the two components is maintained constant while their ratio is varied. The plot of absorbance against mole-fraction will show a maximum at the stoichiometry of the complex. Job's method is superior to the molar ratio method and has been employed in a large number of investigations. In both methods, it is important that Beer's law is obeyed in the concentration ranges employed. Job's method has been extended to cases where a series of complexes is formed between the components[126].

REFERENCES

[1] ORNDORFF, W. R., GIBBS, R. G., McNULTY, S. A. and SHAPIRO, C. V., *J. Amer. Chem. Soc.*, 1928, **50**, 831.

[2] CAPPER, N. S. and MARSH, J. K., *J. Chem. Soc.*, 1926, 724.

[3] FARRAR, K. R., HAMLET, J. C., HENBEST, H. B. and JONES, E. R. H., *J. Chem. Soc.*, 1952, 2657.

[4] BRINK, N. G. and FOLKERS, K., *J. Amer. Chem. Soc.*, 1949, **71**, 2951.

[5] MORTON, R. A., *The Application of Absorption Spectra to the Study of Vitamins, Hormones and Coenzymes*, Hilger, London, 1942.

[6] DOISY, E. A., BINKLEY, S. B. and THAYER, S. A., *Chem. Revs.*, 1941, **28**, 477.

[7] TRENNER, N. R., *Anal. Chem.*, 1950, **22**, 405.

[8] WOODWARD, R. B., BREHM, W. J. and NELSON, A. L., *J. Amer. Chem. Soc.*, 1947, **69**, 2250.

[9] WOODWARD, R. B. and McLAMORE, W. M., *J. Amer. Chem. Soc.*, 1949, **71**, 379.

[10] PASTERNAK, R., CONOVER, L. H., BAVLEY, A., HOCHSTEIN, F. A., HESS, G. B. and BRUNINGS, K. J., *J. Amer. Chem. Soc.*, 1952, **74**, 1928.

[11] CELMER, W. D. and SOLOMONS, I. A., *J. Amer. Chem. Soc.*, 1952, **74**, 1870, 3838.

[12] BOOKER, H., EVANS, L. K. and GILLAM, A. E., *J. Chem. Soc.*, 1940, 1453.

[13] WOODWARD, R. B., *J. Amer. Chem. Soc.*, 1941, **63**, 1123; 1942, **64**, 72, 76.

[14] EVANS, L. K. and GILLAM, A. E., *J. Chem. Soc.*, 1943, 565.

[15] FIESER, L. F. and FIESER, M., *Natural Products Related to Phenanthrene*, Reinhold, New York, 1949.

[16] FIESER, L. F. and CAMPBELL, W. P., *J. Amer. Chem. Soc.*, 1938, **60**, 159.

[17] FIESER, L. F., FIESER, M. and RAJAGOPALAN, S., *J. Org. Chem.*, 1948, **13**, 800.

[18] GILLAM, A. E. and WEST, T. F., *J. Chem. Soc.*, 1942, 671; 1944, 49.

[19] WOODWARD, R. B. and SINGH, G., *J. Amer. Chem. Soc.*, 1950, **72**, 1428, 5321.

[20] BRAUDE, E. A. and COLES, J. A., *J. Chem. Soc.*, 1951, 2085.

[21] BRAUDE, E. A., *Ann. Repts. on Progr. Chem.*, 1945, **42**, 105.

[22] KOCH, H. P., *Chem. & Ind.* (*London*), 1942, **61**, 273.

[23] ZECHMEISTER, L., *Chem. Revs.*, 1944, **34**, 267.

[24] BIQUARD, D., *Ann. Chem.*, 1933, **20**, 97.

[25] RAMART-LUCAS and BIQUARD, D., *Compt. rend*, 1932, **194**, 187.

[26] HAWTHRONE, F. and CRAM, D. J., *J. Amer. Chem. Soc.*, 1952, **74**, 5859.

[27] GROSSMAN, P., *Z. Phys. Chem.*, 1924, **109**, 305.

[28] MORTON, R. A., HASSAN, A. and CALLOWAY, T. C., *J. Chem. Soc.*, 1934, 883.

[29] MORTON, R. A. and STUBBS, A. L., *J. Chem. Soc.*, 1939, 1321.

[30] KOCH, H. P., *J. Chem. Soc.*, 1949, 401.

[31] SURESH, K. S., RAMACHANDRAN, J., RAO, C. N. R., *J. Sci. Ind. Research* (*India*), 1961, 20B, 203.

[32] STERN, E. S., *J. Chem. Soc.*, 1949, 1664.

[33] LIEBER, E., RAMACHANDRAN, J., RAO, C. N. R. and PILLAI, C. N., *Can. J. Chem.*, 1959, **37**, 563.

[34] BURAWOY, A. and THOMPSON, A. R., *J. Chem. Soc.*, 1953, 1443.

[35] PACSU, E. and HILLER, L. A., *J. Amer. Chem. Soc.*, 1948, **70**, 523.

[36] GILLAM, A. E. and HEILBORN, I. M., *Biochem. J.*, 1936, **30**, 1253.

[37] MORTON, R. A. and HEILBORN, I. M., *Biochem. J.*, 1928, **22**, 987.

[38] ZSCHEILE, F. P., Jr., *J. Phys. Chem.*, 1934, **38**, 95.

[39] GRIDGEMAN, N. T., *Analyst*, 1951, **76**, 449.

[40] WOODROW, J. W., *Phil. Mag.*, 1928 (7), **5**, 944.

[41] MORTON, R. A., *J. Pharm. Pharmacol.*, 1950, **2**, 128.

[42] MELLON, M. G., *Anal. Chem.*, 1949, **21**, 3; 1950, **22**, 2; 1951, **23**, 2; 1952, **24**, 2; 1954, **26**, 2; MELLON, M. G. and BOLTZ, D. F., *ibid.*, 1956, **28**, 559; 1958, **30**, 554.

[43] ROSENBAUM, E. J., *Anal. Chem.*, 1949, **21**, 16; 1950, **22**, 14; 1951, **23**, 12; 1952, **24**, 14; 1956, **26**, 20; HIRT, R. C., *ibid.*, 1956, **28**, 579; 1958, **30**, 589.

[44] MELLON, M. G., *Analytical Absorption Spectroscopy*, John Wiley, N. Y., 1950.

[45] SCOTT, J. F., in *Physical Techniques in Biological Research*, Vol. I, Edited by OSTER, G. and POLLISTER, A. W., Academic Press, New York, 1955.

[46] STUCKEY, R. E., *J. Pharm. Pharmacol.*, 1952, **4**, 345.

[47] MILLER, F. A., *Quantitative Biological Spectroscopy*, Burgess, Minneapolis, 1940.

[48] HIRT, R. C., KING, F. T. and SCHMITT, R. G., *Anal. Chem.*, 1954, **26**, 1270.

[49] DEWAR, M. J. S. and URCH, D. S., *J. Chem. Soc.*, 1957, 345.

[50] COMAR, C. L., *Anal. Chem.*, 1942, **14**, 877.

[51] GOODWIN, T. W. and MORTON, R. A., *Biochem. J.*, 1946, **40**, 628.

[52] COGGESHALL, N. D., in *Physical Chemistry of Hydrocarbons*, Vol. I, Edited by FARKAS, A., Academic Press, New York, 1950.

[53] McGOVERN, J. J., GRIM, J. M. and TEACH, W. C., *Anal. Chem.*, 1948, **20**, 312.

[54] HILDITCH, T. P., PATEL, C. B. and RILEY, J. P., *Analyst*, 1951, **76**, 81.

[55] GILLAM, A. E., *Biochem. J.*, 1934, **28**, 79.

[56] CUNNINGHAM, K. G., DAWSON, W. and SPRING, F. S., *J. Chem. Soc.*, 1951, 2305.

[57] BARRY, V. C., McCORMICK, J. E. and MITCHELL, P. W. D., *J. Chem. Soc.*, 1955, 222.

[58] BRAUDE, E. A. and JONES, E. R. H., *J. Chem. Soc.*, 1945, 498.

[59] ROBERTS, J. I. and GREEN, C., *J. Amer. Chem. Soc.*, 1946, **68**, 214.

[60] DJERASSI, C. and RYAN, E., *J. Amer. Chem. Soc.*, 1949, **71**, 1000.

[61] RILEY, J. P., *J. Chem. Soc.*, 1952, 2108.

[62] BROWN, H. C., McDANIEL, D. H. and HAFLIGER, O., in *Determination of Organic Structures by Physical Methods*, Edited by BRAUDE, E. A. and NACHOD, F. C., Academic Press, New York, 1955, Chapter 14.

[63] FLEXSER, L. A., HAMMETT, L. P. and DINGWALL, A., *J. Amer. Chem. Soc.*, 1935, **57**, 2103.

[64] SAGAR, E. E., SCHOOLEY, M. R., CARR, A. S. and ACREE, S. F., *J. Research Nat. Bur. Standards*, 1945, **35**, 521.

[65] HAMMETT, L. P., *Chem. Revs.*, 1935, **16**, 67.

[66] BROWN, H. C. and McDANIEL, D. H., *J. Amer. Chem. Soc.*, 1955, **77**, 3752.

[67] KING, F. T. and HIRT, R. C., *Appl. Spectroscopy*, 1953, **7**, 164.

[68] BRAUDE, E. A. and JONES, E. R. H., *J. Chem. Soc.*, 1944, 436 and later papers.

[69] ELLIS, C., WELLS, A. and HEYROTH, F. E., *The Chemical Action of Ultraviolet Rays*, Reinhold, New York, 1941.

[70] DIMROTH, K., *Ber.*, 1937, **70**, 1631.

[71] MOWRY, D. T., BRODE, W. R. and BROWN, J. B., *J. Biol. Chem.*, 1942, **142**, 671, 679.

[72] BARTHROP, J. A., HAYES, P. M. and CALVIN, M., *J. Amer. Chem. Soc.*, 1954, **76**, 4348.

[73] FAGLEY, T. F., SUTTER, J. R. and OGLUKIAN, R. L., *J. Amer. Chem. Soc.*, 1956, **78**, 5567.

[74] ROUGHTON, F. J. W. and MILLIKAN, G. A., *Proc. Roy. Soc. (London)*, 1936, **A155**, 258, 269, 277.

[75] CHANCE, B., *Rev. Sci. Instr.*, 1951, **22**, 619.

[76] DALZIEL, K., *Biochem. J.*, 1953, **55**, 79.

[77] CHANCE, B. and WILLIAMS, G. R., *Advances in Enzymology*, 1956, **17**, 65.

[78] CROMWELL, T. M. and SCOTT, R. L., *J. Amer. Chem. Soc.*, 1950, **72**, 3825.

[79] HARVEY, A. E. and MANNING, D. L., *J. Amer. Chem. Soc.*, 1950, **72**, 4488.

[80] GILLAM, A. E. and MORTON, R. A., *Proc. Roy. Soc. (London)*, 1929, **A124**, 604; 1931, **A132**, 152.

[81] BROOME, F. K., RALSTON, A. W. and THORNTON, M. H., *J. Amer. Chem. Soc.*, 1946, **68**, 849.

[82] BUCKLES, R. E., POPOV, A. I., ZELENZY, W. F. and SMITH, R. J., *J. Amer. Chem. Soc.*, 1951, **73**, 4525.

[83] POPOV, A. I., BISI, C. C. and CRAFT, M., *J. Amer. Chem. Soc.*, 1958, **80**, 6513.

[84] CHABEREK, S. and MARTELL, A. E., *Organic Sequestering Agents*, John Wiley, New York, 1959.

[85] BELL, R. P. and McDOUGALL, A. O., *Trans. Faraday Soc.*, 1960, **56**, 1281.

[86] DAVIS, M. M. and co-workers, *J. Research Nat. Bur. Standards*, 1947, **39**, 221 1948, **41**, 27; 1949, **42**, 595.

[87] KLOTZ, I. M., *Chem. Revs.*, 1947, **41**, 373 and later papers.

[88] TAKASHIMA, S., *Nature (London)*, 1952, **169**, 192.

[89] MORTON, R. A., *Ann. Repts. on Progr. Chem.*, 1949, **46**, 259.

[90] SHEPPARD, S. E. and GEDDES, A. L., *J. Amer. Chem. Soc.*, 1944, **66**, 2003.

[91] MATTOON, R. W., *J. Chem. Phys.*, 1944, **12**, 268.

[92] BRODE, W. R., *J. Amer. Chem. Soc.*, 1924, **46**, 581.

[93] CAMA, H. R., DALVI, P. D., MORTON, R. A. and SALAH, M. K., *Biochem J.*, 1952, **52**, 542.

[94] Publications of RAYMOND-HAMET.

[95] Articles on alkaloids in *Fortschr. Chem. org. Naturstoffe*.

[96] ZECHMEISTER, L., *Fortschr. Chem. org. Naturstoffe*, 1960, **18**, 223.

[97] FERGUSON, L. N. and KELLY, I., *J. Amer. Chem. Soc.*, 1951, **73** 3707 and the references listed here.

[98] CAMA, H. R., COLLINS, F. D. and MORTON, R. A., *Biochem. J.*, 1951, **50**, 48.

[99] CALDERBANK, A., JOHNSON, A. W. and TODD, A. R., *J. Chem. Soc.*, 1954, 1285.

[100] BROCKMANN, H. and DORLARS, A., *Chem. Ber.*, 1952, **85**, 1168.

[101] BRAND, J. C. D. and SCOTT, A. I., in *Elucidation of Structures by Physical and Chemical Methods*, Part 1, Ed. by K. W. Bentley, Chap. II, Interscience, New York, 1963.

[102] HALPERN, O. and SCHMIDT, H., *Helv. chim. Acta*, 1958, **41**, 1109.

[103] STORK, G., *J. Amer. Chem. Soc.*, 1951, **73**, 504.

[104] BLANDON, P., HENBEST, H. B. and WOOD, G. W., *J. Chem. Soc.*, 1952, 2737.

[105] FIESER, L. F. and FIESER, M., *Steroids*, Reinhold, New York, 1959.

[106] BARTON, D. H. R. and SCOTT, A. I., *J. Chem. Soc.*, 1958, 1767.

[107] WOODWARD, R. B. and YATES, P., *J. Amer. Chem. Soc.*, 1963, **85**, 551, 553.

[108] EDWARDS, O. E., *Canad. J. Chem.*, 1952, **30**, 672.

[109] COOKSON, R. C. and TREVETT, M. E., *J. Chem. Soc.*, 1956, 3864.

[110] BEALE, R. N. and ROE, E. M. F., *J. Chem. Soc.*, 1953, 2755.

[111] MURTHY, A. S. N., BALASUBRAMANIAN, A., RAO, C. N. R. and KASTURI, T. R., *Canad. J. Chem.*, 1962, **40**, 2267.

[112] KASTURI, T. R., MYLARI, B. N., BALASUBRAMANIAN, A. and RAO, C. N. R., *Canad. J. Chem.*, 1962, **40**, 2272.

[113] DEV, S., *Tetrahedron*, 1960, **9**, 1.

111

[114] SORM, F., *Fortschr. Chem. Org. Nuturstoffe*, 1961, **19**, 27.

[115] MORTON, R. A. and STUBBS, A. L., *Biochem. J.*, 1947, **41**, 525.

[116] ASTWOOD, E. B., GREER, M. A. and ETTLINGER, M. S., *J. Biol. Chem.*, 1949, **181**, 121.

[117] ENGLANDER, S. W. and EPSTEIN, H. T., *Arch. biochem. Biophys.*, 1957, **68**, 144.

[118] MORTON, R. A. and STUBBS. A. L., *Analyst*, 1946, **71**, 348.

[119] BENESI, H. A. and HILDEBRAND, J. H., *J. Amer. Chem. Soc.*, 1949, **71**, 2703.

[120] MOORE, R. L. and ANDERSON, R. C., *J. Amer. Chem. Soc.*, 1945, **67**, 168.

[121] KETELAAR, J. A. A., van de STOLPE, C., GOULDSMIT, A. and DZCUBAS, W., *Rec. Trav. chim.*, 1952, **71**, 1104.

[122] ROSE, N. J. and DRAGO, R. S., *J. Amer. Chem. Soc.*, 1959, **81**, 6138.

[123] LANDAUER, J. and McCONNELL, *J. Amer. Chem. Soc.*, 1952, **74**, 1221.

[124] BJERRUM, J., *Metal Ammine Formation in Aqueous Solution*, Haase and Son, Copenhagen, 1941.

[125] JOB, P., *Ann. Chim.*, 1928, **10**, 113.

[126] VOSBURGH and COOPER, G. R., *J. Amer. Chem. Soc.*, 1941, **63**, 437.

[127] ZIMMERMAN, H. E. and PAUFLER, R. M., *J. Amer. Chem. Soc.*, 1960, **82**, 1514.

[128] VAN TAMELEN and PAPPAS, S. P., *J. Amer. Chem. Soc.*, 1963, **85**, 3297.

[129] BIRNAUM, P. P. and co-workers, *Trans. Faraday Soc.*, 1953, **49**, 735.

CHAPTER 8
STERIC EFFECTS

STERIC effects may decrease or increase electronic interactions or may even cause new electronic interactions. A majority of the studies reported in the literature, however, deal with the effects of twisting bonds in conjugated systems on absorption spectra. The explanation of the observed effects is based on the principle that the coplanarity of the system is a necessary requirement for maximal resonance. Several reviews[1-11] have appeared on the electronic absorption spectra of sterically hindered molecules. In this chapter, the generalities regarding the various types of steric effects on the electronic spectra of conjugated molecules have been discussed with specific examples. The effect of bent benzene rings and strain in three-membered rings on the absorption spectra of their derivatives have been dealt with at the end of the chapter.

Steric Effects Causing Decreased Electronic Interactions
Effect of Twisting a 'Single' Bond in a Conjugated System—The 'single' bonds in conjugated systems have considerable double-bond character, the latter being greater in the excited state than in the ground state. The strength of the 'single' bond or the resonance energy of the molecule is maximal when all the atoms attached to the bond are coplanar and hence steric effects that cause twists of the 'single' bonds have profound effect on the electronic spectra. The magnitude of the effect depends on the extent of twist. When the twist is small, there may be decrease in the absorption wavelength and/or intensity. Small or intermediate twists reduce the double-bond character (i.e. raise the energy) of the excited state and consequently the absorption maximum is shifted to shorter wavelengths. When twists are very large, there is little or no *p*-electron interaction (i.e. least resonance) across the bond and the spectrum will be similar to the additive spectra of the two component parts of the molecule.

We shall now exemplify some of the ideas discussed till now by the absorption data of *ortho*-substituted biphenyls[7]. The resonance energy of biphenyl, I, is determined by the double-bond character between the rings. In the absence of steric effects, the most stable configuration would be the one

I

where the two benzene rings are coplanar. Due to steric effects of groups in *ortho*-positions to the central bond, twists are produced and the resonance energy is found to vary in proportion to the square of the cosine of the angle of twist[12].

In *Figure 8.1*, the spectra of symmetrical dimethylbiphenyls are compared with the spectrum of biphenyl. Biphenyl shows a broad intense $\pi \to \pi^*$ band (conjugation band) around 245 mμ which is probably due to a combination of the bands due to the allowed (shifted 200 mμ primary band of benzene) and the forbidden (weak 'benzenoid' band around 260 mμ) transitions of benzene. In 4,4'-dimethylbiphenyl, the band is shifted to a longer wavelength

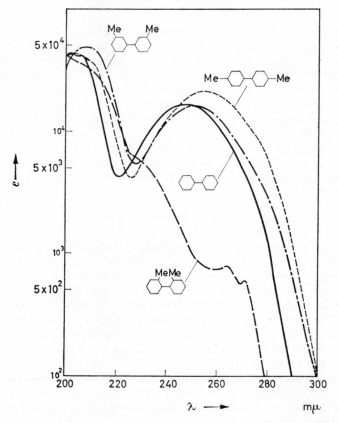

Figure 8.1. Absorption spectra of biphenyl and 2,2'-, 3,3'-, and 4,4'-dimethylbiphenyls[7]

and the intensity is also increased. However, there is very little difference between the spectra of 3,3'-dimethylbiphenyl and biphenyl. The spectra of 4,4'- and 3,3'-derivatives may easily be understood in terms of the usual electrical effects of *p*- and *m*-alkyl groups on the benzene spectrum. In 2,2'-dimethylbiphenyl, the high-intensity band (200 mμ primary band of benzene) is seen as an inflection of a much lower intensity, around 222 mμ, and in addition the low-intensity 'benzenoid' band with vibrational structure appears around 260 mμ. Substitution by additional methyl groups in the *ortho*-positions causes progressive disappearance of the high-intensity 'primary' band and the increasing resolution of the low-intensity 'benzenoid' band (*Figure 8.2*). Thus, the spectrum of 2, 6, 2', 6'-tetramethylbiphenyl shows a broad inflection around 218 mμ and the benzenoid band at 260 mμ.

114

The spectrum of decamethylbiphenyl is quite similar to that of hexamethyl-benzene in double concentration (*Figure 8.3*). The replacement of the *ortho*-methyl groups by bulkier groups, like the *t*-butyl group, results in a further decrease in intensity and increase in the fine structure of the benzenoid band at 260 mμ. In addition, the primary band also undergoes a blue-shift. The effect of increasing the size of the substituents in 2,2'-disubstituted biphenyls

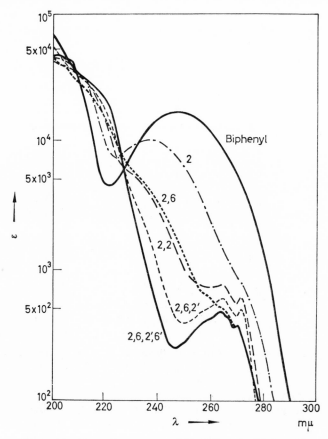

Figure 8.2. Absorption spectra of the 2(6)-methylbiphenyls[7]

has also been studied with halogen substituents[7]. The spectra of these derivatives show a progressive decrease in intensity and increase in blue-shift of the 200 mμ benzene band in the order F, Cl, Br. The absorption spectra of *ortho*-substituted biphenyls are consistent with the hypothesis that increasing deviation from coplanarity due to the progressive introduction of groups in the four *ortho*-positions, results in progressive decrease of con-jugation across the central bond.

The effects of twisting 'single' bonds in conjugated systems away from coplanarity on the absorption spectra may be classified into three types: (1) Decrease in the absorption intensity and no change in wavelength, caused

115

by small twists; (2) shift to shorter wavelengths and decrease in absorption intensity, caused by twists larger than those causing the Type 1 effect; and (3) similarity of the observed spectrum to the additive spectra of the two component parts caused by very large twists. Such a classification of steric

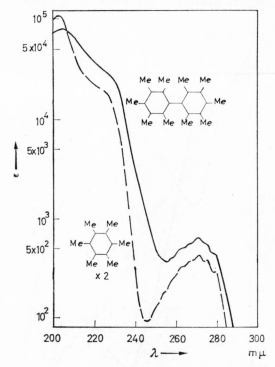

Figure 8.3. Absorption spectra of decamethylbiphenyl and hexamethylbenzene (2 moles)[7]

effects into three types, put forward by Braude and co-workers[13] and Forbes[10], has been criticized[14] since there are also cases where steric effects cause shifts to longer wavelengths. A unified approach should only consider the partial bond orders for the twisted bonds. Non-coplanarity, in principle, may cause hypsochromic or bathochromic shifts. However, the above classification is quite useful[10] and fairly general as long as twists of 'single' bonds are being considered. Examples may be given for each type of steric effect on the absorption spectra of conjugated systems.

There have been several investigations reported on the Type 1 steric effect caused by relatively small twists[5]. In *Table 8.1*, the results on some substituted dimethylanilines have been summarized[15,16]. O'Shaughnessy and Rodebush[17] observed that 2,6-dimethylacetophenone absorbs with much lower intensity ($\epsilon \sim 2000$) than acetophenone ($\epsilon \sim 12,000$). From a study of the absorption spectra of nitroaniline derivatives, Arnold and Craig[18] have found that steric hindrance decreases in the order CH_3 > six-membered ring > five-membered ring.

116

Braude and co-workers[4,13] explained the Type 1 effect by suggesting that some fraction of the molecules in the ground electronic state at room temperature might be vibrationally excited such that the molecule could be

Table 8.1. *Molar Extinction Coefficients of some Substituted Dimethylanilines*

Substituents	ϵ_{max}*
none	14,000
4-CH$_3$	15,000
2-CH$_3$	6,000
2,6-Di-CH$_3$	2,500
2-C(CH$_3$)$_3$	1,000
2-F	12,000
2-Cl	7,500
2-Br	6,000
4-NO$_2$	18,400
4-NO$_2$-3-CH$_3$	16,500
4, NO$_2$-3,5-Di-CH$_3$	6,500

* There is little change in the absorption maximum in related series of compounds.

sufficiently distorted to become near-planar in the electronic transition. To test this hypothesis, Waight and Erskine[11] have recently studied the absorption spectra of substituted acetophenones at 20°C and −196°C (*Table 8.2*). The results indicate that there is no marked variation (decrease) in absorption intensity at low temperatures and do not support Braude's mechanism[4,13]. The three mono-*o*-methylacetophenones have very similar extinctions at

Table 8.2. *Absorption Spectra of Substituted Acetophenones at 20° and −196°C in* iso-*Pentane Solution*[11]

Substituents	20°C		−196°C	
	λ_{max}, mμ	ϵ_{max}	λ_{max}, mμ	ϵ_{max}
none	237	12,050	241	12,050
	244*		248	10,000
3-CH$_3$	241	12,400	243·5	13,300
	248*	9,400	251	11,350
4-CH$_3$	246	18,100	248	17,950
			257*	11,600
2-CH$_3$	237	10,700	240	11,800
	245·5	8,360	248	11,500
2,4-Di-CH$_3$	246	12,350	247	12,950
	254	10,300	255	11,700
2,5-Di-CH$_3$	240	9,750	241	12,250
	247	8,400	250	11,100
2,6-Di-CH$_3$	~235*	2,010	~235*	1,480

* Inflection.

−196°C, suggesting thereby that at this temperature they exist mainly in the relatively unhindered conformation, II. As the temperature is increased, a proportion of the molecules probably takes up the less stable non-planar conformations, III, which contribute very little to the light absorption in the

117

250 mμ region. The 2,6-dimethylacetophenone has no unhindered conformation and therefore absorbs with very low intensity in this region at both the temperatures.

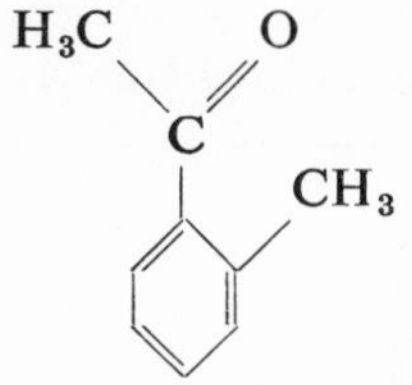

II
III 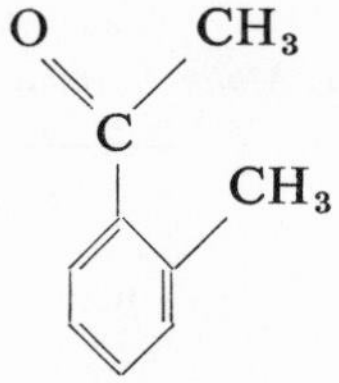

When the steric effects are great enough to cause larger twists than those responsible for the Type 1 effect, the absorption maximum is shifted to shorter wavelengths and the absorption intensity is also decreased (Type 2). The absorption spectra of o-substituted biphenyls, discussed earlier, exemplify the Type 2 effect. The absorption spectra of o-substituted benzoic acids have been studied[19] and their absorption maxima found to be at lower wavelengths than the p-isomers.

The similarity between the absorption spectra of decamethylbiphenyl and hexamethylbenzene[7] (*Figure 8.3*) may be taken as experimental evidence for very large twists (Type 3). Similarly, the absorption spectra of bimesityl and 2,2′, 4,4′, 6,6′-hexachlorobiphenyl may be compared with the spectra of mesitylene and sym-trichlorobenzene respectively[20]. The spectra of the two non-planar phenanthrene derivatives, IV and V, are similar to the spectrum of phenanthrene itself[21]. The naphthalene derivative, VI, exhibits the same

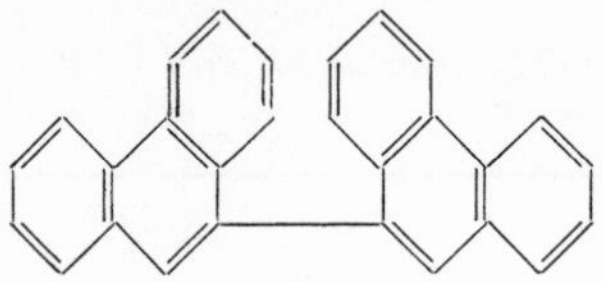

IV
V 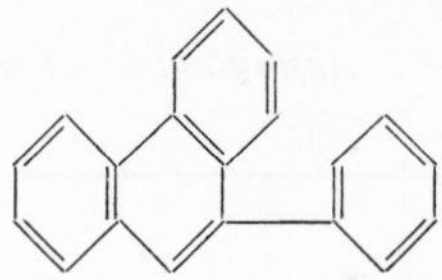

spectrum as naphthalene[22]. Unlike the 2,2′-alkyl- and 2,2′-halo-derivatives of biphenyl (Type 2), the 2,2′-dicarboxy and 2,2′-dinitro-biphenyls exhibit

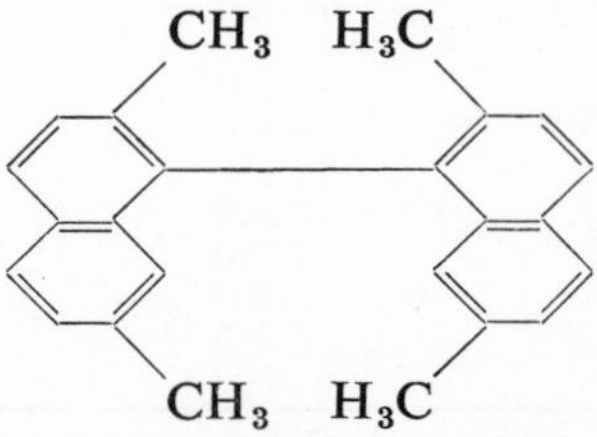

VI

spectra which indicate large twists of Type 3 in these systems[23]. The similarity between the spectra of substituted benzils and the corresponding benzaldehydes has been interpreted by Leonard and colleagues[24] in terms of the skew structures of benzil. Benzil shows the long wavelength absorption at 370 mμ

118

($\epsilon \sim 75$) compared to glyoxal which absorbs around 450 mμ. The relation between the angle of twist and the $n \to \pi^*$ absorption maxima of α-diketones have already been discussed in Chapter 4. Interaction between formally non-conjugated double bonds or hetero atoms with carbonyl groups was discussed in Chapter 3.

The absorption spectra of tetraphenylethylene and triphenylethylene are found to be similar to the spectrum of *trans*-stilbene (diphenylethylene)[25]. This has been explained as due to the unsymmetrical twists of the phenyl groups. While two of the phenyl groups are non-coplanar in tetraphenyl-ethylene, the other two give the spectrum of *trans*-stilbene. Ingraham[5] has discussed this aspect in detail and has given examples where unsymmetrical twists are more probable. Symmetrically and unsymmetrically twisted isomers are possible when three phenyl groups are on the same carbon atom: one isomer with a symmetrical propeller-like structure and the other with a propeller-like structure with one blade bent backwards. This type of iso-merism has been noticed in crystal violet[26].

S-*cis* and S-*trans* isomerization about a bond normally written as a single bond, but with considerable double-bond character (S-bond), was first pro-posed by Mulliken for the 2,3-bond in butadiene[27]. The S-*cis* form shows lower absorption intensity than the S-*trans* form[28]. 2-Methyl-l-acetyl-cyclohexene, VII, may exist in S-*cis* and S-*trans* forms about the bond marked S. The absorption spectrum only shows a relatively low-intensity

VII, S-*cis*   VII, S-*trans*

band ($\epsilon \sim 6,300$) around 247 mμ. This molecule was assigned the S-*trans* structure by Braude and Timmons[29]. Earlier, Turner and Voitle[30] had proposed the planar S-*cis* structure for the compound. Forbes[31] has suggested that equal amounts of the non-planar S-*trans* and the planar S-*cis* forms are present, but the former does not contribute significantly to the absorption. Waight and Erskine[11] have studied the infra-red and the ultra-violet absorp-tion spectra of a number of $\alpha\beta$-unsaturated ketones and have shown that the S-*cis* form itself is non-planar. They explain the low absorption intensity of VII as due to the non-planar S-*cis* form. Waight and Erskine[11] have similarly shown that β-ionone, VIII, exists in S-*trans* form with the diene system non-planar and thus explain the low-intensity absorption.

VIII

119

Effect of Twisting an 'Essential' Double Bond in a Conjugated System—
Till now, the effect of twisting a 'single' bond in a conjugated system was
discussed. If the twist is about an 'essential' double bond[5,32] (e.g. double
bond in butadiene), the absorption spectrum is shifted to a longer wavelength. This is because the double-bond character of the bond is greater in
the ground state than in the excited state. The larger λ_{max} of dibiphenylene-
ethylene compared to dibiphenylene-butadiene has been explained as due to
steric effects that twist the central double bond in the former compound.

A bathochromic shift due to a similar type of steric hindrance (i.e. increasing the energy of the ground state more than that of the excited state) was
noticed by Brunings and Corwin[33] in the cyanine dyes, IX and X. Brooker and
colleagues[2] and Dewar[9] have discussed the effect of non-coplanarity on the

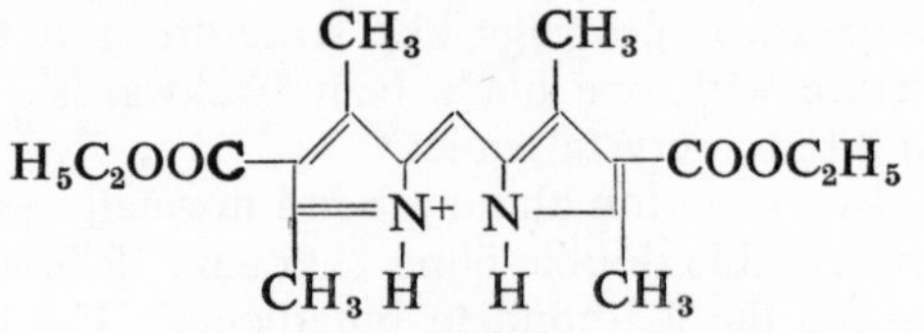

IX

λ_{max} 473 mμ

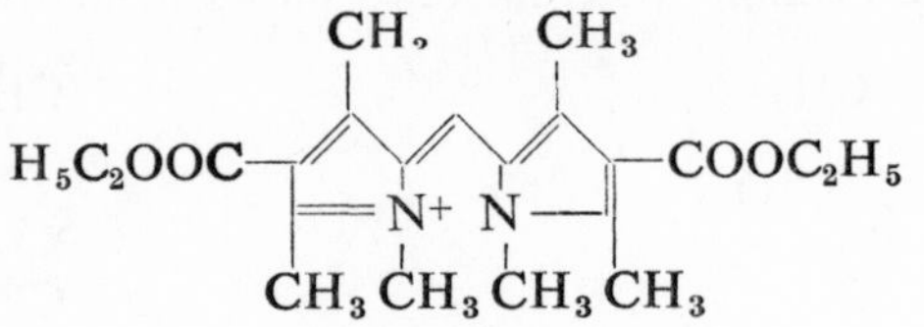

X

λ_{max} 510 mμ

spectra of cyanine dyes. Steric effects shift the absorption maxima of basic di-
and triphenylmethane dyes (Michler's hydrol blue, malachite green and crystal
violet) also to longer wavelengths.

Steric Effects causing Increased or New Electronic Interactions

Electronic interactions occur through the overlap of *p*-orbitals and there
are two types of overlap possible, resulting in the formation of the $2p\sigma$ and
the $2p\pi$ bonds. The $2p\sigma$ bonds are stronger than the $2p\pi$ bonds at larger
distances and therefore the interaction between non-bonded atoms occurs
only when $2p\sigma$ bonds are possible[5]. Leonard and Blout[34] have found that,
although the carbonyls in benzil are non-planar, they can be forced into
planarity by *ortho*-groups to allow $2p\pi$ interaction across the bond between
the two carbonyl groups. The effect of coplanarity on resonance in the case
of diketones[35] was already discussed in Chapter 4. The spectra of triptycene[36]
and di-*p*-xylylene[37] have been explained in terms of $2p\sigma$ bonds.

Ortho substituents may also exert non-steric effects on the absorption
spectra. They may increase the conjugation between the two component
parts of the molecule and shift the absorption to longer wavelengths (e.g.
2-nitrobiphenyl[33]).

120

Spectra of Bent Benzene Rings

When aromatic rings are bent out of the planar configuration, the characteristic fine structure is lost in the electronic absorption spectra[5]. This effect has been found in the spectra of a number of alkyl substituted condensed ring

XI   XII

hydrocarbons of the angular series (e.g. 4,5-dimethylphenanthrene and 4,5-dimethylchrysene). Cram, Allinger and Steinberg[38] have recently prepared compounds with warped benzene rings of the type XI and XII, and found that they did not show any fine structure in their absorption spectra. Warped benzene rings also shift the absorption maxima to longer wavelengths[40]. Helicenes also show such bathochromic shifts.

Strain in Three-Membered Rings

The strain in three-membered ring compounds results in their ability to conjugate with adjacent double bonds. Consequently, cyclopropyl and ethylene oxide derivatives exhibit absorption maxima at wavelengths intermediate to the corresponding alkyl and vinyl derivatives. The absorption spectrum of cyclopropane (λ_{max} 190 mμ) was explained in Chapter 3 as due to the unsaturation property of the ring resulting from strain. The spectrum of cyclopropylbenzene was explained in terms of cyclopropyl conjugation in Chapter 5. Kosower[39] has recently given unequivocal evidence for conjugation in cyclopropyl ketones.

REFERENCES

[1] JONES, R. N., *Chem. Revs.*, 1943, **32**, 1.

[2] BROOKER, L. G. S., WHITE, F. L., SPRAGUE, R. H., DENT, S. G., Jr. and VAN ZANDT, G., *Chem. Revs.*, 1947, **41**, 325.

[3] FERGUSON, L. N., *Chem. Revs.*, 1948, **43**, 385.

[4] BRAUDE, E. A. and WAIGHT, E. S., in *Progress in Stereochemistry*, Vol. I, Edited by Klyne, W., Butterworths, London, 1954.

[5] INGRAHAM, L. L., in *Steric Effects in Organic Chemistry*, Edited by Newman, M. S., John Wiley, New York, 1956, Chapter 11.

[6] WEPSTER, B. M., in *Progress in Stereochemistry*, Vol. 2, Edited by Klyne, W. and de la Mare, P. B. D., Butterworths, London, 1958.

[7] BEAVEN, G. H., *Steric Effects in Conjugated Systems*, Edited by Gray, G. W., Butterworths, London, 1958, Chapter 3.

[8] BARKER, C. C., *Steric Effects in Conjugated Systems*, Edited by Gray, G. W., Butterworths, London, 1958, Chapter 4.

[9] DEWAR, M. J. S., *Steric Effects in Conjugated Systems*, Edited by Gray, G. W., Butterworths, London, 1958, Chapter 5.

[10] FORBES, W. F., *Steric Effects in Conjugated Systems*, Edited by Gray, G. W., Butterworths, London, 1958, Chapter 6.

[11] WAIGHT, E. S. and ERSKINE, R. L., *Steric Effects in Conjugated Systems*, Edited by Gray, G. W., Butterworths, London, 1958, Chapter 7.

[12] DEWAR, M. J. S., *J. Amer. Chem. Soc.*, 1952, **74**, 3341.

[13] BRAUDE, E. A., JONES, E. R. H., KOCH, H. P., RICHARDSON, R. W., SONDHEIMER, F. and TOOGOOD, J. B., *J. Chem. Soc.*, 1949, 1890.

[14] DEWAR, M. J. S., see *Steric Effects in Conjugated Systems*, Edited by Gray, G. W., Butterworths, London, 1958, Chapter 6, p. 71.

[15] REMINGTON, W. R., *J. Amer. Chem. Soc.*, 1945, **67**, 1838.

[16] BROWN, W. G. and REAGAN, H., *J. Amer. Chem. Soc.*, 1947, **69**, 1032.

[17] O'SHAUGHNESSY, M. T. and RODEBUSH, W. H., *J. Amer. Chem. Soc.*, 1940, **62**, 2906.

[18] ARNOLD, R. T. and CRAIG, P. N., *J. Amer. Chem. Soc.*, 1950, **72**, 2728.

[19] MOSER, C. M. and KOHLENBERG, A. I., *J. Chem. Soc.*, 1951, 804.

[20] PICKETT, L. W., WALTER, G. F. and FRANCE, H., *J. Amer. Chem. Soc.*, 1936, **58**, 2296.

[21] HENRI, V. and BERGMANN, E., *Nature (London)*, 1939, **143**, 278.

[22] FRIEDEL, R. A., ORCHIN, M. and REGGEL, L., *J. Amer. Chem. Soc.*, 1948, **70**, 199.

[23] WILLIAMSON, B. and RODEBUSH, W. H., *J. Amer. Chem. Soc.*, 1941, **63**, 3018.

[24] LEONARD, N. J., RAPALA, R. T., HERZOG, H. L. and BLOUT, E. R., *J. Amer. Chem. Soc.*, 1949, **71**, 2997.

[25] JONES, R. N., *J. Amer. Chem. Soc.*, 1943, **65**, 1818.

[26] LEWIS, G. N., MAGEL, T. T. and LIPKIN, D., *J. Amer. Chem. Soc.*, 1942, **64**, 1774.

[27] MULLIKEN, R. S., *Rev. Mod. Phys.*, 1942, **14**, 265.

[28] MULLIKEN, R. S., *J. Chem. Phys.*, 1939, **7**, 121.

[29] BRAUDE, E. A. and TIMMONS, C. J., *J. Chem. Soc.*, 1955, 3766.

[30] TURNER, R. B. and VOITLE, D. M., *J. Amer. Chem. Soc.*, 1951, **73**, 1403.

[31] FORBES, W. F., in *Steric Effects in Conjugated Systems*, Edited by Gray, G. W., Butterworths, London, 1958, Chapter 7, p. 76.

[32] LONGUET-HIGGINS, H. C., *J. Chem. Phys.*, 1950, **18**, 265.

[33] BRUNINGS, K. J. and CORWIN, A. H., *J. Amer. Chem. Soc.*, 1942, **64**, 693.

[34] LEONARD, N. J. and BLOUT, E. R., *J. Amer. Chem. Soc.*, 1950, **72**, 484.

[35] LEONARD, N. J. and MADER, P. M., *J. Amer. Chem. Soc.*, 1950, **72**, 5388.

[36] BARTLETT, P. D. and LEWIS, E. S., *J. Amer. Chem. Soc.*, 1950, **72**, 1005.

[37] CRAM, D. J. and STEINBERG, H., *J. Amer. Chem. Soc.*, 1951, **73**, 5691.

[38] CRAM, D. J., ALLINGER, N. L. and STEINBERG, H., *J. Amer. Chem. Soc.*, 1954, **76**, 6132.

[39] KOSOWER, E. M., *J. Amer. Chem. Soc.*, 1958, **80**, 3261.

[40] CRAM, D. J. and co-workers, *J. Amer. Chem. Soc.*, 1957, **81**, 5963, 5971 and 5977.

CHAPTER 9

FAR ULTRA-VIOLET ABSORPTION SPECTRA

IN spite of several decades of academic research on the far ultra-violet absorption spectra of organic molecules, this region has not been fully exploited by chemists for analytical and structural work. The major cause for this delay is probably the lack of adequate instrumentation. The far ultra-violet absorption spectra of various types of organic compounds have been investigated by the photographic technique. Particular mention must be made of the studies by Platt and co-workers on aromatics and other unsaturated hydrocarbons[1-8], by Duncan and co-workers on aliphatic ketones and ethylene oxide[9,10] and by Carr, Pickett and their co-workers on olefins, diolefins, cyclic unsaturates, ethers and alcohols[11-19]. For the past few years, measurements of analytical accuracy have been possible by the use of photoelectric spectrophotometers[20]. Jones and Taylor[20] have recorded the absorption spectra of 69 pure hydrocarbons in the 170–220 mμ region using a photoelectric spectrophotometer.

The major problems in spectroscopy in the far ultra-violet region are: the source of radiation, window materials and mirrors. Absorption of radiation by air is another problem.

Instrumentally, the far ultra-violet region may be divided into two parts: the far ultra-violet region from 210 to 170 mμ made accessible to most spectrophotometers by simple modification of their optics and detectors and by purging or flushing the instruments with nitrogen, and the vacuum ultra-violet region below 170 mμ which requires efficient evacuation of the instrument in addition to special instrumentation. There are now photoelectric instruments commercially available (Beckman DK, Cary 14 etc.) which may be operated down to 185 or 170 mμ by nitrogen purging and by use of high quality quartz and fused silica prisms. Taylor and Jones[21] have described the conversion of the Beckman DU spectrophotometer for operation down to 192 mμ, by using a photomultiplier tube with fused silica window, an Allen-Nester hydrogen lamp and nitrogen flushing. Several instruments, techniques and improvements have been discussed in the literature[20-22]. Kaye[30,31] and Turner[36] have recently reviewed the techniques and applications of far ultra-violet spectroscopy. These reviews are bound to be of immense value particularly because of the extensive collection of literature data and references.

Kaye[30] in his review discusses various instrumental problems and various parameters affecting performance. Wavelength calibration in the far ultraviolet region is probably best accomplished by employing the oxygen absorp-

123

tion bands listed[30] in the next page. The mercury resonance line at 1849·6 Å is also very useful for this purpose.

λ, Å	λ,	λ, Å	λ, Å
1998·2	1902·6	1846·4	1792·6
1972·4	1882·3	1830·7	1783·0
1947·4	1863·6	1816·4	1774·9
1924·1	—	1803·7	1768·3

Spectra of pure liquids can be recorded with very short path cells. Solution spectra are best recorded either in heptane or in water, down to 170–175 mμ. The purity of these solvents is very critical since oxygen dissolved in the solvent gives very characteristic absorption bands. Pure perfluorinated solvents can be employed down to about 157 mμ. Pure methanol and acetonitride can be used down to 185 and 178 mμ respectively. The spectra of a few solvents are shown below in *Figure 9.1*.

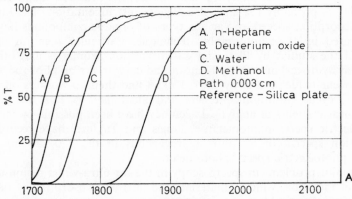

Figure 9.1. Solvent spectra. (From W. I. Kaye[31] by courtesy of the Society for Applied Spectroscopy)

The thickness of cells employed in the far ultra-violet region is generally small (0·03 mm). It is important to note that solvent compensation in double-beam operation should not be pushed too far because of stray light problems[30].

Spectra of gases can be recorded by using vacuum-tight cells. Use of mercury manometers in the vacuum lines is sufficient to show the lines at 1849Å.

Table 9.1. Molar Absorptivities in the Far Ultra-violet Region
(From W. I. Kaye[31] by courtesy of Society for Applied Spectroscopy.)

Compound	L/mol-cm	Wave-length, Å	Compound	L/mol-cm	Wave-length, Å
	Olefins			Ethers	
Ethylene	33,000	1704	Diethyl ether	2,000	1880
Propylene	13,000	1710	Divinyl ether	15,600	2030
			Furan	31,000	1915
	Dienes				
1-*trans*-3-Pentadiene	27,500	2148		Halogens	
			Methyl iodine	20,000	2013
	Aromatics		Ethyl bromide	10,000	1700
Benzene	109,000	1791			
Naphthalene	122,000	2210			
Anthracene	21,500	1885		Miscellaneous	
			Oxygen	500	1700
	Aldehyde and Ketone		Water vapour	3,000	1700
Formaldehyde	18,000	1750	Nitric oxide	900	1830
Acetaldehyde	10,000	1815	Ammonia	12,000	1940
Acetone	9,000	1950			

Leakage of air should be avoided to prevent oxygen absorption lines.

Sample purity is *extremely important* since even very small traces of impurities show up prominently owing to the high absorption coefficients in this region. The molar absorptivities of a few typical compounds as listed by Kaye[31] are given in *Table 9.1*.

Kaye[31] has summarized the data and references on the far ultra-violet spectra of a number of organic and inorganic compounds. These tabulations will be of great value in analytical or structural work. Kaye's reviews[30,31] are available as Beckman reprints from Beckman Instruments Inc.

Saturated Hydrocarbons and their Derivatives

Saturated hydrocarbons are generally transparent down to 170 mμ and are therefore suitable for use as solvents. The transitions in paraffins and

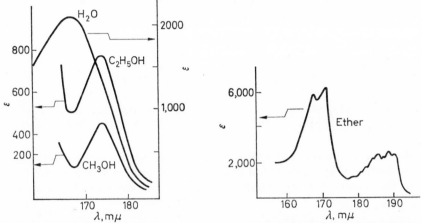

Figure 9.2. Far ultra-violet spectra (n$\rightarrow\sigma$ bands) of water, methanol, ethanol and ether. (From Tsubomura and colleagues[32] by courtesy of The Chemical Society of Japan)

some of their simple derivatives were discussed earlier in Chapter 3. Simple paraffins exhibit bands due to $\sigma \rightarrow \sigma^*$ transitions (CH_4, λ_{max} 125 mμ; C_2H_6 λ_{max} 135 mμ) which occur just prior to the sharp Rydberg bands caused by the ionization of the molecules. Quite often it is difficult to distinguish bands due to $\sigma \rightarrow \sigma^*$ transitions from the ionization bands. The derivatives of the saturated hydrocarbons containing atoms with unshared pairs of electrons (e.g. CH_3OH, CH_3Cl, $(CH_3)_3N$, CH_3OCH_3), however, absorb at longer wavelengths due to $n \rightarrow \sigma^*$ transitions (see Chapter 3). Some of the far ultra-violet absorption bands of a few alcohols and ethers have been summarized in *Table 9.2*. The spectra of a few compounds[32] are shown in *Figures 9.2* and

Table 9.2. Far Ultra-violet Absorption Bands of some Ethers and Alcohols in Vapour Phase

Compound	λ_{max}^*, mμ	Compound	λ_{max}^*, mμ
Methanol[32]	174	Diethyl ether[18]	188
Ethanol[32]	174	Ethylene oxide[10]	157, 171
1-Propanol[17]	183	Tetrahydrofuran[13]	170, 190
2-Propanol[17]	181	Tetrahydropyran[13]	175, 189
Dimethyl ether[18]	184	1,4-Dioxan[13]	188

* Approximate centres of bands

125

9.3. Absorption data on several saturated heterocyclic compounds are given in Chapter 6.

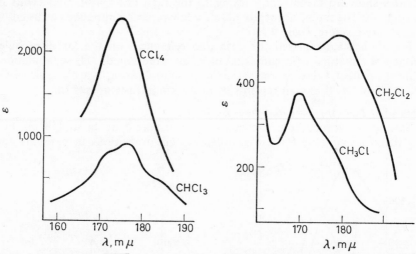

Figure 9.3. Far ultra-violet absorption bands of chloromethanes. (From Tsubomura and colleagues[32] by courtesy of The Chemical Society of Japan)

Olefins

With the exception of ethylene, all the olefins exhibit very similar absorption spectra. They show broad and intense absorption bands ($\epsilon \sim 10,000$) with the maxima in the region 172–194 mμ (*Figure 9.4*). The bands are

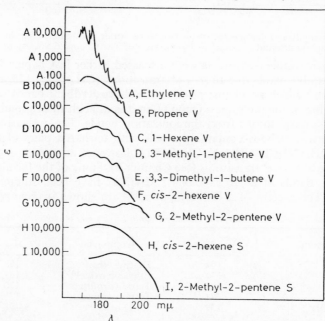

Figure 9.4. Far ultra-violet absorption spectra of olefins[20]: V, vapour state; S, heptane solution

126

assigned to the $\pi \rightarrow \pi^*$ (N $\rightarrow$ V) transitions associated with the double bonds. For analytical purposes, the olefins may be conveniently grouped according to the number of alkyl groups attached to the carbons of the double bond. A further subdivision into *cis*- and *trans*-isomers may also be useful. The average positions and intensities of the absorption bands of different types of alkenes are summarized in *Table 9.3*. Vibrational structure is noticed in the vapour phase spectra (*Figure 9.4*), which is more pronounced in olefins with two or more alkyl groups.

In a given series of olefins, the absorption intensity at the absorption maximum seems to increase with increasing symmetry of the molecule[20]. Thus, the intensity increases in the series: 4-methyl-*trans*-2-pentene $<$ *trans*-2-hexene $=$ *trans*-2-pentene $<$ *trans*-2-butene $<$ *trans*-3-hexene. The vibrational structure and the absorption intensity of the bands decrease in solution

Table 9.3. *Far Ultra-violet Absorption Bands of Olefins in Vapour Phase*[20]

Olefin Type	Average position λ_{max}, mμ	Approximate ϵ_{max}
1-Alkenes	175 ± 2.5	$11,800 \pm 1200$
cis-2-Alkenes	176.5 ± 1.5	$12,300 \pm 200$
trans-2-Alkenes	179 ± 1	$11,700 \pm 800$
2-Alkyl-1-alkenes	187.5 ± 1.5	$8,900 \pm 1200$

spectra (*Figure 9.1*). The differences between the spectra of individual olefins and between the average spectra of different olefin classes are so small that the far ultra-violet spectrophotometry will not be of much use in the determination of individual constituents in mixtures or even in estimating the relative amounts of the various olefin types. However, the close similarity of the absorption spectra of various olefins would suggest that determination of total olefin content may be possible even in complex mixtures[20].

Recently, the far ultra-violet absorption spectra of cyclic olefins[12,20], small ring olefins[19], and olefins of the steroid and triterpenoid families[23] have been studied. Turner[23] has suggested that it is necessary to apply a correction for hydrocarbon skeletal absorption when determining the λ_{max} of the olefinic band in steroid and triterpenoid compounds. A general correlation of the λ_{max} with the number of ethylenic substituents, n, is possible[23]: $n = 2$, λ_{max} 182–188 mμ; $n = 3$, λ_{max} 188–193 mμ and $n = 4$, λ_{max} 196–200 mμ. However, there are exceptions to this correlation. Reliable information on the degree of substitution can be obtained from the knowledge of the wavelength at which ϵ is 1000. Data on a number of compounds have been given by Turner[36]. Turner[23] has correlated certain features of the far ultra-violet spectra of olefins with steric strain.

Diolefins

The far ultra-violet absorption spectra of diolefins, where the double bonds are insulated by two or more methylene groups, are very similar to those of the mono-olefins[20]. A single methylene group cannot effectively insulate the two double bonds.

Conjugated dienes generally exhibit broad and intense absorption bands (ϵ 20,000–28,000) around 215 mμ[20], which may be assigned to the $\pi \rightarrow \pi^*$

transition (K- or conjugation band). In vapour state the absorption bands show vibrational structure which is absent in solution spectra[5,20]. Turner[36] has discussed the features of the far ultra-violet absorption of dienes and polyenes. The far ultra-violet absorption spectra of cyclopentadiene and cyclohexadiene have been studied[11]. The spectrum of furan has also been reported[13].

Acetylenes and Allenes

Platt, Klevens and Price[6] have reported the absorption spectra of 1-octyne and 2-octyne. 2-Octyne exhibits a strong band ($\epsilon \sim 9,500$) at 180 mμ while 1-octyne shows only a shoulder ($\epsilon \sim 2,000$) around 185 mμ. In addition, both of them show a weak band ($\epsilon \sim 150$) at 225 mμ. Jones and Taylor[20] have found that 1-butyne shows a shoulder around 185 mμ ($\epsilon \sim 800$) and a maximum at 172 mμ ($\epsilon \sim 4,500$). Monosubstituted allenes are found[20] to give a band at about 178 mμ ($\epsilon \sim 20,000$) and a shoulder at 188 mμ. Disubstituted allenes exhibit the same features at about 181 and 171 mμ respectively.

Aromatics

Benzene exhibits two bands in the far ultra-violet region, around 179 and 200 mμ in vapour phase and around 184 and 203 mμ in heptane solution. The transitions responsible for these bands were already mentioned (Chapter 5). Platt and Klevens[3] and Jones and Taylor[20] have studied the far ultra-violet absorption spectra of a number of alkyl substituted benzenes in

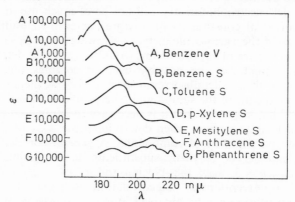

Figure 9.5. Far ultra-violet absorption spectra of aromatics[20]: V, vapour state; S, heptane solution

heptane solution. Both the bands are shifted to longer wavelengths with increasing alkyl substitution and the 200 mμ band has about the same molar extinction coefficient for all the alkyl substituted benzene derivatives. The absorption curves for benzene and some of the derivatives are shown in *Figure 9.5*. The relative concentrations of mono-, di-, tri- and more highly substituted benzenes may be determined by measuring the extinctions at the average positions of the absorption maxima (of the 180 mμ band) for these classes. Data on a number of benzene derivatives have been tabulated by Turner.[36]

128

Catacondensed hydrocarbons do not absorb very strongly in the 180–200 mμ region[20]. Platt[24] noted that the absorption spectra of all catacondensed aromatic hydrocarbons containing the same number of aromatic rings are similar with regard to the number and location of their absorption bands. The intensity varies due to changes in molecular symmetry. The similarity of the absorption curves of anthracene and phenanthrene[20] may be seen in *Figure 9.5*. Far ultra-violet absorption data on heteroaromatics have been summarized by Turner[36]

Carbonyl Compounds

It was pointed out in Chapters 2 and 3 that a carbonyl group exhibits two intense bands in the far ultra-violet region due to the $n \rightarrow \sigma^*$ and $\pi \rightarrow \pi^*$ transitions. McMurry[25] assigned the 190 mμ band in ketones to the $n \rightarrow \sigma^*$ transition and the 150 mμ band to the $\pi \rightarrow \pi^*$ transition. Holdsworth and Duncan[9] have reported these absorption bands for several aliphatic ketones in vapour phase (*Table 9.4*). Kosower[26] has reported the $n \rightarrow \sigma^*$ bands of acetone and cyclopropyl ketones in *iso*-octane and water solutions. The $n \rightarrow \sigma^*$ bands of saturated ring ketones have also been reported[27,28]. Recently, the $\pi - \pi^*$ and $n \rightarrow \sigma^*$ transitions of various carbonyl compounds have been assigned[33,34,36]. The $\pi \rightarrow \pi^*$ transitions of carboxylic acids and esters have been assigned in the region 155–165 mμ[34].

Turner[29,36] has recorded the absorption spectra of cyclic imides and amides in the 175–200 mμ region. The effect of progressive C_α-alkyl substitution on the intensity has been studied. The shift of the absorption band to a longer wavelength in glutarimide has been ascribed to steric strain.

Table 9.4. Far Ultra-violet Absorption Spectra of Aliphatic Ketones
(R_1R_2CO) in Vapour Phase[9]

R_1	R_2	$\pi \rightarrow \pi^*$ transition approximate λ_{max}, mμ	$n \rightarrow \sigma^*$ transition approximate λ_{max}, mμ
CH_3	CH_3	167	192
CH_3	C_2H_5	169	194
CH_3	$i\text{-}C_3H_7$	172	194
CH_3	$t\text{-}C_4H_9$	174	194
C_2H_5	C_2H_5	172	193
$i\text{-}C_3H_7$	$i\text{-}C_3H_7$	174	197
$t\text{-}C_4H_9$	$t\text{-}C_4H_9$	171	197

Inorganic Compounds

Inorganic compounds such as alkali metal halides, mercury halides, nitrogen oxides, hydrides, oxides and sulphides of various elements all show absorption in the vacuum or far ultra-violet regions. Simple gases or vapours such as oxygen, mercury, ozone, tin, sulphur show absorption in the far ultra-violet region itself. The data and references on the inorganic compounds have been listed by Kaye[31]. Little use has been made of the far ultra-violet region for analytical work on inorganic compounds.

Analytical Applications of Far Ultra-Violet Spectroscopy

Although there has not been much activity till now in this area it is bound to get increasingly popular in the near future. There have been some instances where analysis of substances has been carried out based on far ultra-violet absorption bands[33]. A few such examples quoted by Kaye[31] are listed below, (i) Ammonia in nitrogen employing the 204 mμ band of ammonia (detectability 7 p.p.m.) (ii) Water vapour in air. (iii) Number of double bands in fatty acids. (iv) Acetone in acetylene. (v) Mercury vapour.

Kaye[35] has reported the use of far ultra-violet detection of effluents in vapour phase chromatography. Various hydrocarbon mixtures and gasoline have been deleted and analysed by this method.

REFERENCES

[1] PLATT, J. R., ROSOFF, I. and KLEVENS, H. B., *J. Chem. Phys.*, 1943, **11**, 535.

[2] MANN, D. E., PLATT, J. R., KLEVENS, H. B., *J. Chem. Phys.*, 1949, **17**, 481.

[3] PLATT, J. R. and KLEVENS, H. B., *Chem. Revs.*, 1947, **41**, 301.

[4] PLATT, J. R. and KLEVENS, H. B., *J. Chem. Phys.*, 1948, **16**, 832.

[5] JACOBS, L. E. and PLATT, J. R., *J. Chem. Phys.*, 1948, **16**, 1137.

[6] PLATT, J. R., KLEVENS, H. B. and PRICE, W. C., *J. Chem. Phys.*, 1949, **17**, 466.

[7] KLEVENS, H. B. and PLATT, J. R., *J. Chem. Phys.*, 1949, **17**, 470.

[8] KLEVENS, H. B., *J. Polymer Sci.*, 1953, **10**, 97.

[9] HOLDSWORTH, R. S. and DUNCAN, A. B. F., *Chem. Revs.*, 1947, **41**, 311.

[10] LIU, T. and DUNCAN, A. B. F., *J. Chem. Phys.*, 1949, **17**, 241.

[11] CARR, E. P., *Chem. Revs.*, 1947, **41**, 293.

[12] PICKETT, L. W., MUNTZ, M. and McPHERSON, E. M., *J. Amer. Chem. Soc.*, 1951, **73**, 4862.

[13] PICKETT, L. W., HOEFLICH, N. J. and LIU, T., *J. Amer. Chem. Soc.*, 1951, **73**, 4865.

[14] GARY, J. T. and PICKETT, L. W., *J. Chem. Phys.*, 1954, **22**, 599, 1266.

[15] SEMENOW, D., HARRISON, A. J. and CARR, E. P., *J. Chem. Phys.*, 1954, **22**, 638.

[16] FLEMING, G., ANDERSON, M. M., HARRISON, A. J. and PICKETT, L. W., *J. Chem. Phys.*, 1959, **30**, 351.

[17] HARRISON, A. J., CEDERHOLM, B. J. and TERWILLIGER, M. A., *J. Chem. Phys.*, 1959, **30**, 355.

[18] HARRISON, A. J. and PRICE, D. R. W., *J. Chem. Phys.*, 1959, **30**, 357.

[19] LOEFFLER, B. B., EBERLIN, E. and PICKETT, L. W., *J. Chem. Phys.*, 1958, **28**, 345.

[20] JONES, L. C., Jr. and TAYLOR, L. W., *Anal. Chem.*, 1955, **27**, 228.

[21] TAYLOR, L. W. and JONES, L. C., Jr., *Anal. Chem.*, 1956, **28**, 1706.

[22] HIRT, R. C., *Anal. Chem.*, 1956, **28**, 579; 1958, **30**, 589.

[23] TURNER, D. W., *J. Chem. Soc.*, 1959, 30

[24] PLATT, J. R., *J. Chem. Phys.*, 1949, **17**, 484.

[25] McMURRY, H. L., *J. Chem. Phys.*, 1941, **9**, 231.

[26] KOSOWER, E. M., *J. Amer. Chem. Soc.*, 1958, **80**, 3261.

[27] PRUGGER, H. and DORR, F., *Z. Elektrochem.*, 1960, **64**, 425.

[28] RAO, C. N. R., GOLDMAN, G. K. and RAMACHANDRAN, J., *J. Indian Inst. Sci.*, 1961, **43**, 10.

[29] TURNER, D. W., *J. Chem. Soc.*, 1957, 4555.

[30] KAYE, W. I., *Appl. Spec.*, 1961, **15**, 89.

[31] KAYE, W. I., *Appl. Spec.*, 1961, **15**, 130.

[32] TSUBOMURA, H., KIMURA, K., KAYA, K., TANAKA, J. and NAGAKURA, S., *Bull. Chem. Soc. Japan*, 1964, **37**, 417.

[33] BARNES, E. E. and SIMPSON, W. T., *J. Chem. Phys.*, 1963, **39**, 670.

[34] NAGAKURA, S., KAYA, K. and TSUBOMURA, H., *J. Mol. Spec.*, 1964, **13**, 1.

[35] KAYE, W. I., *Anal. Chem.*, 1962, **34**, 287.

[36] TURNER, D. W. in *Determination of Organic Structures* by Physical Methods, Vol. 2, ed. by NACHOD, F. C. and PHILLIPS, W. D., Chapter 5, Academic Press, New York, 1962.

CHAPTER 10

FLUORESCENCE*

FLUORESCENCE is the process of emission of light which accompanies the spontaneous transition of a molecule from an excited state to a lower energy level. When a molecule is raised from the ground level, S (*Figure 10.1*), to an excited state, S', by light absorption, it undergoes deactivation by collision with other molecules either of its own kind or otherwise and emission of radiation takes place when it reverts from the excited state S' to vibrationally excited levels of the ground state, S. This emission process is called luminescence and may consist of the direct transition of the excited electron from the level S' to S in a very short time of the order of 10^{-9} sec or the transition of the electron from the level S' to S through an intermediate meta-stable triplet state, T', of lower energy, the life of the excited state being fairly long ($\sim 10^{-3}$ sec). The former process is known as fluorescence and

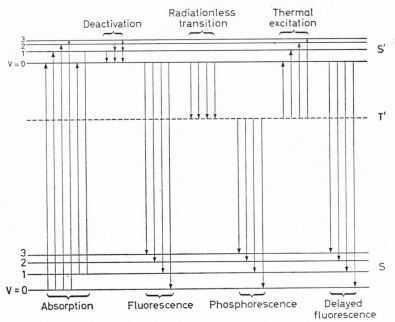

Figure 10.1. Processes occurring in fluorescence and phosphorescence

the latter, phosphorescence. This triplet-singlet transition may be delayed a good deal at low temperatures, and at still lower temperatures it may be

* This Chapter originally written by N. Rajalakshimi has now been modified.

'frozen in'. Delayed fluorescence is observed when a molecule in the state T′ is thermally excited to the state S′ before reverting to the ground state S. The phenomenon of predissociation is found whenever two excited states have crossing potential energy curves.

Luminescence is exhibited by almost all substances possessing selective absorption, and under the proper choice of chemical and physical conditions it can be excited in all forms of matter. In solids and liquids, the excited molecules are apt to lose a part of the absorbed energy in the form of heat motion to the surrounding molecules and hence the frequency of the emitted light will be less than that of the exciting light. In fact, Stokes' law states that fluorescent light always has a greater wavelength than the exciting light. Hence, violet fluorescence is excited by the ultra-violet light, green by blue, red by orange, etc. Even infra-red fluorescence has been observed in chlorophyll by excitation with red light; and some luminescent molecules containing heavy atoms emit bright fluorescence under x-ray excitation[1].

Normal fluorescence and phosphorescence are mono-molecular processes which decay according to the exponential law[2]

$$I = I_0 e^{-t/\tau}$$

where I is the intensity of emission at time t after the cessation of the exciting light of intensity I_0, and τ is the average decay period, being the time required for the intensity of emission to fall to $1/e^{I}0$.

Theoretical considerations of the Einstein theory of thermodynamic equilibrium between matter and radiation give rise to the following relation[3] between the probability of radiational emission from an excited state and the integrated intensity of the corresponding absorption band.

$$\int \epsilon d\bar{\nu} = 3\cdot47 \times 10^8 \frac{1}{\bar{\nu}_A^2 \, n^2} \frac{g_u}{g_1} k_e$$

where ϵ is the molar extinction coefficient and the integration is over the whole absorption band, whose maximum is at $\bar{\nu}_A$, n is the refractive index of the medium, g_u and g_1 are the multiplicities of the upper and lower states and k_e is the rate constant of the emission process. Since $\tau \leqslant 1/k_e$, the mean life of the excited state is inversely proportional to the corresponding integrated absorption intensity.

The simplest examples of fluorescence are afforded by monatomic vapours like that of sodium at low pressures, and by paramagnetic atoms such as those of group VIII or the transition group and the rare earths, which give rise to discrete and line-like spectra. In solids with activating elements causing a strain in the structure, similar line-like spectra are observed. Most diamagnetic solids, on the other hand, exhibit broad continuous bands produced by energy forces of neighbouring particles. Continuous spectra are also observed in the solid state when the displaced electrons associate with other atoms in the system and then become free and absorb energy. This situation resembles the 'metallic state' and transitions to and from such a state give rise to broad bands.

Fluorescence is radically affected by chemical elements and changes in physical environment which cause a decrease in intensity, duration of emission or width of the bands. This process is known as quenching. Fluorescein and rhoduline-orange are the best examples for the effect of temperature on the quenching of fluorescence. Addition of potassium iodide also quenches the fluorescence of fluorescein, rhoduline-orange and uranin. Quenching involves processes like internal quenching, concentration quenching[2,4], etc. Many of the saturated hydrocarbons, alcohols, ethers and acids do not show ultra-violet fluorescence on account of internal quenching caused by pre-dissociative transitions. Concentration quenching[2] is observed in certain dyes where the increase in concentration causes the formation of non-fluorescent dimers or higher aggregates. Fluorescence is said to be quenched by internal conversion, when competitive radiationless electronic transitions occur within the molecule itself. Dissolved gases like O_2, SO_2, HCl and trimethyl-amine also inhibit fluorescence[5], well-known cases being quenching of fluorescence of diacetyl by oxygen[6] and that of benzpyrene by O_2 and SO_2[5].

The efficiency of quenching can be reduced considerably by employing viscous solvents and low temperatures. These effects are well illustrated during the photoreduction of triphenylmethane dyes[7].

Photoelectric Measurement of Fluorescence Spectra

Burdett and Jones[8] have described a convenient attachment that makes possible the determination of the fluorescence spectra with the Beckmann spectrophotometer. Lipsett[9] has suggested a versatile apparatus for auto-matic recording of absolute fluorescence. In recent years, fluorescence attach-ments have become available for most commercial photo-electric spectro-photometers.

Various standards, such as quinine bisulphate[10], rhodamine 6G[11] and colloidal silica[12] have been proposed for the calibration of spectrofluoro-meters.

Fluorescence of Organic Compounds

A fluorescence spectrum is usually the mirror image of the absorption spectrum and a study of the fluorescence spectrum of a substance yields information concerning its molecular structure of essentially the same nature as that derived from its absorption spectrum. When vibrational structure appears in the fluorescence spectra of molecules in solution, a more or less complete vibrational analysis of the ground electronic state may be made analogous to that derived from Raman or infra-red spectra.

In monatomic molecules, where strictly electronic transitions are the source of luminescence, resonance spectra are observed. The resonance radiation has the same frequency as the absorption frequency. In diatomic molecules, since transitions occur from the excited state to rotational states in a number of vibrational states of the ground state the spectra consist of a series of lines, one coinciding with the absorption line and the others at longer wave-lengths at intervals determined by the energy differences between the vibra-tional states in the ground state. Spectra of polyatomic vapours such as that of benzene at low pressures are quite complicated, since excitation by ultra-violet light may cover several quantized transitions and also since the excited state can revert to a number of vibrational levels in the ground state. At higher vapour pressures or in solution, before fluorescent emission occurs, almost all

133

the excited molecules are in the vibrationless state due to vibrational deactivation by collision. The spectrum therefore consists of bands whose separation is determined by the vibrational intervals in the ground state. Thus, in the case of many organic compounds, special fluorescent properties appear to be attendant with given structures. This constitutive property of fluorescence is often appreciated in the aromatic, cyclic or closed ring structures. However, the ring system is not always an exclusive requisite to a bright fluorescence, since aliphatic compounds like palmitates and stearates are also fluorescent. Generally, compounds which absorb in the far ultra-violet or in the far end of the near ultra-violet region do not show fluorescence because of predissociation. Thus, saturated or simple olefins do not fluoresce.

Thus, the characteristic feature of the fluorescence of cyclic compounds like 1-methyl decapentaene-ω-carboxylic acid, $H_3C(CH=CH)_5COOH$, and the polyene dicarboxylic ester, isomethylbixin, $C_{26}H_{36}O_8$, is the conjugated chain which has relatively low energy of excitation associated with the absorption bands of long wavelengths[2]. Aliphatic aldehydes and ketones which have an absorption maximum around 270 mμ exhibit vibrational structure in the low frequency edge, while the high frequency part shows the characteristics of predissociation. The fluorescence of acetone has drawn the attention of several workers especially on account of the photochemical decomposition of acetone to biacetyl. Acetone vapour yields visible luminescence containing blue and green components[13]. The green component is attributed to biacetyl which originates by the photochemical decomposition of acetone. Other compounds like acetaldehyde and methyl ethyl ketone which contain the acetyl group exhibit[14] this green fluorescence of biacetyl. Very recently, Murad[15] has attempted to put forward a mechanism for the fluorescence behaviour of acetaldehyde vapour.

Fluorescence and absorption spectra of the aromatic hydrocarbons, benzene, naphthalene, anthracene, naphthacene and pentacene exhibit vibrational structure with well-defined maxima. The wavelengths of the absorption and emission processes increase linearly through the series and vary from the ultra-violet region for benzene and naphthalene to the visible region for the higher members. The fluorescence regions (mμ) and yields (ϕ) of a few aromatics are given below[2]:

	λ	ϕ		λ	ϕ
Benzene	270–310	0·11	Anthracene	370–460	0·46
P-xylene	270–320	0·42	Phenanthrene	280–470	0·27
Hexamethyl benzene	280–330	0·04	Biphenyl	290–360	0·23
Naphthalene	300–360	0·38	Triphenyl-methane	280–340	0·23

The quantum yield of fluorescence in dilute solution increases from a value of about 0·1 for benzene to about 0·46 for anthracene and then diminishes to a low value for pentacene[2]. Fluorescence spectra of angularly annulated condensed ring hydrocarbons are at shorter wavelengths than those of the linear compounds with the same number of rings. Pure phenanthrene, though isomeric with anthracene, fluoresces almost wholly in the ultra-violet with a quantum yield lower than that of naphthalene whereas anthracene gives blue fluorescence of higher efficiency. Perylene (I) is the only substance among the unsubstituted condensed ring molecules which is noted for powerful fluorescence[16]; its vapour fluoresces in ordinary light.

(I)

Substitution of aromatic molecules is known to diminish fluorescence[2]. The data on a few substituted benzenes are given below[2]:

R	λ region, $m\mu$	Fluorescence intensity
H	270–310	10
CH$_3$	270–320	17
F	270–320	10
Br	290–380	5
I	—	0
OH	285–365	18
NH$_2$	310–405	20
COOH	310–390	3
CN	280–360	20
NO$_2$	—	0

Taking the simplest case of the substituted benzenes[16], introduction of F, Cl, Br and I atoms diminishes the fluorescence in the order given. In fact, iodobenzene is not fluorescent, because it probably undergoes predissociation. Similarly, the NO$_2$ group completely eliminates fluorescence by causing a rapid dissipation of the energy of electronic excitation. Further, the bond that the NO$_2$ group forms with the nucleus has a low bond energy which favours predissociation. The phenyl group is another example of a radical of large mass held by loose constraints. It is a powerful dissipative agent when it becomes a part of conjugated structures. But the conjugation of the phenyl group should not be too strong, except to give to the connecting link a large double bond character so that the constraints of this link become sufficiently great to permit vibrations of low energy. Hydroxyl and methoxyl groups increase the fluorescence of aromatic compounds with a bathochromic displacement, whereas the carboxyl group exerts a depressant effect. The sulphonic acid group exerts little influence on the fluorescence or absorption of aromatic compounds. All of these groups or radicals which cause a rapid dissipation of the energy of electronic excitation are comparable to loose bolts in some moving parts of a machine. This Lewis–Calvin[16] 'loose bolt effect' provides a process by which the energy of the system is lost or degraded. Fluorescence data on many of the substituted benzenes and other compounds have been given by West[2], Pringsheim[26] and others.

Solutions of unsubstituted monoheterocyclic compounds, pyridine, pyrrol, furan and thiopene are non-fluorescent. According to Kasha and Reid[17], the near ultra-violet absorption spectra of N-heterocyclic compounds like pyridine, pyrazine and phenazine include $n \rightarrow \pi^*$ transitions and the excited

135

state undergoes, with high probability, a radiationless transition to a lower triplet metastable state and hence few molecules remain in the excited state long enough to fluoresce. The presence of molecules in the triplet state has been shown by their phosphorescence.

Fusion of a benzene ring to a heterocyclic nucleus causes a bathochromic shift and increases the intensity of absorption. Thus, quinoline, isoquinoline, indole and quinolium and isoquinolium ions fluoresce in the ultra-violet. Acridine, acridone and carbazole exhibit visible fluorescence. Porphyrin[18] and some of its derivatives are characterized by narrow well-defined vibrational bands and their fluorescence bands are in the red region of the spectrum.

Another characteristic feature of fluorescence is the study of dilute solutions of one compound in the crystal of another compound, absorbing at shorter wavelengths. A well-known example is the fluorescence of naphthacene in anthracene[19]. Dissolved naphthacene fluoresces when excited by blue light which it absorbs. When an exciting wavelength of 365 mμ is used, pure anthracene fluoresces a violet colour (bands 403–445 mμ), whereas a solid solution of as little as one mole of naphthacene in 10^4 moles of anthracene fluoresces with the characteristic green colour of naphthacene, and at a mole ratio of 5:10^4, the green is very strong and anthracene emission is largely suppressed. This behaviour of solid solutions has been explained in terms of the 'exciton effect'[19,20]. This explains why the fluorescence of solid organic compounds is liable to be much more sensitive to traces of impurities embedded in the crystal than the corresponding solutions in liquids.

Fluorescence of Common Dyestuffs

Turning now to common dyes, fluorescence is highly restricted. The fluorescent dyes mostly belong to the five classes: anthraquinone, indigo, azine, xanthene and acridine dyes. The anthraquinone and the indigo dyes resemble the condensed rings and represent fairly rigid structures. In the indigos and thioindigos, the two halves are separated by a double bond which produces large constraints. The most remarkable fluorescence is found in xanthenes, acridines and azines, each of which has a rigid structure in the upper part and a heavy group not very strongly held, namely, the lower phenyl group. Hence, the main absorption band and the band corresponding to the observed re-emission as fluorescence are due to the horizontal oscillation in the upper part of the molecule. Substituents such as OH, $N(CH_3)_2$, $NH(C_2H_5)$ and $N(C_2H_5)_2$ may be introduced into either of the side rings without destroying fluorescence, but the $NH(C_6H_5)$ group which introduces a phenyl group in a place where it becomes a part of the oscillating system, is not conducive to fluorescence[16]. Thus rhoduline violet and methyl heliotrope O differ only in that the $N(CH_3)_2$ group in the former has been replaced by the $NH(C_6H_5)$ group in the latter. The former fluoresces, the latter does not. The number of fluorescent dyes may be greatly increased and possibly may eventually be extended to include all coloured substances by proper choice of solvent and temperature. For example, non-fluorescent dyes such as crystal violet and malachite green show brilliant fluorescence when they are dissolved in glycerol and slightly cooled. In concentrated sulphuric acid, xanthone exhibits the blue fluorescence of its cation, while in the same solvent the visibly coloured o-dihydroxybenzophenone is non-fluorescent[2]. Solvent effects on fluorescence have been extensively studied by Mataga and Tsuno[21].

Xanthone o-dihydroxybenzophenone

That the compact structure associated with ring closure enhances fluorescence is indicated by the non-fluorescent malachite green as against the fluorescence of rosamine. A simpler example would be that of fluorene

Malachite green   Rosamine

(efficiency $= 1$) compared to biphenyl (efficiency $= 0.23$). Dyes such as amethyst violet, capri blue and methylene blue, which have compact structures, are fluorescent, whereas the triphenyl methane dyes with looser structure are non-fluorescent in solution. However, the latter become fluorescent in viscous media[7]. These green dyes in glucose glass give green fluorescence on excitation in the short wavelength range, while excitation in the long wavelength range gives red fluorescence. This implies the existence of two electronic excitation systems. Oster, Dubien and Broyde[7] have derived an empirical relation connecting the temperature, viscosity and intensity of fluorescence for the triphenyl methane dyes.

Fluorescence of Metallo-Organic Compounds

The introduction of one or more metal atoms into the structure of an aromatic compound may accentuate fluorescence in the ultra-violet. Sodium and other members of the alkali metal group show this characteristic more than the other metallic elements. Those of greater atomic number and further down in the electromotive series show little effect on the emission, or definitely tend towards quenching as in the case of copper on di-o-tolyl guanidine[22]. Chlorophyll a and b, which are the magnesium complexes of dihydroporphyrin, have their absorption and fluorescence spectra at longer wavelengths than those of other complexes of the porphyrins, their fluorescence being deep red[2]. The strong fluorescence of compounds like Zn, Cd, and Mg salts of 8-hydroxyquinoline in colloidal suspension as against the low fluorescence of 8-hydroxyquinoline, shows that ring closure by metal chelation favours fluorescence[2]. Of the several hundred metal-organic compounds tested for ultra-violet emission with three types of excitation energies, only three substances emitted wavelengths as low as 275 mμ: sodium benzene sulphonate, sodium formaldehyde-sulphoxylate in ethanol, and calcium hexose diphosphoric acid in water[22]. The metal derivatives of mesoporphyrin provide an excellent series of compounds to illustrate the effect of increased spin-orbital interaction on the emission spectra. By considering the types of emission obtained together with their relative intensities and lifetimes, deductions have been made regarding the nature of the metal–porphyrin bonding and the magnetic character of the central metal ion of these molecules[23].

Fluorescence of Inorganic Compounds

The number of pure inorganic substances possessing fluorescence as a characteristic property of their molecules is very small. Substances predominantly fluorescing in the ultra-violet region are water and the alkali and alkaline earth halides like sodium chloride, sodium bromide and calcium fluoride[24]. The ultra-violet fluorescence of pure water has been a popular topic for study by Russian physicists. But whether this is a property of pure water or due to traces of impurities, is still a matter of dispute. In general, fluorescent inorganic substances consist essentially of the rare earth ions[25], the platinum cyanide radical[1], $Pt(CN)_4^{2-}$, and the siloxene group[1], $Si_6H_6O_3$. The luminescence of the rare earth ions is a case of delayed fluorescence. Their characteristic fluorescence corresponds to forbidden transitions and consists of typical atomic line spectra. Molecular band spectra arising out of delayed fluorescence are observed in many of the uranyl compounds[26]. The only fluorescent metal ion outside the rare earth group is the thallous ion[1], Tl^+. Other inorganic compounds which exhibit fluorescence are zinc sulphide, calomel, the manganese halides and silicates and calcium tungstate.

As in the case of organic compounds, fluorescence of inorganic compounds is easily influenced by traces of impurities. This effect is largely utilized in the activation of phosphors[26,27]. Promethium[28], whose fluorescence could not be studied on account of its intense radioactivity, was rendered amenable for investigation by preparing crystals of various compositions in lanthanum chloride matrix.

Dependence of Fluorescence on pH

The strengths of aromatic acids and bases are functions of the electron distribution in the aromatic ring and hence the molecules will show a change in acidity or basicity in the excited state. Thus, when ionizable compounds are investigated in dissociating media, the changes in fluorescence run parallel with the changes in absorption caused by varying pH. For example, the fluorescence of β-naphthylamine[29] extends into the visible region corresponding to the relatively long wavelength absorption band ($n \rightarrow \pi^*$ in character) associated with the resonating structures below.

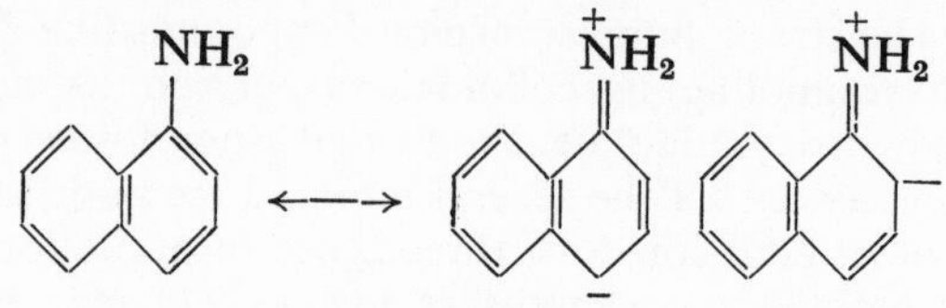

In sufficiently acidic solutions, the unshared pair of electrons of the nitrogen accept a proton and the absorption spectrum loses its long wavelength band and becomes similar to that of naphthalene. The fluorescence spectrum is, therefore, limited to the ultra-violet region. But in the case of phenol[2], in acid or weakly alkaline medium, it has no important resonance structures in addition to those of benzene, whereas in more strongly alkaline solutions, a long wavelength absorption band develops with a corresponding long wavelength fluorescence due to the three structures below.

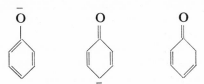

The dependence of fluorescence spectra and intensity of fluorescence of ionizable compounds on the pH of the solution enables them to be used as fluorescence indicators. The naphthyl sulphonic acids are typical examples. In the case of hydroxy and amino pyrene sulphonic acids, sharp changes in fluorescence do not occur at the same pH values as changes in absorption. This has been explained by Forster[30] by considering the attainment of the ionic equilibrium appropriate to the excited state within its lifetime. The fluorescence of some purines and pyrimidines also depends on the acidity or alkalinity of the medium[31].

Stereoisomerism

Stereoisomers can be easily recognized by a study of their fluorescence spectra. When two stereoisomeric forms of a substance are excited, it is possible that they both produce the same electronically excited state and become merely phases of rotation or vibration belonging to a single state. On the other hand, it is conceivable that even when no isomers exist in the normal state, they may be found in a state of electronic excitation. Olson and his associates[32] have investigated several such isomeric pairs. The *cis-trans* isomers of stilbenes are good examples for illustrating the dependence of fluorescence on the steric changes involved during the transition of one form to the other. In the planar *trans*-stilbene, the phenyl groups are able to vibrate out of plane, but since the electronic oscillation is entirely in the plane, it is unable to stimulate these transverse vibrations. Hence, it exhibits strong fluorescence; but in *cis*-stilbene, its non-planar structure inhibits fluorescence. The photochemical isomerization of *cis-trans* isomers of stilbenes was therefore followed fluorometrically by Lewis and his associates[33].

That fluorescence requires an extended resonating system is exhibited in the *trans-trans* form of 1,4-diphenylbutadiene[34], which shows more intense fluorescence than the *cis-trans* isomer in which resonance is partly inhibited

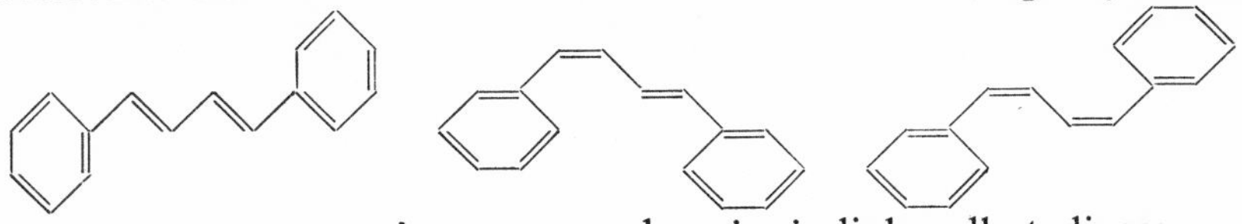

trans-trans-,   *cis-trans-*   and   *cis-cis*-diphenylbutadienes

139

by steric hindrance. The fluorescence observed for other arylated dienes[35] is also in keeping with the *trans-trans* structure ascribed to them on the basis of their absorption spectra. Prolonged irradiation causes stereoisomerization of the 1,4-diarylbutadienes. Substituents which extend the resonating system in 1,4-diphenyl butadiene increase the fluorescence intensity; methoxy and phenyl groups in the para position and especially β-naphthyl instead of phenyl are examples. Inhibition of resonance by substituents like o-methyl decrease the fluorescence intensity.

9,9'-phenanthroin[36] under the influence of ultra-violet light undergoes a *trans-cis* isomerization in the same manner as a stable enediol and does not form a tautomeric mixture. This shows the powerful conjugating influence of the 9-phenanthryl radical. The spectrum of sym-di-(9-phenanthry-ethylene) illustrates rather strikingly the fact that the 9, 10 double bonds of the phenanthrene nuclei participate in the polyenic system; the absorption curve approaches closely the visible region of the spectrum and resembles somewhat the spectrum of 1,6-diphenyl hexatriene. This active extension of the resonating system is substantiated by the fact that the hydrocarbon as well as 9,9'-phenanthroin fluoresce distinctly.

Tautomerism

If tautomeric forms of a substance are present in a solution, discrepancies between the absorption and excitation spectra will be found, provided the tautomers differ in both absorption spectra and quantum yield. The dissociation of the carboxyl group in fluorescein produces changes in absorption and fluorescence spectra and quantum yield as indicated[37] on *Table 10.1*. At pH 5–7, where both tautomers are present in appreciable amounts, the absorption and excitation spectra differ appreciably. The change in quantum yield has been shown to be due to a long-lived tautomer and not to quenching by H^+ ions, since the polarization of fluorescence of dilute solution remains equal to 0.022 ± 0.001 between pH 14 and 1.5.

Table 10.1. Dissociation of the Carboxyl Group in Fluorescein

	Absorption maximum of band of least frequency (mμ)	Emission max. (mμ)	Width of fl. band in wave nos. (cm⁻¹)	Quantum yield
Doubly charged anion(N/10NaOH)	490	577	1,100	0·93
Uncharged molecule (pH 2)	437	520	2,300	0·31

Polarized Fluorescence

Partial polarization of fluorescent light has been observed in crystalline uranyl salts, rubies at very low temperatures and simple aromatic hydrocarbons like anthracene, phenanthrene and perylene, in glycerine solution[22]. The mechanism of this polarization of fluorescent light has been clearly explained by Bowen[38]. Well-formed crystals of uranyl compounds[26] show a distinct pleochromism. When observed through a Nicol prism, their colour changes from yellow-green to very pale yellowish-white as the plane of the prism is rotated through +90°. Such changes in colour in the double chlorides of rubidium, ammonium, potassium and caesium are connected with the striking and significant variations in their absorption and fluorescence spectra and often shifts occur in their fluorescence spectra at low temperatures. Similar shifts are also observed in the polarized spectra of many uranyl salts. Polarization of anthracene[40] and stilbene[39] crystals has also been studied.

As polarization arises from the mode of vibration of an atom or molecule, both bands and lines in luminescence spectra suffer polarization. Since polarization of fluorescent light is closely associated with the lifetime of the excited state, a lower limit for the lifetime of the excited state of many organic compounds was obtained[37] by consideration of the linear polarization of fluorescence in media of high and low viscosity by using Perrin's law of depolarization[41], which connects polarization with the lifetime of the excited state and the relaxation time of molecular rotation.

Low-Temperature Fluorescence

Fluorescence spectra undergo drastic changes with change of temperature. When the temperature is raised, vibrational and rotational energies increase on account of thermal agitation and a general broadening of the emission spectrum takes place. But the effect of large decreases in temperature approximating that of liquefied gases is to break up the broad bands of the liquid spectrum into finer bands due to the reduction of thermal agitation and the simplification of the modes of vibration and rotation of the molecules. The emission lines at these low temperatures, therefore, arise from one or at most a few low-lying levels. The spectra arising from higher levels vanish because of the disappearance of the population of the atoms in these levels and hence low-temperature conditions become favourable for the existence of metastable states. Thus, short-lived fluorescence at higher temperatures becomes phosphorescence at low temperatures.

Many inorganic solids such as the various halides of metals like Zn, Cd, Cu, Sn, Sb, Mn, that do not show appreciable emission at room temperatures, frequently emit rather strongly at very low temperatures of the order of $-185°C$[42]. Uranyl salts are the best illustrations of the effect of low temperature on luminescence bands.

A study of the low-temperature (77°K) emission and absorption spectra of naphthalene[43] has established the nature of the comparatively weak absorption band on the long wavelength side of its ultra-violet spectrum; the lowest singlet-singlet band in the crystal has been shown to be at 322 mμ. Low-temperature fluorescence study of some molecular and ionic hydroxynaphthalenes in rigid solvents[44] shows that emission occurs from the Franck-Condon state at a temperature of 77°K, whereas at room temperature, normal fluorescence is observed.

Thermochromism

The phenomenon of change of colour exhibited by a number of organic compounds when the temperature is raised is known as thermochromism. The compounds showing this property are usually the substituted ethylenes

141

with multiple or fused aromatic rings as substituents. Some of the well-known compounds exhibiting this phenomenon are diphenyl- and dianisyl-methylene anthrones which, on heating, change from yellow to red-orange on account of the broadening of near ultra-violet absorption bands caused by the change in the distribution of molecules among the vibrational states[45]. Similarly, thermal broadening is attributed to the change of colour associated with 2,2'-dibenzothiazolyl disulphide (I) and tetramethylthiuram disulphide (II) which become yellow on heating. It has been postulated that free radicals are important in this process[46].

$$(CH_3)_2N—\overset{\overset{\displaystyle S}{\|}}{C}—S—S—\overset{\overset{\displaystyle S}{\|}}{C}N(CH_3)_2$$

I   II

Thiocarbonyl compounds and aryl disulphides are, in general, weakly thermochromic; the thermochromism is visually not striking, but the colour of the melt or solution deepens on heating and regains its normal colour on cooling. The visual thermochromism of some thiocarbonyl compounds[47] is probably associated with the $n \rightarrow \pi^*$ electronic absorption band and is due to a redistribution of intensity with temperature, the integrated intensity being constant. At higher temperatures, the band broadens and moves slightly $(100–150 \text{ cm}^{-1})$ to lower frequencies. The broadening is attributable to the change with temperature of the relative population of the lower vibrational levels of the ground state; the frequency shift is a new effect explained by a diminution of solvent–solute interaction with rising temperature.

The thermochromism of dianthrone and its 2,2'-dicarboxylic acid[45], which change from yellow through green to blue-green, has been explained as due to the existence of a distinct low triplet electronic level situated 3·5 kcal above the ground state.

Like fluorescence, thermochromism is influenced by steric effects. Thus, substitution of dixanthylene in the positions 1 and 1' which hinders the planarity of the molecule is detrimental to the development of thermo-chromic properties[48].

A case of negative thermochromism has been observed[49] during the study of the magnetic properties of the deep red-violet prisms, N-ethyl phenazyl radicals, which show strong bands at 80°K but none at room temperature.

Phosphorescence

Phosphorescence is associated with considerably longer decay times (10^{-4} sec to a few seconds) than fluorescence (10^{-9} to 10^{-6} sec). Phosphorescence has been shown to involve emission to the ground level from a metastable triplet state. Phosphorescence in certain inorganic substances is due to the presence of impurities which act as activators and the energy levels of the crystals are responsible for the phosphorescence rather than those of the individual molecules. In most organic compounds, phosphorescence is a molecular property. Phosphorescence spectra are generally found at longer wavelengths than the absorption or the fluorescence spectra. Since phosphorescence is due to a triplet-singlet transition it has forbidden character. Molecules with heavy atoms or solvents with heavy atoms favour the transition due to spin-orbit coupling. Data on the phosphorescence spectra[50] of a few aromatics are given below.

	λ, mμ	τ, sec		λ, mμ	τ, sec
Naphthalene	470	2·6	Benzene	340	7·0
α-Fluoronaphthalene	477	1·5	Toluene	347	8·8
α-Chloronaphthalene	483	0·30	Phenol	350	2·9
α-Bromonaphthalene	483	0·018	Benzoic acid	368	2·5
α-Iodonaphthalene	526	0·0025	Acetophenone	384·5	0·008
α-Aminonaphthalene	526	1·5	Chrysene	505	2·5
α-Nitronaphthalene	521	0·049	Coronene	525	9·4
Tetraphenylmethane	350	5·4	Triphenylene	420	15·9

Phosphorescence quantum yield is increased by the presence of a heavy atom while the fluorescence yield is decreased. Both the fluorescence and phosphorescence yields are independent of the exciting wavelength as well as concentration[51].

Triplet-Triplet Absorption Spectra

Excited triplet states have sufficiently long lifetimes and in fact, triplet-triplet absorption has been observed in some cases. The first observation was by Lewis and co-workers[52] in the case of fluorescein (505 mμ, ϵ 18,000 and 650 mμ, ϵ 20,000). A number of studies have been carried out in recent years in rigid glasses at low temperatures. Flash photolysis has been employed to study triplet-triplet absorption in several molecules.

Triplet-triplet absorptions have been found to be responsible for thermochromism and photochromism in some molecules. In photochromism, a substance which is normally colourless becomes coloured on irradiation.

Fluorometry

Fluorometry is an important analytical tool for the determination of traces of substances which exhibit fluorescence. The Beer–Lambert law is also applied in fluorometry in the form

$$\log \frac{I_{\text{solvent}}}{I_{\text{sample}}} = \epsilon_f C l$$

where ϵ_f is the absorptivity of the fluorescent material, C the concentration and l the path length. I_{solvent} and I_{sample} are the values of intensity of the incident radiant energy and of the transmitted energy respectively, just as in absorption spectrophotometry. Thus $I_{\text{solvent}} - I_{\text{sample}}$ gives the intensity of the radiation absorbed. The intensity of fluorescence is given by

$$F = k \left(I_{\text{solvent}} - I_{\text{sample}} \right)$$

143

where k is the proportionality constant (< 1). It follows,

$$F = k\, I_{\text{solvent}}\, (1 - 10^{-\epsilon_f CL})$$

$$F = F_n\, (1 - 10^{-\epsilon_f CL})$$

where $F_n = k\, I_{\text{solvent}}$

$$\frac{F - F_n}{F_n} = -10^{-\epsilon_f CL}$$

Thus,
$$\log \frac{F_n}{F_n - F} = \epsilon_f Cl$$

For $\epsilon_f Cl \leqslant 0.01$, $F \approx 2.303\, k\, I_{\text{solvent}}\, \epsilon_f Cl$. This equation holds for concentrations down to a few p.p.m.

Several commercial spectrofluorometers are available (Cenco, Coleman, Farrand, Fisher, Hilger, Klet, Lumetron, Photovolt, etc.) for routine analytical work. Applications of various kinds have been described in the literature[53,54]. Determination of several elements by fluorometry has been discussed in several books[55-57]. Organic reagents like 8-hydroxyquinoline and morin have been particularly useful in inorganic analysis. For aluminium, pentachrome Blue–Black R has been used, while for boron benzoin has been found to be excellent. Uranium can be estimated by employing fused salts for preparing samples in the form of glasses. A number of spot tests are known for elements, where, by addition of suitable reagents, fluorescent products are obtained[58].

Fluorometry has been employed for determination of organic substances, the determination of quinine being a classic example. There are several biochemical applications for this technique. The determination of thiamine (vitamin B_1), riboflavin (vitamin B_6 or G), vitamin A and folic acid are typical instances[53-56].

REFERENCES

[1] PRINGSHEIM, P. and VOGEL, M., *Luminescence of Liquids and Solids*, Interscience, New York, 1943.
[2] WEST, W., *Chemical Applications of Spectroscopy*, Interscience, New York, 1956, Chapter VI.
[3] LEWIS, G. N. and KASHA, M., *J. Amer. Chem. Soc.*, 1945, **67**, 994.
[4] PLATT, J. R., *Ann. Rev. Phys. Chem.*, 1959, **10**, 349.
[5] MILLER, J. A. and BAUMANN, C. A., *J. Amer. Chem. Soc.*, 1943, **65**, 1540.
[6] ALMY, G. M. and ANDERSON, S., *J. Chem. Phys.*, 1940, **8**, 805.
[7] OSTER, G., DUBIEN, J. J. and BROYDE, B., *J. Amer. Chem. Soc.*, 1959, **81**, 1869.
[8] BURDETT, R. A. and JONES, L. C., *J. Opt. Soc. Am.*, 1947, **37**, 554.
[9] LIPSETT, F. R., *J. Opt. Soc. Am.*, 1959, **40**, 673.
[10] MELHUISH, W. H., *J. Phys. Chem.*, 1960, **64**, 762.
[11] NIHONGI, T. and IWASCHI, S., *Chem. Abst.*, 1960, **54**, 17045i.

[12] HERCULES, D. M. and FRANKEL, H., *Science*, 1960, **131**, 1611.
[13] HUNT, E. and NOYES, W. A., *J. Amer. Chem. Soc.*, 1948, **70**, 467.
[14] MATHESON, M. S. and ZABOR, J. W., *J. Chem. Phys.*, 1939, **7**, 536.
[15] MURAD, E., *J. Phys. Chem.*, 1960, **64**, 942.
[16] LEWIS, G. N. and CALVIN, M., *Chem. Revs.*, 1939, **25**, 273.
[17] Quoted by KASHA, M., *Discussions Faraday Soc.*, 1950, **9**, 14.
[18] HAUROWITZ, F., *Ber.*, 1938, **71**, 1404.
[19] BOWEN, E. J., *J. Chem. Phys.*, 1945, **13**, 306.
[20] FRANCK, J. and TELLER, E., *J. Chem. Phys.*, 1938, **6**, 861.
[21] MATAGE, N. and TSUNO, S., *Bull. Chem. Soc., Japan*, 1957, **30**, 711; 1959, **38**, 481.
[22] JACK, DE MENT, *Fluorochemistry*, Chemical Publishing Co., New York, 1945, p. 577.
[23] ALLISON, J. B. and BECKER, R. S., *J. Chem. Phys.*, 1960, **32**, 1410.
[24] CURIE, M., *Luminescence of Solid Bodies*, University of France Press, 1934, Chapter I.
[25] TOMASCHEK, R. and DEUTSCHBIN, O., *Ann. Physik*, 1937, **29**, 311.
[26] PRINGSHEIM, P., *Fluorescence and Phosphorescence*, Interscience, New York, London, 1949.
[27] *Preparation and Characteristics of Solid Luminescent Materials*, Cornel Symposium of the American Physical Society, Wiley, 1948; see also
KIRK-OTHMER, *Encyclopedia of Chemical Technology*, Interscience, N.Y., 1952, Vol. 8, pp. 540–553.
[28] CONWAY, J. G. and GRUBER, J. B., *J. Chem. Phys.*, 1960, **32**, 1586
[29] REID, C., *Excited State in Chemistry and Biology*, Butterworths, London, 1957, p. 68.
[30] FORSTER, T., *Z. Elektrochem.*, 1950, **54**, 42.
[31] STIMSON, M. M. and REUTER, M. A., *J. Amer. Chem. Soc.*, 1941, **63**, 697.
[32] OLSON, A. R. and HUDSON, F. L., *J. Amer. Chem. Soc.*, 1933, **55**, 1410.
[33] LEWIS, G. N., LIPKIN, D. and MAGEL, T. T., *J. Amer. Chem. Soc.*, 1940, **62**, 2973.
[34] SANDOVAL, A. and ZECHMEISTER, L., *J. Amer. Chem. Soc.*, 1947, **69**, 553.
[35] HIRSHBERG, Y., BERGMANN, E. and BERGMANN, F., *J. Amer. Chem. Soc.*, 1950, **72**, 5117.
[36] HIRSHBERG, Y. and BERGMANN, F., *J. Amer. Chem. Soc.*, 1950, **72**, 5118.
[37] WEBER, G. and TEALE, F. W. J., *Trans. Faraday Soc.*, 1958, **54**, 640.
[38] BOWEN, E. J., *Trans. Faraday Soc.*, 1939, **35**, 16.
[39] VARFOLMEYEVA, V. N. and ZHAVANDROV, N. D., *Doklady Akad. Nauk S.S.S.R.*, 1957, **115**, 1115.
[40] CHAUDHURY, N. K., *Z. Physik*, 1958, **151**, 93.
[41] WEBER, G., *Advances in Protein Chem.*, 1953, **8**, 415.
[42] RANDALL, J. T., *Trans. Faraday Soc.*, 1939, **35**, 7.
[43] KASHA, M. and NAUMANN, R. V., *J. Chem. Phys.*, 1949, **17**, 576.
[44] HERCULES, D. M. and ROGERS, L. B., *J. Phys. Chem.*, 1960, **64**, 397.
[45] GRUBB, W. T. and KISTIAKOWSKY, G. B., *J. Amer. Chem. Soc.*, 1950, **72**, 419.
[46] DAVIS, R. E. and PERRIN, C., *J. Amer. Chem. Soc.*, 1960, **82**, 1590.
[47] BRAID, J. C. D. and DAVIDSON, J. R., *J. Chem. Soc.*, 1956, 15.
[48] MUSTAFA, A. and SOBHY, M. E., *J. Amer. Chem. Soc.*, 1955, **77**, 5124.
[49] HAUSSER, K. H. and BIRKOFER, *Die Naturwiss.*, 1955, **42**, 97.
[50] MCCLURE, D. S., *J. Chem. Phys.*, 1949, **17**, 905.
[51] GILMORE, E. H., GIBSON, G. E. and MCCLURE, D. S., *J. Chem. Phys.*, 1952, **20**, 829.
[52] LEWIS, G. N., LIPKIN, D. and MAGEL, T. T., *J. Amer. Chem. Soc.*, 1941, **63**, 3005.
[53] RADLEY, J. A. and GRANT, J., *Fluorescence Analysis in the Ultraviolet Light*, Van Nostrand, New York, 1954.
[54] Reviews in *Analytical Chemistry*, by C. E. White and others (1949–1956)

[55] WILLARD, H. H., MERRITT, Jr., L. L. and DEAN, J. A., *Instrumental Methods of Analysis*, Van Nostrand, New York, 1958.

[56] EWING, G. W., *Instrumental Methods of Chemical Analysis*, McGraw Hill Co., New York, 1960.

[57] SANDELL, E. B., *Colorimetric Determination of Traces of Metals*, Interscience, New York, 1950.

[58] FEIGL, F., *Spot Tests*, Elsevier, 1954.

Chapter 11

CHARGE TRANSFER SPECTRA*

CHEMISTS have long been familiar with the formation of intensely coloured molecular complexes when certain aromatic hydrocarbons, amines, phenols, etc., are mixed with a large class of aromatic nitro-compounds, quinones, carboxylic acids, sulphonic acids, halogens and the like. Pfeiffer[1], who was the first to classify these complexes, suggested the utilization of secondary valencies for their formation. The beautiful dark green crystals of quin-hydrone which may be obtained from a mixture of quinone and hydroquinone in alcoholic media and the brightly coloured crystalline picrates of alkyl benzenes and of condensed ring aromatic hydrocarbons are striking examples of these complexes. Often it may not be possible to isolate solid complexes. However, when the solutions of the two reagents are mixed, the profound change in colour clearly indicates the formation of a complex. Thus iodine, which is violet in inert solvents such as carbon tetrachloride, forms red to brown solutions in aromatic solvents. The principal feature of this type of complex formation is the appearance of a new and intense absorption band in the ultra-violet or visible region of the spectrum.

The formation of these complexes may be proved and their compositions established from a study of the associated characteristic abrupt changes from ideal behaviour in certain physical properties. These properties[2,3] include melting points, vapour pressure, viscosity, surface tension, dielectric constant, refractive index, conductivity and absorption of visible or ultra-violet radiation. Recently, valuable information has been obtained from nuclear magnetic resonance spectroscopy[4], optical dichroism of crystals[5,6] and flash photolysis[7] as well as through structural studies employing x-ray diffraction[8,9], magnetic[10] and dipole moment measurements[11,12], and from the measurements of the infra-red[13,14] and Raman[15] frequency shifts which accompany the formation of the complex.

The various aspects of such complex formation are best described on the charge-transfer basis as has been done by Mulliken[16-23]. The main spectral feature accompanying complex formation is the broad intense absorption band in the visible or ultra-violet region due to an electronic transition. Just as the excitation of an electron in an individual molecule by a quantum of radiation may be associated with intra-molecular rearrangement of charge, similarly in the complex formed by the association of two molecular or ionic species, the excitation of an electron by a photon can involve a charge re-arrangement in the complex. This rearrangement, according to the Mulliken theory, involves a transfer of an electron or part of it from one component of the complex to the other. This is analogous to the photochemical oxidation–reduction reactions in inorganic systems. Thus, the ion-pair $(Fe^{3+}, (CNS)^-)$ absorbs radiation in the visible range and an electron is transferred to the cation from the thiocyanate ion giving rise to a CNS radical.

* This chapter originally written by R. M. Mallya has now been modified.

147

Absorption Spectra of Alkali Halides

The general features of charge transfer spectra may be illustrated from the ultra-violet absorption spectra of alkali halides. These have been studied extensively by Hilsch and Pohl[24-29] for the crystalline halides and by Franck, Kuhn and Rollefson[30] for the gaseous halides. The chlorides usually give rise to single absorption peaks whereas the bromides and iodides of the alkali metals show a pair of absorption maxima. The difference in λ_{max} for the two peaks corresponds to an energy difference of 0·48–0·60 eV for the alkali bromides and to 0·95–1·19 eV in the case of the alkali iodides. This separation corresponds closely to the separation of the energy states of the halogen atoms. The two lowest energy levels of the halogen atoms of the same electronic configurations, viz. the $2P_{3/2}$ and $2P_{\frac{1}{2}}$ states, are very close together in chlorine, 0·46 eV apart in bromine and 0·94 eV apart in iodine. It may therefore be concluded that during irradiation with ultra-violet radiation, a charge transfer process has occurred giving rise to the formation of halogen and alkali metal atoms. Hilsch and Pohl[24-26] have obtained further evidence for the charge transfer process in the case of rubidium halides. The separation of λ_{max} of two bands in the rubidium halides corresponds to an energy difference of 1·51 to 1·53 eV, which is the separation between the ground and first excited states of the rubidium atom.

It has to be clearly understood, however, that the electronic excitation and the formation of the metal and halogen atoms are different processes. Thus temperature, which has little effect on the ultra-violet absorption spectrum of potassium bromide in a wider range (100–400°C) has a marked influence on the quantum efficiency of the reaction forming colour centres[31,32]. Thus at −100°C no metal atoms are formed whereas at 400°C almost every quantum absorbed gives rise to a metal atom. The quantum efficiency at 0°C is ¼. This implies that the production of metal atoms is a secondary process, dependent on the thermal oscillations of the crystal lattice, which, however, has little or no effect on the primary process of electron excitation on absorption of light quanta. The reaction may therefore be represented as follows for the alkali halide, MX.

$$M^+ + X^- + h\nu \rightleftharpoons (M^+, X^-)^* \to M + X$$

where either or both the products M and X may be in the excited state. The primary excitation process is reversible and the excited complex $(M^+, X^-)^*$ will return to the ground level unless a secondary interaction can take place during its life span to give rise to the products M and X. It is the very short lifetime of the excited state (10^{-8} sec) which restricts the quantum efficiency of the reaction giving rise to colour centres[33].

There is considerable evidence that in the excited state of the complex considerable charge transfer has occurred and that the primary process of photo-excitation is more akin to the reaction

$$(M^+, X^-)_g + h\nu \rightleftharpoons (M, X)^*$$

where $(M^+, X^-)_g$ represents the ion pair which is the ground state of the complex. In such a case, the energy for excitation $h\nu$ should be given by

$$h\nu = I_{X^-} - E_{M^+} + \Delta \quad . \quad . \quad . \quad . \quad . \quad . \quad (1)$$

where $I_X{}^-$ is the ionization potential of the halide ion and $E_M{}^+$ the electron affinity of the alkali metal cation. $I_X{}^-$ and $E_M{}^+$ may be replaced by E_X and I_M respectively. Here Δ represents the difference in energy of the crystal due to a pair of adjacent ions being replaced by a pair of the corresponding neutral atoms.

In a series of alkali halides, if it is assumed that Δ is constant, then, for the halides of a given alkali metal, the energies of the quanta required for electron excitation should depend on the electron affinities of the halogen atoms. Actual measurements have shown that the frequencies of maximum absorption (ν_{max}) of the halides for a given alkali metal increase in the order $I^- < Br^- < Cl^-$. This provides strong support for the theory, although the ν_{max} calculated by estimating the interaction term Δ on a simple electrostatic model was much too large[34,35]. Klemm[36] and also Von Hippel[37] have improved these calculations by considering the repulsive interactions between ions, the attractive force between the neutral atoms and the crystal lattice, the changes in the lattice dimensions and the non-symmetrical potential field in the region around the excited ion pair due to the associated charge transfer. The frequencies calculated in this manner were very close to the absorption maxima frequencies obtained experimentally.

General Spectral Features of Charge Transfer Complexes

Any theory of charge transfer complexes should explain satisfactorily the following general features of the absorption spectra and energy changes associated with such complex formation.

1. The characteristic absorption of visible or ultra-violet radiation by the complex. This is ascribed to the excitation of an electron in the complex. Often, the λ_{max} is several thousand Ångstroms greater than the wavelengths of absorption by the individual components of the complex. This indicates a decrease in energy of the order of 20 kcal/mole for the most loosely bound electron in the complex. In some instances where the two peaks are fairly close, it has been suggested by Bayliss[38,39] that it is mainly due to a perturbation of the optical transition and not due to complex formation.

2. Although the electron excitation energy decreases considerably on complex formation, the heats of formation for several of these complexes are of a much smaller order[2,40] ($\sim$ 1–5 kcal/mole). This indicates the weak nature of binding in the ground state of the complex.

3. The high intensity of the absorption band. The extinction coefficient is often of the order of 10^4 litre/mole cm. Several of the earlier theories of such complex formation could not account for the high intensities of charge transfer absorption bands.

4. The absorption band extends over a range of wavelength continuously. The breadth of the band suggests the loose nature of binding in the ground state of the complex. Thus, each different configuration of the ground state of the complex leads to a slightly different absorption frequency, the lack of fine structure indicating a continuous range of configurations in the ground state. The ν_{max} corresponds to the energy required to excite the electron from the most probable ground state of the complex. When several ground state configurations have equal probabilities no well-defined absorption peaks are obtained. The characteristic absorption peak for the charge transfer

complexes may be obtained in such cases by minimizing the vibrations and rotations of the components of the complex with respect to each other. For complexes of iodine in inert solvents, this has been achieved by compression or by working at very low temperatures, around $-190°C$ as was done by Ham[42].

5. A systematic study of complex formation has shown that it invariably occurs between species one of which has a low ionization potential and the other a high electron affinity, i.e. complex formation occurs with charge transfer from the electron donor component of the complex to the electron acceptor component. Weiss[45,46] therefore suggested that the stability of the complex is due to the Coulombic interaction in the ion-pair formed by charge transfer. In complexes of various donors with a given acceptor, the ν_{max} has been found to vary directly with the ionization potential of the donor[19,43]. This has been shown to be the case for the halides of a given alkali metal, as mentioned earlier; for complexes of sulphur dioxide with aromatic compounds[47], aromatic compounds with iodine[41-44] and for several other systems. Thus Keefer and Andrews have shown for complexes of benzene and its derivatives with I_2 and ICl that substitution of methyl groups which lower the ionization potential of the donor causes an increase in the λ_{max} as well as in the equilibrium constant unless steric effects oppose the formation of the complex as in hexaethylbenzene[62,63].

Theory of Charge Transfer Complexes

The account of the absorption spectra of alkali halides presented earlier shows how the energies of optical excitation are governed by the electron affinities of the halogen atoms and the ionization potentials of the alkali metal atoms. The electron donor and acceptor character of the components (D and A) of complexes, led Weiss to suggest the formation of ion pairs (D^+, A^-). Woodward[48], however, believed that the components of the complex were bound by means of a semi-polar bond. The low heats of formation of these complexes as obtained by Briegleb[49,50] suggested only dipole-dipole, dipole-induced dipole or dispersion interactions which would explain the loose nature of the complex. However, the main spectral feature, namely, the broad intense characteristic absorption band in the visible or ultra-violet region, could not be sufficiently accounted for in these terms and Brackman[51] suggested this to be the characteristic of the complex formed as follows.

$$D + A \rightleftharpoons (D, A), (D^+A^-)$$

and existing in various canonical forms. The interaction between these canonical forms would contribute a resonance energy stabilizing the complex. In terms of this 'complex resonance' theory, Brackman explained the variation of ν_{max} with the electron affinities of acceptors for a given donor.

The most satisfactory account of this phenomenon is due to Mulliken, according to whom a complex (D, A) is formed from a donor (D) species and an acceptor (A) species. This complex can exist in two energy states, the difference in energy between the two being equal to the energy of a quantum at the maximum of the absorption band. In the ground state of the complex the binding between the components is chiefly due to the Van der Waals interactions, including dipole orientation, induced dipole, London dispersion and other effects. Where conducive hydrogen bonding might also occur, this is the 'no bond' configuration (D, A). In addition, there is a definite, though small, contribution to the stability of the ground state arising from the transfer of charge from the donor to the acceptor. This configuration, $(D^+ - A^-)$ represents bonding due to electrostatic, polarization and possibly covalent interactions. The extent of charge transfer, and hence the strength of binding, between the components in the ground state is determined by I_D, the ionization potential of the donor, and E_A, the electron affinity of the acceptor. In the excited state of the complex, the predominant structure is that involving the complete transfer of an electron from D to A. Between these two states optical transitions are permissible giving rise to the absorption spectrum.

Mulliken's theoretical treatment[16-23] stresses that resonance occurs between configurations differing in the occupation of molecular orbitals rather than atomic orbitals and also between the no-bond configurations and the bonded structures derived from them by charge transfer. A non-rigorous account, nevertheless presenting the essential features, of Mulliken's theory is given below.

The wave-function, Ψ_N, for the normal or ground state of a charge transfer complex may be expressed as a linear combination of the wave-functions for the no-bond structure (D, A) and the bonded (largely ionic) configuration $(D^+ - A^-)$ as

$$\Psi_N = a\Psi_{0(D,A)} + b\Psi_{1(D^+A^-)} \qquad \text{. . . . (2)}$$

In view of the electron-donating and accepting tendencies of D and A respectively, the contribution of the ionic structure $(D^- - A^+)$ may be neglected. The ratio b^2/a^2 determines the ionic contribution to the ground state of the complex.

This representation of the ground state wave function Ψ_N is quite analogous to the usual manner of representing resonance between covalent and ionic states. By extending the analogy, the excited state of the complex may be represented similarly and the corresponding wave-function Ψ_E is given by

$$\Psi_E = a^*\Psi_{1(D^+A^-)} - b^*\Psi_{0(D,A)} \qquad \text{. . . . (3)}$$

Here the coefficients a^* and b^* which determine the ionic and no-bond contributions to the excited state of the complex are almost equal, respectively, to coefficients a and b in (2) which describe the contributions of the no-bond and ionic states to Ψ_N for the complex in the ground state. Consequently, the excited state of the complex is almost completely ionic with a small contribution from the no-bond arrangement.

Between these two states optical transitions are permissible and occur if the period of vibration of the components is long enough for a quantum of radiation to be absorbed. On this basis Mulliken was able to account for the high intensity of the absorption band in terms of the dipole strength of the transition which gives rise to a high intensity factor. This is in accord with the high intensity of the absorption spectra involving a transition from a covalent to an ionic state when, as shown by Mulliken, certain conditions are fulfilled[23,52].

The fairly strong coupling which persists in the excited state between the excited electron and the electron with which it was paired in the ground state molecular orbital prior to excitation accounts for the stability of the complex.

As in the case of the alkali halides, the energy of the photon causing electron excitation may be expressed in terms of the ionization potential of the donor and the electron affinity of the acceptor as

$$hv = I_D - E_A - \Delta + \left[\frac{2\,\beta^2}{I_D - E_A - \Delta} \right] \quad \cdots \quad (4)$$

The last two terms account for the various interactions that alter the energies of the ground and excited states and hence the absorption frequency. However, when the constant β is small, the approximate expression

$$hv = I_D - E_A - \Delta \qquad \cdots \quad (5)$$

may be employed. The various interactions which alter the energy difference between the excited and ground states of the complex from $I_D - E_A$ are: (a) the decrease in energy accompanying the formation of the complex (D, A) from D and A in the ground state and of the complex $(D^+ - A^-)$ from D^+ and A^- in the excited state; (b) the alterations in the energies of the two states due to the factor b, that is, the decrease in energy of the ground state due to the ionic contribution and the increase in energy of the excited state due to the no-bond structure; (c) the solvation energies of the complex in its ground and excited states may be different and alter hv correspondingly by a small amount.

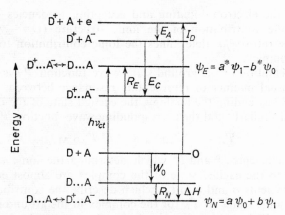

Figure 11.1. Schematic potential energy diagram for spectra of charge transfer complexes

The various contributions to the energy are shown in *Figure 11.1.* As can be easily seen from the figure

$$hv = I_D - (E_A - E_C + W_0) + R_E - R_N = I_D - E_A - \Delta \quad \cdots \quad (6)$$

and $\qquad W_N = \Delta H = W_0 - R_N$

where $\qquad R_N$ is the resonance energy.

In complexes between species of weak electron-donating and electron-accepting capacities the structure $(D^- - A^+)$ will also contribute to the stability of the complex. The wave function of the ground state of the complex will then be given by

$$\Psi_N = a\Psi_{(D,A)} + b\Psi_{(D^+A^-)} + c\Psi_{(D^-A^+)} \quad \ldots \ldots \quad (7)$$

where $c < b$.

The spread of absorption frequencies is clearly due to the loose coupling between the donor and acceptor components in the ground state of the complex. This loose coupling permits a continuous range of relative orientations of the two and therefore generally causes a continuous variation in the energy of the ground state, although some of the orientations may be energetically equivalent. The wave-function for the ground state of the complex will then be represented by

$$\Psi_N = a\Psi_{0(D,A)} + \Sigma b_i \, \Psi_{21i(D^+A^-)} + \Sigma C_j \Psi_j \, (D^-A^+) \quad \ldots \quad (8)$$

for a series of permitted values of i and j which describe the alignments of D and A on a suitable basis. Corresponding to each value of b_{ij} there will be an excited state represented by

$$\Psi_{Eij} = a^*\Psi_{11(D_i^+A_j^-)} - b^* \, \Psi_{0(D,A)} + d^*\Psi_{31(D^*A)} \quad \ldots \quad (9)$$

However, for a given donor and acceptor certain specific relative orientations in the ground state might lower the energy of the system to a minimum, and these arrangements will be favoured for dipole and induced-dipole interactions as well as for charge transfer. The maximum absorption corresponds to the transition from the most probable ground state alignment of the donor and acceptor species.

Charge transfer complexes range widely in their energies of formation in their ground states. At one end are the strongly bound complexes generally with specific relative orientations and considerable contribution to the stability of the ground state by the dative structure $(D^+ - A^-)$. In such cases the infra-red and Raman spectra of one or both components are modified markedly. Thus, in complexes of oxalyl chloride with aromatics[53,54] on formation of the complexes, the $C=O$ frequency is shifted from 1700 cm^{-1} to 1,777 cm^{-1} and the C—Cl stretching frequency at 777 cm^{-1} decreases to 757 cm^{-1}. Intensity enhancement of the vibrational bands of the component species on complex formation have also been found, as for example, in the infra-red spectrum of complexes of benzene and toluene with iodine and bromine[55].

At the other extreme are the transitory 'contact charge transfer' complexes arising out of the collisions between donor and acceptor species provided optical absorption takes place during the contact interval. In such contact pairs[70] $a \approx 1$ and $b^* \approx 0$. In loosely bound as well as contact charge transfer complexes the vibrational bands are modified little or not at all. However, the characteristic intense charge transfer absorption bands are still obtained for these complexes when other methods indicate slight complex formation and even, in some cases, when the equilibrium constant K for complex formation is virtually zero. This is the case for iodine in saturated hydrocarbons when a new band at 260 mμ appears, whereas gaseous iodine absorbs only at wavelengths < 200 mμ. All other evidence indicates no complex forma-

153

tion[56,57,89]. Similar behaviour has been observed for solutions of bromine,[56] oxygen[56,58] and tetranitromethane[59] in saturated hydrocarbons.

The intense absorption bands of contact charge transfer complexes have been explained by Mulliken[23] on the basis of the relatively greater range of charge transfer forces with respect to the corresponding range of Van der Waals forces. The stability of the ground state of the complex due to the charge transfer force is related to the contribution of the dative structure $(D^+ - A^-)$, which is governed by the square of the factor b in equation (2). When the donor and acceptor components are in their singlet ground states Mulliken[18] has shown that under certain conditions b is approximately proportional to the overlap integral

$$S_{DA} = \int \phi_D \, \phi_A \, d\tau \qquad \dots \dots (10)$$

between ϕ_D, the molecular orbital of the donor from which the electron is transferred, and ϕ_A, that of the acceptor to which the electron is transferred in the structure $(D^+ - A^-)$. The 'volume' corresponding to this overlap and known as the *electron-acceptation 'volume'*, S_{DA}, can sometimes be much greater than the *Van der Waals 'volume'*, S_{VDW}, which corresponds to the overlap of the outermost molecular orbitals of the donor and acceptor species in their ground states and in contact. Here S_{DA}^2 will chiefly determine the attractive resonance forces and S_{VDW}^2 the repulsive exchange forces of the electronic closed shells of D and A. If the acceptor orbital is strongly anti-bonding, as in the case of the iodine molecule, this orbital will reach out further into space. Consequently, when the donor and acceptor are in contact, or even a little further apart than corresponds to the Van der Waals contact, ϕ_D and ϕ_A can overlap giving rise to a non-zero S_{DA} and hence a net charge transfer force of attraction between the components. This 'contact pair' will constitute the ground state of the complex to which the charge transfer theory of Mulliken may be applied and the intense absorption spectrum explained[71]. Murrell[85] has pointed out that the intensity of contact pair transitions may be partly borrowed from the intra-donor transitions which can occur due to partial mixing of Ψ_{31} with Ψ_{11} in equation (9).

When the donor and acceptor species are ionic, then the ground state of the complex which depends largely on the Coulombic interaction between the components is influenced markedly by the dielectric of the medium. Consequently, the position of the charge transfer band is extremely sensitive to the nature of the solvent. These effects have been studied for certain pyridinium iodide complexes by Kosower[82] and employed to classify the solvents as 'associating' (acetic acid), 'normal' (chloroform, alcohols, etc.) or 'dissociating' (dimethyl formamide, dimethyl sulphoxide).

Mulliken's theory has met with a large degree of success in explaining most of the observed features of *c.t.* complexes. Thus, it is found that with one particular acceptor, the frequency of the *c.t.* band increases linearly with the ionization potential of the donor. The linear relation:

$$h\nu_{ct} = I_D - C_1 + \frac{C_2}{I_D - C_1} \qquad \dots \dots (10A)$$

is found to fit the observed *c.t.* band frequencies of a large variety of donors with an acceptor like iodine. Strong donors like amines do not follow this relation. It is now realized that linearity between $h\nu_{ct}$ and I_D is not a universal rule, since with the change of donor other factors such as the overlap integral vary as well[86].

In iodine complexes, the visible iodine band is shifted towards shorter wavelengths by an amount which is related to the stability and/or the strength of the complex. According to Mulliken[23], the blue-shift of the acceptor absorption band is greater when there is greater contact or overlap of the D and A in the ground state of the complex.

Classification of Donor-Acceptor Systems

Mulliken[88] has recently classified various types of donors and acceptors that would give rise to *c.t.* interactions of varying magnitude (*Table 11.1*).

Table 11.1 Classification of Donors and Acceptors

Number of electrons	Functional Type	Donor Types		Acceptor Types	
		Structure	Examples	Structure	Examples
Odd	Free radical	R	No,C_2H_5,H	Q	X,H,OH
Even	(a) Increvalent	n	R_3N, R_2S, R_2O, R_2CO	v	Br_3,AlR_3SnCl_4
	(b) Sacrificial	σ	Aliphatic hydrocarbons	σ	X_2, CCl_4 (X = halogen)
		π	Aromatic and unsaturated hydrocarbons — Intramolecular π-donor island groups.	π	Aromatic and unsaturated hydrocarbons fortified by electron-withdrawing groups—Intramolecular π-acceptor island groups.

It can be seen that almost all chemical interactions come under this general classification of D and A systems. The D–A systems vary widely in their energies of formation in the ground state. At one extreme we have the strong Lewis acid–Lewis base addition compounds, and, at the other, the weak contact pairs. The various types of D–A interactions commonly encountered are shown in *Table 11.2* along with the approximate energy ranges.

Table 11.2. D-A Systems and Their Energy Ranges

Type	Examples	Energy range, kcal mole⁻¹
1. Contact pairs	Cyclohexane + I_2 Benzene + CCl_4	<2
2. π—σ	Benzene + I_2 Phenanthrene + I_2	1–4
3. π—π	Naphthalene + *Sym*-trinitrobenzene	1–4
4. n—σ	Carbonyl compounds +I_2	3–15
5. n— v	Amines + I_2 BF_3 + Ether	Very strong addition compounds (>10)

It can be seen that the energy ranges for the weak π—σ complexes and the contact pairs are nearly the same. In fact, it is difficult to distinguish the so-called contact pairs from the weak complexes on the basis of the enthalpies of formation[89]. The n—σ interaction as in the case of amines $+I_2$ or thioureas $+ I_2$, can be very strong and the energies of formation in some cases are as large as in n—v systems[88,90].

The interaction of highly electron-withdrawing or -donating substituents with the π-system of the benzene ring in benzene derivatives may also be considered to be an intramolecular c.t. interaction. The intense transitions of acetophenones or nitrobenzenes are often referred to as c.t. bands (see Table 11.1). Intramolecular c.t. interaction of the C=O with formally non-conjugated C=C has already been discussed in Chapter 3. Many anions (such as I^-, Br^- or $S^=$) give rise to intense bands in the ultra-violet region due to charge-transfer to solvent[91,92].

Thermodynamics of Charge Transfer Complexes

An evaluation of the thermodynamic properties of charge transfer complexes, such as the changes in enthalpy, ΔH, entropy, ΔS°, and standard free energy, ΔG°, occurring on complex formation, provides useful evidence regarding the nature and strength of the binding in the complex. These thermodynamic quantities can be determined from a knowledge of the equilibrium constant K for complex formation from ideal solutions of the components D and A, and by experimentally determining the variation of the equilibrium constant with temperature. The thermodynamic relationships

$$\Delta G^\circ = -RT\ln K$$

$$\frac{d \ln K}{dT} = \frac{\Delta H}{RT^2}$$

and

$$\Delta G^\bullet = \Delta H^\circ - T\Delta S^\circ \qquad \cdots \cdot (11)$$

are employed to evaluate the changes in these thermodynamic properties.

Although several physical methods, which have been listed earlier, may be employed to evaluate the equilibrium constants for complex formation, the spectrophotometric method has been used most often. Following Ketelaar[60], the acceptor concentration may be maintained at a constant low value and the extinction coefficients of the complex (ϵ) and donor (ϵ_D) species followed at various donor concentrations [D], by measuring the intensity of the characteristic absorption spectrum of the complex. In such a case, the optical density d, when corrected for absorption by the donor, at a given wavelength is given by Ketelaar's relationship

$$\frac{L}{(d/[A]) - \epsilon_A} = \frac{1}{K(\epsilon - \epsilon_A)[D]} + \frac{1}{\epsilon - \epsilon_A} \qquad \cdots \cdot (12)$$

where K is the equilibrium constant for the formation of the 1:1 complex (D, A). Here the optical path, L, the extinction coefficient of the acceptor, ϵ_A, and the acceptor concentration [A] are kept constant.

The corrected optical density

156

$$d = \log_{10}\left(\frac{I_0}{I}\right) - \epsilon_D \; [D]_{free} \; L$$

$$= \left\{ \epsilon \, [DA] + \epsilon_A \, [A]_{free} \right\} L \quad \cdots \cdots \quad (13)$$

where I_0 and I are the intensities of the incident and transmitted light, respectively.

If ϵ_A is negligibly small relative to ϵ then the Ketelaar equation reduces to

$$\frac{L[A]}{d} = \frac{1}{K\epsilon[D]} + \frac{1}{\epsilon} \quad \cdots \cdots \quad (14)$$

which was used by Benesi and Hildebrand[61] in their studies on charge transfer (1:1) complexes of iodine with benzene and various other aromatic solvents. They found that the experimentally determined values of $(L\,[I_2])/d$ at various mole fractions of benzene in solvent gave a linear plot for $(L\,[I_2])/d$ versus $1/[C_6H_6]$. Values of K and ϵ were calculated from the slope and intercept of this plot. A number of other equations for use in the determination of K were discussed towards the end of Chapter 7 under 'Physicochemical Studies'. The general equation of Rose and Drago[87] is particularly useful in the evaluation of K in c.t. equilibria. Person[93] has recently pointed out the importance of using appropriate donor concentrations while evaluating equilibrium constants by the Benesi–Hildebrand or some other procedure. Typical plots employed for the evaluation of K are shown in *Figure 11.2*.

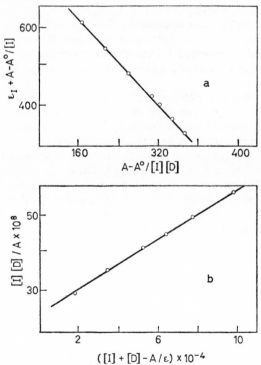

Figure 11.2. Typical plots employed for the evaluation of equilibrium constants. (a) modified Rose-Drago plot for acetone + iodine: (b) modified Benesi-Hildebrand plot for thiozolidine-2-thione+iodine. (From Bhaskar, K. R. and colleagues[94] by courtesy of The Faraday Society)

The spectrophotometric method has established the charge transfer complex formation between various aromatic compounds and bromine[62], iodine chloride[63], chlorine[64], sulphur dioxide[65], oxalyl chloride[66], etc., and the equilibrium constants derived using the Benesi-Hildebrand method. Some of the recent publications discusses the interaction of carbonyl and thiocarbonyl donors with iodine[90,94], amines $+ I_2$[95], triphenyl derivatives of Vb elements $+ I_2$[96] and interaction of π-donors with sym-trinitrobenzene and tetracyanoethylene as acceptors[97]. An excellent discussion of Donor-Acceptor Complexes may be found in the book by Briegleb[97].

The equilibrium constants K_c or K_x, expressed respectively in concentration or mole fraction units, as calculated above, are true thermodynamic constants only when the concentrations of D, A and DA correspond to the respective activities of the same species[69]. However, as has been pointed out by Orgel and Mulliken[70], the above thermodynamic treatment does not distinguish between one well-defined complex and several isomeric 1:1 complexes, so that the experimentally determined $K = \Sigma K_i$, where K_i refers to the ith species. The small enthalpy changes observed for loosely bound complexes indicate that the different orientations probably arise due to rotational freedom for the components. The enthalpy change $\Delta H = (\Sigma K_i \Delta H_i)/K$. Therefore, unless all the alignments of the 1:1 complex have the same enthalpy change, which is independent of temperature, $\ln K$ versus $1/T$ will not be linear. Also, $\epsilon = (\Sigma K_i \epsilon_i)/K$ will vary with temperature if several energetically non-equivalent 1:1 alignments are possible for the complex. Consequently, the linearity of the plot $\ln K$ versus $1/T$ and temperature independence of ϵ constitute thermodynamic criteria for the formation of definitely oriented 1:1 complexes in preference to 1:1 complexes in which the components have considerable rotational freedom[2].

Study of c.t. complexes by Electronic Spectroscopy

Electronic spectroscopy can give information on several aspects of *c.t.* complexes. To get the best out of the study one has to make very careful and detailed measurements under a variety of conditions.

(*a*) *c.t. band* — $\lambda_{c.t.}$ (or $h\nu_{c.t.}$); ϵ_{max}; $f_{c.t.}$ (oscillator strength), D (transition moment); $\Delta\nu$ (half-band width of the band). The $h\nu_{c.t.} - I_D$ correlation will be informative if data are available for a series of donors with the same acceptor. Sometimes *c.t.* bands may be hidden under the donor bands.

(*b*) *Donor band*—What happens to the donor absorption on charge-transfer may give some information on the interaction.

(*c*) *Acceptor band*—What happens to the acceptor absorption on charge-transfer provides information on the magnitude of the interaction. For example, the blue-shift, f, ϵ_{max} and $\Delta\nu_{\frac{1}{2}}$ of the iodine band have been useful in studies of *c.t.* complexes with iodine[88].

(*d*) *c.t. equilibria*—By employing suitable methods one can get K (therefore $\Delta F°$) and $\Delta H°$ of the equilibria. These thermodynamic quantities are of importance to understand the nature and magnitude of *c.t.* interaction.

Typical absorption curves obtained in the study of thiourea + iodine complexes[90] are shown in *Figures 11.3* and *11.4*.

Additional information on *c.t.* complexes may be obtained from infra-red spectroscopy, dipole moment measurements, etc.

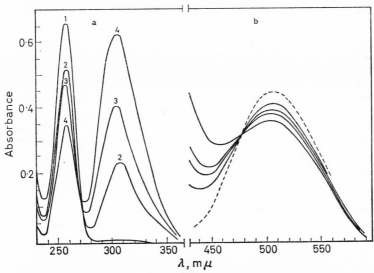

Figure 11.3. Absorption spectra of N,N'-di-t-butylthiouria + I$_2$ complex in CH$_2$Cl$_2$. (a) Curves 2–4: effect of varying iodine concentration (in the range 1-2·5 × 10^{5}M) keeping donor concentration constant (at 4·9 × 10^{5}M): curve 1: absorption spectrum of the pure donor at the same concentration. (b) Effect of varying donor concentration (in the range 1·2 × 10^{-5} to 1·5 × 10^{-4}M) keeping the iodine concentration constant (at 5·1 × 10^{-4}M); spectrum of the pure acceptor is shown by the dotted curve. Notice the *c.t.* band at ∼ 308 mμ. (From Bhaskar, K. R. and colleagues[40] by courtesy of The Faraday Society)

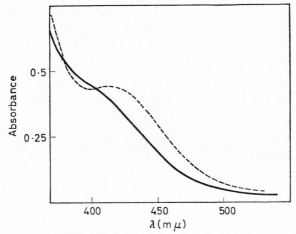

Figure 11.4. Effect of high donor concentration ∼8 × 10^{-4}M) on the visible absorption band of iodine (concentration ∼1·0 × 10^{-4}M); CCl$_4$ solvent (dotted line): CHCl$_3$ (full line). (From Bhaskar, K. R. and colleagues[40] by courtesy of The Faraday Society)

In some *n*-donor-σ-acceptor complexes the *c.t.* band intensity decreases with time due to the transformation of the associate *outer complex* to a dissociative *inner complex*. The kinetics and mechanism of transformation of the outer *c.t.* complexes to inner *c.t.* complexes have been examined in detail recently[98]. The systems studied are: Mφ$_3$(M = As and Sb) + I$_2$, RCN + I$_2$ and DMSO + I$_2$. The transformation may be represented as: D + I$_2$ ⇄ D.I$_2$ → DI$^+$I$^-$ (I$^-$ may give rise to I$_3^-$).

Structural Alignment in Charge Transfer Complexes

The preferential alignment of the donor and acceptor components in certain specific arrangements in charge transfer complexes has been predicted by Mulliken[23] by applying the overlap and orientation principle to the highest energy filled orbital of the donor, ϕ_D, and the unfilled orbital of the lowest energy of the acceptor, ϕ_A. This principle requires the donor and acceptor components in the complex to tend towards a mutual alignment so as to make the overlap integral S_{DA} a maximum. In the benzene–iodine complexes[18] one of the (e_{1g}) electrons of benzene in the ground molecular orbital arrangement $(a_{2u})^2 (e_{1g})^4$ is donated to the vacant $\bar{\sigma}_{4u}(5p_z)$ antibonding molecular orbital of iodine which has the ground state molecular orbital configuration

$$\sigma_g(5s)^2 \ \bar{\sigma}_u(5s)^2 \ \sigma_g(5p_z)^2 \ \pi_u(5p_x, 5p_y)^4 \ \bar{\pi}_g(5p_x, 5p_y)^4$$

The probable models for the complex are, therefore:

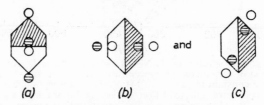

(a)   (b)   (c)

with the iodine molecule above the plane of the benzene ring and its centre lying on the sixfold rotation axis of the benzene ring. As is evident from the models, (a) and (b) give rise to a greater overlap of the molecular orbitals and therefore constitute the predominant arrangement in the complex[72]. Other models have also been proposed and certainly do occur as evidenced by the effect of high pressure on the intensity of the absorption bands[73,74].

Similar considerations for a non-zero overlap integral between the occupied π_u molecular orbital of ethylene and the unfilled $5s$ atomic orbital of the silver ion Ag^+ in ethylene–silver ion complexes indicate that the silver ion will be above the ethylenic plane over the $C{=}C$ rather than in the ethylenic plane itself. An alternative consideration of the overlap of the $\bar{\pi}_g$ unfilled antibonding molecular orbital of ethylene and the filled $4d$ orbital of the silver ion (with the charge transfer in reverse direction) also leads to the same alignment as above. The possibility of charge transfer occurring in both directions in the olefin-complexes of Pt and Pd leads to a double-bond character for the metal–olefin linkage in these complexes[75-77]. Special mention must be made of the recent studies of Hassel *et al.*[99] who have determined the structures of a variety of D—A systems in solid state. On the basis of these studies, one can differentiate 1:1 pairs from $\infty : \infty$ pairs[88].

Of interest are the self-complexes formed by *p*-nitroaniline, quinhydrone, etc, where the same species has both donor and acceptor character in different portions of the molecule. In such a case the ground state of the complex is given by equation (7) with $b = c$. The presence of charge transfer forces in these species leads to a closer packing of these molecules in their crystals than would occur in the absence of these forces[33,43,78].

The orientation of charge transfer forces predicted by Mulliken on the principle of maximum overlap of molecular orbitals has been confirmed by

Nakamoto's work[5,79] on the optical dichroism of the crystalline complex between hexamethyl benzene and chloranil and the quinhydrone self-complex. The long wavelength spectra of these crystals are polarized, the component perpendicular to the plane of the two interacting molecules being larger than that parallel to this plane.

A study of the luminescent spectra of some charge transfer complexes has led to the recognition of the mirror image relationship between the charge transfer absorption band and the emission spectra, as has been shown by Bier[80,81]. This relationship has been confirmed by the shift in the emission spectrum to longer wavelengths with increasing electron affinity of the acceptor for their complexes with a given donor. This has been clearly shown by Czekalla[83,84], who studied a series of complexes DA, D being durene, hexamethyl benzene, naphthalene, phenanthrene, anthracene and 1,2-benzanthracene in each case and A being chloranil, 2,5-dichloroquinone, 2,4,7-trinitrofluorenone, trinitrobenzene, tetrachlorophthalic anhydride and trimesyl chloride in the order of decreasing electron affinity.

For a detailed account of the classification of donors, acceptors and donor-acceptor interactions as well as the energetics of charge-transfer complexes, the reader is referred to the reviews by Booth[2], Andrews[3], Orgel[33], McGlynn[71] and Mulliken[86, 88]. The excellent book on electron donor-acceptor complexes by Briegleb[97] is a must for those interested in doing research in this area. Andrews and Keefer[100] have discussed c.t. complexes in some detail in their book on molecular complexes in organic chemistry.

REFERENCES

[1] PFEIFFER, P., *Organische Molekulverbindungen*, 2nd Edition, Ferdinand Enke, Stuttgart, 1927.
[2] BOOTH, D., *Sci. Progr.*, 1960, Vol. XLVIII, 435.
[3] ANDREWS, L. J., *Chem. Revs.*, 1954, **54**, 713.
[4] REEVES, L. W. and SCHNEIDER, W. G., *Can. J. Chem.*, 1957, **35**, 251.
[5] NAKAMOTO, K., *J. Amer. Chem. Soc.*, 1952, **74**, 1739.
[6] NAKAMOTO, K., *Spectrochim. Acta*, 1956, **8**, 142.
[7] RAND, S. J. and STRONG, R. L., *J. Amer. Chem. Soc.*, 1960, **82**, 5.
[8] HASSEL, O., *Proc. Chem. Soc.*, 1957, 250.
[9] HASSEL, O., *Mol. Phys.*, 1958, **1**, 241.
[10] KONDO, M., KISHITA, M., KIMURA, M. and KUBO, M., *Bull. Chem. Soc., Japan*, 1956, **29**, 305.
[11] FAIRBROTHER, F., *J. Chem. Soc.*, 1948, 1051.
[12] FAIRBROTHER, F., *J. Chem. Soc.*, 1950, 180.
[13] FERGUSON, E. E., *J. Chem. Phys.*, 1956, **25**, 577.
[14] FERGUSON, E. E. and MATSEN, F. A., *J. Chem. Phys.*, 1958, **29**, 105.
[15] TAUFEN, H. J., MURRAY, M. J. and CLEVELAND, F. F., *J. Amer. Chem. Soc.*, 1941, **63**, 3500.
[16] MULLIKEN, R. S., *J. Amer. Chem. Soc.*, 1950, **72**, 600.
[17] MULLIKEN, R. S., *J. Chem. Phys.*, 1951, **19**, 514 (I).
[18] MULLIKEN, R. S., *J. Amer. Chem. Soc.*, 1952, **74**, 811 (II).
[19] MULLIKEN, R. S., *J. Phys. Chem.*, 1952, **56**, 801 (III).
[20] MULLIKEN, R. S., *Symposium on Molecular Physics, Nikko, Japan*, 1953, p. 45.
[21] MULLIKEN, R. S., *J. Chim. phys.*, 1954, **51**, 341.
[22] MULLIKEN, R. S., *J. Chem. Phys.*, 1955, **23**, 397.

[23] MULLIKEN, R. S., *Rec. trav. chim.*, 1956, **75**, 845.
[24] HILSCH, R. and POHL, R. W., *Z. Physik*, 1929, **57**, 145.
[25] HILSCH, R. and POHL, R. W., *Z. Physik*, 1930, **59**, 812.
[26] HILSCH, R. and POHL, R. W., *Z. Physik*, 1930, **64**, 606.
[27] POHL, R. W., *Proc. Phys. Soc. (London)*, 1937, **49**, E3.
[28] HILSCH, R. and POHL, R. W., *Trans. Faraday Soc.*, 1938, **34**, 883.
[29] POHL, R. W., *Kolloid-Z.*, 1939, **71**, 257.
[30] FRANCK, J., KUHN, H. and ROLLEFSON, G., *Z. Physik*, 1927, **43**, 155.
[31] SMAKULA, A., *Z. Physik*, 1930, **63**, 762.
[32] HILSCH, R. and POHL, R. W., *Nachr. ges. Wiss. Göttingen, Jahresber. geschöftsjahr Math-Physik kl.*, 1934, No. 9; 1935, No. 19.
[33] ORGEL, L. E., *Quart. Revs. (London)*, 1954, **8**, 422.
[34] WOLF, K. L. and HERZFELD, K. F., *Ann. der Physik*, 1925, **78** (4), 35 and 195.
[35] BORN, M., *Z. Physik*, 1932, **79**, 62.
[36] KLEMM, W., *Z. Physik*, 1933, **82**, 529.
[37] VON HIPPEL, A., *Z. Physik*, 1936, **101**, 680.
[38] BAYLISS, N. S. and McRAE, E. G., *J. Phys. Chem.*, 1954, **58**, 1002.
[39] BAYLISS, N. S. and BRACKENRIDGE, C. J., *J. Amer. Chem. Soc.*, 1955, **77**, 3959.
[40] AINSCOUGH, J. B. and CALDIN, E. F., *J. Chem. Soc.*, 1956, 2528, 2540, 2546.
[41] BHATTACHARYA, R. and BASU, S., *Trans. Faraday Soc.*, 1958, **54**, 1286.
[42] HAM, J. S., *J. Amer. Chem. Soc.*, 1954, **76**, 3875, 3881.
[43] ANDREWS, L. J., *Chem. Revs.*, 1954, **54**, 713.
[44] McCONNELL, H., HAM, J. S. and PLATT, J. R., *J. Chem. Phys.*, 1953, **21**, 66.
[45] WEISS, J., *J. Chem. Soc.*, 1942, 245.
[46] WEISS, J., *J. Chem. Soc.*, 1943, 462.
[47] BOOTH, D., DAINTON, F. S. and IVIN, K. J., *Trans. Faraday Soc.*, 1959, **55**, 1293.
[48] WOODWARD, R. B., *J. Amer. Chem. Soc.*, 1942, **64**, 3058.
[49] BRIEGLEB, G., *Z. physik. Chem.*, 1936, **B31**, 58.
[50] BRIEGLEB, G. and KAMBEITZ, J., *Z. physik. Chem.*, 1936, **B32**, 305.
[51] BRACKMAN, W., *Rec. trav. chim.*, 1949, **68**, 147.
[52] MULLIKEN, R. S., *Rep. Progr. Physics*, 1941, **8**, 231.
[53] MARTIN, G. T. O. and PARTINGTON, J. R., *J. Chem. Soc.*, 1936, 1178.
[54] SAKSENA, B. D., *Proc. Indian Acad. Sci.*, 1940, **12A**, 416.
[55] FERGUSON, E. E., *J. Chem. Phys.*, 1956, **25**, 1577.
[56] EVANS, D. F., *J. Chem. Phys.*, 1955, **23**, 1424, 1426.
[57] HASTINGS, S. H., FRANKLIN, J. L., SCHILLER, J. C. and MATSEN, F. A., *J. Amer. Chem. Soc.*, 1953, **75**, 2900.
[58] MUNCK, A. U. and SCOTT, J. F., *Nature (London)*, 1956, **177**, 587.
[59] EVANS, D. F., *J. Chem. Soc.*, 1957, 4229.
[60] KETELAAR, J. A. A., VAN DE STOLPE, C. and GERSMANN, H. R., *Rec. trav. chim.*, 1952, **70**, 499.
[61] BENESI, H. A. and HILDEBRAND, J. H., *J. Amer. Chem. Soc.*, 1949, **71**, 2703.
[62] KEEFER, R. M. and ANDREWS, L. J., *J. Amer. Chem. Soc.*, 1950, **72**, 4677, 5170.
[63] ANDREWS, L. J. and KEEFER, R. M., *J. Amer. Chem. Soc.*, 1952, **74**, 4500.
[64] ANDREWS, L. J. and KEEFER, R. M., *J. Amer. Chem. Soc.*, 1951, **73**, 462.
[65] ANDREWS, L. J. and KEEFER, R. M., *J. Amer. Chem. Soc.*, 1951, **73**, 4169.
[66] SAKSENA, B. D. and KAGARISE, R. E., *J. Chem. Phys.*, 1951, **19**, 994.
[67] FOSTER, R., HAMMICK, D. Ll. and WARDLEY, A. A., *J. Chem. Soc.*, 1953, 3817.
[68] LANDAUER, J. and McCONNELL, H., *J. Amer. Chem. Soc.*, 1952, **74**, 1221.
[69] SCOTT, R. L., *Rec. trav. chim.*, 1956, **75**, 787.
[70] ORGEL, L. E. and MULLIKEN, R. S., *J. Amer. Chem. Soc.*, 1957, **79**, 4839.
[71] McGLYNN, S. P., *Chem. Revs.*, 1958, **58**, 1113.
[72] DALLINGA, G., *Acta Cryst.*, 1954, **7**, 665.
[73] GIBSON, R. E. and LOEFFLER, O. H., *J. Amer. Chem. Soc.*, 1940, **62**, 1324.

[74] HAM, J., *J. Amer. Chem. Soc.*, 1954, **76**, 3875, 3881.
[75] CHATT, J. and DUNCANSON, L. A., *J. Chem. Soc.*, 1953, 2939.
[76] DEMPSEY, J. N. and BAENZIGER, N. C., *J. Amer. Chem. Soc.*, 1955, **77**, 4984.
[77] WUNDERLICH, J. A. and MELLOR, D. P., *Acta Cryst.*, 1955, **8**, 57.
[78] ABRAHAMS, S. C., *J. Amer. Chem. Soc.*, 1952, **74**, 2693.
[79] NAKAMOTO, K., *J. Amer. Chem. Soc.*, 1952, **74**, 390, 392.
[80] BIER, A., *Rec. trav. chim.*, 1956, **75**, 866.
[81] BIER, A. and KETELAAR, J. A. A., *Rec. trav. chim.*, 1954, **73**, 264.
[82] KOSOWER, E. M., *J. Amer. Chem. Soc.*, 1958, **80**, 3253.
[83] CZEKALLA, J., BRIEGLEB, G., HERRE, W. and GLIER, R., *Z. Elektrochem.*, 1957, **61**, 537.
[84] CZEKALLA, J., SCHMILLEN, A. and MAGER, K. J., *Z. Elektrochem.*, 1957, **61**, 1053.
[85] MURREL, J. N., *Quart. Revs. (London)*, 1961, **15**, 191.
[86] MULLIKEN, R. S. and PERSON, W. B., *Ann. Revs. Phys. Chem.*, 1962.
[87] ROSE, N. J. and DRAGO, R. S., *J. Amer. Chem. Soc.*, 1959, **81**, 6138.
[88] MULLIKEN, R. S., *J. Chim. Phys.*, 1963, **20**.
[89] BHAT, S. N., BHASKAR, K. R. and RAO, C. N. R., *Proc. Indian Acad. Sci.*, 1967.
[90] BHASKAR, K. R., GOSAVI, R. K. and RAO, C. N. R., *Trans. Faraday Soc.*, 1966, **62**, 29.
[91] (a) SMITH, M. and SYMONS, M. C. R., *Trans. Faraday Soc.*, 1958, **54**, 346.
(b) GRIFFITHS, T. R. and SYMONS, M. C. R., *Mol. Phys.*, 1960, **3**, 90.
[92] SINGH, S. and RAO, C. N. R., *Trans. Faraday Soc.*, 1966, **62**, 3310.
[93] PERSON, W. B., *J. Amer. Chem. Soc.*, 1965, **87**, 167.
[94] BHASKAR, K. R., BHAT, S. N., MURTHY, A. S. N. and RAO, C. N. R., *Trans. Faraday Soc.*, 1966, **62**, 788.
[95] YADA, H., TANAKA, J. and NAGAKURA, S., *Bull. Chem. Soc., Japan*, 1960, **33**, 1660.
[96] BHASKAR, K. R., BHAT, S. N., SINGH, S. and RAO, C. N. R., *J. Inorg. Nucl. Chem.*, 1966, **28**, 1915.
[97] BRIEGLEB, G. *Electronen-Donator-Acceptor Komplexe*, Springer-Verlag, Berlin, 1961.
[98] BHAT, S. N. and RAO, C. N. R., *J. Amer. Chem. Soc.*, 1966, **88**, 3216.
[99] HASSEL, O. and ROMMING, C., *Quart. Revs. (London)* 1962. **16**, 1.
[100] ANDREWS, L. J. and KEEFER, R. M. *Molecular Complexes in Organic Chemistry*, Holden Day Inc., San Francisco, 1964.

CHAPTER 12

MISCELLANEOUS TOPICS

*Colours of Transition Metal Ions and their Complexes: Ligand Field Theory**

The nature of the electronic transitions giving rise to the variety of colours displayed by the transition metal ions and their complexes has been understood only since 1951, when Ilse and Hartmann[1] explained the absorption spectrum of $Ti(H_2O)_6^{3+}$ on the basis of the Crystal Field Theory developed by Bethe[2], Van Vleck[3], Schlapp and Penney[4] and others[5,6]. Then followed a remarkable period of intense investigation and theoretical advance in which Orgel[6], Jørgensen[7] and others[8] have played a prominent part as a result of which the simple crystal field theory of the early days has developed into the contemporary Ligand Field Theory, rationalizing the absorption spectra of the transition metal ions and their complexes in a quite satisfactory manner.

The transition metal ions contain an incomplete d shell of electrons and the correlation between the presence of an incomplete d shell and the display of colours by the transition metal ions can be clearly seen from *Table 12.1*. It is to be noted that ions with no d electron or with the maximum number of d electrons are colourless, while those with half-filled d shells exhibit only a very pale colour.

Table 12.1. Colours of Transition Metal Ion Hydrates in Solution[†]
(Together with those of certain preceding and following ions)
(Sulphates or perchlorates)[17]
Usually ions of the type $[M(H_2O)_6]^{n+}$

Total No. of d electrons	Number of unpaired d electrons	Metal ion	Colour
0	0	K^+, Ca^{2+}, Sc^{3+}	Colourless
1	1	Ti^{3+}	Pink-violet
2	2	V^{3+}	Green
3	3	Cr^{3+}	Violet
4	4	Cr^{2+}	Blue
5	5	Mn^{2+}	Very pale pink
		Fe^{3+}	Very pale violet
6	4	Fe^{2+}	Green
7	3	Co^{2+}	Pink
8	2	Ni^{2+}	Green
9	1	Cu^{2+}	Blue
10	0	Cu^+, Zn^{2+}, Ga^{3+}	Colourless

† By courtesy of The Royal Institution.

The colours of the transition metal ions and their complexes are, in fact, due to electronic transitions involving the d electrons. The d shell in an atom or ion is fivefold degenerate, i.e. there are five d orbitals which are equal in energy in the absence of an external magnetic or electric field. An electron

* Written in collaboration with K. Srinivasan.

can jump from one of these orbitals to the other without any absorption or emission of radiation. But this applies only to the free ion in the gaseous state. The ion in solution is surrounded by a certain number of water molecules co-ordinated to it and so even the aquo ion is a complex with water as the ligand. When a certain number of water molecules, or any other ligand molecules, is attached to the central metal ion, the degenerate d orbitals split up into groups of different energies, and electronic transitions from one set of orbitals to the other can only take place with absorption of energy. The magnitude of energy separation is such as to produce the well-known colours of these complexes.

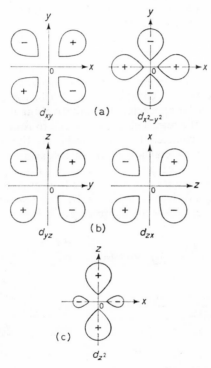

Figure 12.1. Cross sections of the five d orbitals, chosen in real form[6](c)

There are two models by means of which the loss of degeneracy of the d orbitals can be explained: the electrostatic model, and the molecular orbital model. In the first model, the differentiation of the d orbitals is attributed to the electric field produced by the symmetrical disposition of the attached groups, which may be anions like Cl^- or CN^- or dipole molecules like H_2O or NH_3. In a crystal also, the metal ion finds itself in a similar environment and hence the original name Crystal Field Theory. The five d orbitals which may be denoted as d_{xy}, d_{yz}, d_{xz}, $d_{x^2-y^2}$ and d_{z^2} have the shapes as represented in *Figure 12.1*. The d_{xy}, d_{xz} and d_{yz} orbitals have their maximum in a diagonal direction between the co-ordinate axes in each of the three planes. The $d_{x^2-y^2}$ and d_{z^2} orbitals are directed along the co-ordinate axes. Although these five d orbitals are thus disposed in different directions, the solitary d electron in the free Ti^{3+} ion, for example, does not distinguish between them and spends its time equally in all the five orbitals. But when six negative charges in the form of anions or dipoles occupy octahedral positions along the x, y and z axes, the five d orbitals are affected differently by the electric field so produced. The d electron of the central ion avoids the $d_{x^2-y^2}$ and d_{z^2} orbitals where the field is highest and spends its time preferentially in the three orbitals (d_{xy}, d_{yz} and d_{xz}) which are directed between the ligands. The $d_{x^2-y^2}$ and d_{z^2} orbitals which are raised to a higher energy level are called e_g orbitals (or γ_3 orbitals or $d\gamma$ orbitals) and the other three orbitals in which the electron has lower energy are called t_{2g} orbitals (or γ_5 orbitals or $d\epsilon$ orbitals). The energy difference between the two groups of orbitals is variously denoted as 10Dq, E_2-E_1 and more recently as Δ^7.

In tetrahedral complexes, the d_{xy}, d_{xz} and d_{yz} orbitals are nearer the ligands and so become 'unstable' in comparison with the $d_{x^2-y^2}$ and d_{z^2} orbitals. Hence the octahedral order of the levels is inverted in the tetrahedral complexes. Also the energy difference between the two sets of orbitals will not be as much as in the octahedral case; it will be 4/9 of the corresponding octahedral value. This can be appreciated qualitatively if it is remembered that the perturbing field in the tetrahedral case is due to four ligands while in the octahedral case it is produced by six ligands. As the arrangement of the ligands round the central metal ion becomes less symmetrical, the d orbitals split up into more groups of different energies. This happens, for example, in the case of a square planar complex, where four groups of levels come into being out of the original degenerate orbitals. The positions of the different d orbitals in the different cases are represented in *Figure 12.2*.

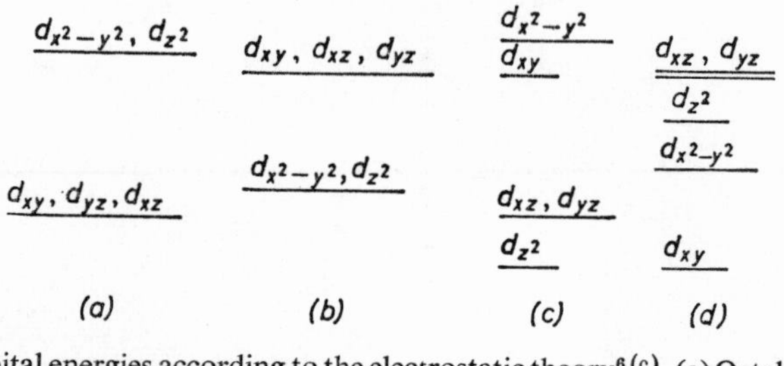

Figure 12.2. Orbital energies according to the electrostatic theory[6(c)]. (a) Octahedral complex, (b) tetrahedral complex, (c) square planar complex, (d) irregular dodecahedral complex.

The molecular orbital method also leads to the same results. Here molecular orbitals are formed from the 3d, 4s and 4p orbitals of the central metal ion and the ligand orbitals. In an octahedral complex, for example, the six σ orbitals are combined to form symmetry orbitals called a_{1g}, e_g and t_{1u} orbitals. From the six σ orbitals, one totally symmetrical a_{1g} orbital, a pair of doubly degenerate e_g orbitals and a trio of triply degenerate t_{1u} orbitals can be formed. Considering the orbitals of the central metal ion, the s orbital belongs to the a_{1g} class, the p orbitals belong to the t_{1u} class and out of the d orbitals, the $d_{x^2-y^2}$ and d_{z^2} orbitals belong to the e_g class while d_{xy}, d_{yz} and d_{xz} orbitals are of the t_{2g} class. In forming molecular orbitals, one has to combine orbitals belonging to the same symmetry class. The a_{1g} orbital of the ligands can be combined with the s orbital of the central ion to give one bonding and one anti-bonding molecular orbital. The three t_{1u} orbitals can be combined with the three p orbitals of the central ion to give six molecular orbitals of which three are bonding and three are anti-bonding.

Finally, the two e_g orbitals of the ligands can be combined with the $d_{x^2-y^2}$ and d_{z^2} orbitals of the central ion to form four molecular orbitals, two of them being bonding and two anti-bonding. It is seen, however, that there are no ligand orbitals belonging to the same class (t_{2g}) as the d_{xy}, d_{yz} and d_{xz} orbitals of the central metal ion. These orbitals remain non-bonding in the molecular orbital method. The manner in which the molecular orbitals are formed and the relative positions of the levels are shown in *Figure 12.3*. If we have n d electrons, there will be a total number of $(n + 12)$ electrons including the ligand electrons. These have to be accommodated in the molecular orbitals. Twelve of these can be put into the six bonding orbitals. The remaining n electrons go into the non-bonding t_{2g} orbitals which are three in number. The lowest anti-bonding orbitals are the e_g^* orbitals and so electronic transition can take place between a non-bonding t_{2g} orbital and an anti-bonding e_g^* orbital and the energy difference between these two orbitals is 10Dq or $E_2 - E_1$ or Δ as stated before.

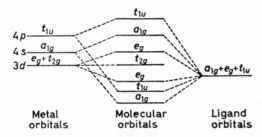

Figure 12.3. The relations between atomic and molecular orbitals in octahedral complexes[6](c)

We thus see that both the electrostatic model and the molecular orbital model lead to the conclusion that the degenerate d orbitals of the free ion are split into groups of different energies when the ion is co-ordinated to other groups in a complex. Taking the example of $Ti(H_2O)_6^{3+}$, which contains only one d electron, this can be put into the t_{2g} orbital. Hence the observed spectrum of the aquo-ion, whose λ_{max} (490 mμ) corresponds to 20,400 cm^{-1}, can be interpreted as being due to the electronic transition from the t_{2g} orbital to the e_g orbital. We can also say that the ground term ^2D in the free ion is split into two terms in the octahedral complex, the upper being called the E_g and the lower being T_{2g}. The electronic transition can therefore be written as $T_{2g} \rightarrow E_g$. The energy separation of 10Dq between the two groups of orbitals is distributed as -4Dq to the lower orbitals and $+6$Dq to the higher orbitals. These numbers follow because, if all the five orbitals are occupied at random by five electrons, the ligand field energy should be zero. With one electron in each of the three t_{2g} orbitals, the energy is given by -4Dq $\times 3 = -12$Dq and with one electron in each of the e_g orbitals the energy is given by $+6$Dq $\times 2 = +12$Dq. Thus, the total energy is zero. In the case of $Ti(H_2O)_6^{3+}$,

$10Dq = 20,400$ cm^{-1}, giving a value of 2,040 cm^{-1} for Dq. The intensity of the absorption is, however, low, the ϵ_{max} being approximately 10. This is understandable because the internal transition involving two levels derived from the same electronic configuration (levels with the same parity) is a forbidden one. In fact, the molar extinction coefficients for the ligand field spectra of transition metal complexes range from 0·01 to 200 only and when values of the order of 1,000 to 10,000 are obtained they are to be ascribed to charge transfer, i.e. electron transfer from the ligand to the central ion.

When considering the filling up of the t_{2g} and e_g orbitals two tendencies will have to be taken into account. First, that of the electrons to occupy systematically the orbitals of lower energy to their maximum. Secondly, there is also the tendency for the electrons to go into different orbitals, including the higher energy ones, with their spins parallel, since thereby the electrostatic repulsion between electrons is lowered and exchange energy is increased. The actual distribution of the d electrons between the two sets of orbitals depends, therefore, on the strength of the ligand field which determines the energy separation of the two sets of orbitals. Two limiting cases can be considered in this connection. In the weak field limit, as for example when water molecules are the ligands, the energy separation Δ between the two sets of orbitals is not sufficiently large to prevent the occupation of the higher set of orbitals by the electrons with their spins parallel. But, in general,

Table 12.2. *Configurations and Ligand Field Stabilization Energies for the Ground States*

	Weak Field			Strong Field		
No. of d electrons	No. of electrons in t_{2g} orbitals	No. of electrons in e_g orbitals	Ligand field stabili- zation energy (in Dq)	No. of electrons in t_{2g} orbitals	No. of electrons in e_g orbitals	Ligand field stabili- zation energy (in Dq)
1	1	0	4	1	0	4
2	9/5	1/5	6	2	0	8
3	3	0	12	3	0	12
4	3	1	6	4	0	16
5	3	2	0	5	0	20
6	4	2	4	6	0	24
7	24/5	11/5	6	6	1	18
8	6	2	12	6	2	12
9	6	3	6	6	3	6

we should not expect to find integral numbers of electrons in the two sets of orbitals. Santen and Wieringen[9] have shown that with two electrons in the d shell, the occupation numbers are 9/5 and 1/5 for the lower and the upper orbitals respectively. Similarly with 7 d electrons, these numbers are 24/5 and 11/5 respectively. In all the other cases the occupation numbers turn out to be integrals. In the strong field limit, on the other hand, Δ is large and so the lower set of three orbitals is filled to the maximum of six electrons before the upper set is occupied. Only in the case of d^4, d^5, d^6 and d^7 and to a slight extent in the case of d^2 will there be a difference in the distribution of electrons between the two sets of orbitals in the two limits. One can calculate the ligand field stabilization energy of the ground state in both cases. For example, in the case of d^2, in the weak field limit it is $-4Dq \times 9/5 + 6Dq \times 1/5 = -6Dq$; that is, the ground state is lowered by 6Dq in comparison with that of the free ion. In the strong field limit, on the other hand, the energy is $-4Dq \times 2 + 6 \times 0 = -8Dq$. Hence we see that the ligand field stabilization is greater in the strong field limit. At the same time, one has to consider the promotion energy necessary to put electrons in the lower set of orbitals with spins opposed. The net stabilization is obtained by subtracting the promotion energy from the ligand field stabilization energy. The configurations and the ligand field stabilization energies for the ground states for different numbers of d electrons are given in *Table 12.2*.

In atomic spectroscopy, the notation S, P, D, F is employed to indicate terms with L values of 0, 1, 2, 3 respectively. The multiplicity is indicated by the number at the top as in ^3P, for example. The spectral terms in an octahedral complex can be expressed in terms of only five ligand field quantum numbers which are written as A_1, A_2, E, T_1 and T_2. The orbital degeneracies of these are 1, 1, 2, 3, 3 respectively. In discussing the absorption spectra of transition metal complexes, one should consider the number of terms into which each term of the free ion splits. The reason for this splitting is of course the differentiation of the degenerate d orbitals into two sets of orbitals. The S and P terms of the free ion are not split but transform as A_1 and T_1 respectively. The D terms are split into E and T_2 while the F terms are split into A_2, T_1 and T_2 [7]. As in atomic spectroscopy, the multiplicity of each term is indicated by the number at the top, as for example $^3T_2$.

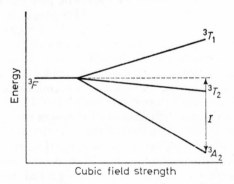

Figure 12.4. The splitting of the ^3F ground state of Ni^{2+} in a field of cubic symmetry[6(a)]

As an example of the application of the ligand field theory in the interpretation of the spectral data of transition metal complexes, we can consider the spectrum of $Ni(NH_3)_6^{2+}$, which gives three bands at 10,700 cm^{-1}, 17,500 cm^{-1} and 28,100 cm^{-1} [10]. Nickel (II) has the configuration d^8 which gives two triplet terms ^3F and ^3P, the second being about 15,800 cm^{-1} higher than the first in the free ion. The ^3F term is split into three terms in $Ni(NH_3)_6^{2+}$ which in the order of increasing energy are $^3A_2$, $^3T_2$ and $^3T_1$. The first corresponds to the distribution $(t_{2g})^6(e_g)^2$ while both $^3T_2$ and $^3T_1$ arise from $(t_{2g})^5(e_g)^3$ distribution. The manner in which the splitting takes place is shown in *Figure 12.4*, which is called the Orgel diagram of energy levels, since Orgel was the first to draw such a diagram[6] [(a)]. However, the diagram given here is not complete since the interaction of the $^3T_1$ from ^3P with $^3T_1$ from ^3F is not taken into account. The first band can be assigned to the transition $^3A_2 \rightarrow {}^3T_2$. The separation of these two terms is 10Dq and hence we get Dq = 1,070 cm^{-1}. Using this value, we can calculate the positions of the other two bands and compare them with the observed values. The second band is obviously due to the transition $^3A_2 \rightarrow {}^3T_1(P)$; that is, from the ground term to the $^3T_1$ term derived from the ^3P term of the free ion. The $^3T_1(P)$ corresponds to the distribution $(t_{2g})^4(e_g)^4$ and so the ligand field energy separation between the two terms is 20Dq, which gives 21,400 cm^{-1}. But the promotional energy for the configuration of the higher term has to be added to this. If this is done, the value of 30,300 cm^{-1} is obtained in comparison with the observed value of 28,100 cm^{-1}. Moffitt and Ballhausen have remarked that the agreement with the experimental values seems to flatter somewhat the basic premises of the theory[10].

Even before the application of the crystal field theory to the spectra of transition metal complexes, it had been noticed that the replacement of water molecules by other ligands changed the λ_{max}, and Tsuchida[11] had arranged the ligands in a spectrochemical sequence in which the ligands shift the absorption maximum of a given metal to shorter wavelengths as one proceeds from left to right in the series. The present arrangement of the more common ligands is as follows[12]:

$$I^- < Br^- < SCN^- < Cl^- < F^- < H_2O < NH_3 < en < NO_2^- < CN^-$$

The shift of λ_{max} has been explained by the ligand field theory as being due to the difference in the strength of the ligand field produced by different ligands. That CN$^-$ should produce a stronger field than F$^-$, for instance, is surprising but the explanation lies in the greater polarizability of the cyanide ion. However, the simple electrostatic model according to which the ligands just serve to produce an electric field has proved itself inadequate in explaining the above sequence in a reasonable manner and in accounting completely for the observed values of Δ. These values range from 7,500–12,500 cm^{-1} for bivalent aquo-ions while for the tervalent aquo-ions it ranges between 13,500–21,000 cm^{-1}. The Δ value is 45% greater for the complexes of the second row transition metals, and 75% greater for those of the third row transition metals compared with the corresponding complexes of the first row transition metals[6] [(c),13]. The molecular orbital method has proved itself versatile where the electrostatic model has proved inadequate. In this method, there is also the possibility of the normally non-bonding electrons in the t_{2g} orbitals forming π bonds with suitable ligand orbitals. This will lead to a change in the magnitude of Δ, the direction of the change depending upon whether the t_{2g} electrons occupy bonding or anti-bonding π orbitals. In the former case Δ increases while in the latter Δ decreases. As Jørgensen has stated[14], the electrostatic model has to be given up, although it has worked quite well, because the molecular orbital method has proved itself more capable of explaining the observed data.

This account of the ligand field theory will be concluded with a brief reference to the Jahn–Teller effect[15]. There are several instances of complexes whose structure is distorted from octahedral or tetrahedral symmetry. The distortion may be towards tetragonal or rhombic symmetry. According to the Jahn–Teller effect, if the ground state of a complex happens to be a degenerate one, there will be distortion towards lower symmetry and thus the degeneracy of the ground state is removed and with it the energy separations between the ground level and the higher levels are increased. This happens when the electron configurations in the free ion are such as to give ground states in the complex belonging to E_g, T_{1g} or T_{2g}. The d^4 and d^9 configurations with $^3T_{1g}$ and ^2E_g as their ground states are typical cases exhibiting marked tetragonal distortion. In the first transition series, the Δ values of the divalent hexa-aquo ions decrease steadily from vanadium (II) ($12,600$ cm^{-1}) to nickel (II) ($8,500$ cm^{-1}); chromium (II) with the d^4 configuration happens to be the exception in this series with a Δ value of $13,900$ cm^{-1}. Copper (II), coming after nickel, gives a value of $12,600$ cm^{-1} and it has the d^9 configuration. The spectrum of $[Cu(H_2O)_6]^{2+}$ has been explained by assuming a tetragonal bipyramidal configuration, the two water molecules along the z-axis being more distant than the other four[16]. By assuming that the cubic contribution to the Δ value in the case of copper (II) complexes is of the same order as the Δ values for the corresponding nickel (II) complexes, Jørgensen[7] has used the ratio ν_{Cu}/ν_{Ni} as a measure of the tetragonality of the copper complexes. While this ratio is $1 \cdot 1$ for $[Cu(dip)_2 (H_2O)_2]^{2+}$, it is $1 \cdot 48$ for $[Cu(H_2O)_6]^{2+}$ and $1 \cdot 7$ for $[Cu(NH_3)_4(H_2O)_2]^{2+}$, indicating low, medium and strong tetragonality respectively.

Readers interested in studying ligand field theory and absorption spectra of complexes in greater detail are referred to the books on the subject[12,123].

Colour Centres in Inorganic Compounds*

It has long been known that alkali halides, when irradiated with ionizing particles or high-energy radiations, develop very deep colours characteristic of the salt[18]. The coloration is very unstable and is bleached away in time by gentle warming. But it can be rendered more stable if the halide is additively coloured; that is, if the colour is introduced by heating the halide in the vapours of the alkali metal or halogen such that the halide takes in a stoichiometric excess of the alkali metal or the halogen[18]. Thus, colours may be produced in KBr and KI by heating them in the corresponding halogen or potassium vapour at high temperatures. KCl develops a deep blue colour when irradiated with x-rays. Alkali and alkaline earth azides have also been found to develop such colours by irradiation[19]. The coloration is primarily due to the formation of F-centres, but also to the existence of certain other centres which absorb in the ultra-violet, called V-centres.

The primary process involved in the x-ray production of colour centres is presumed to be[20]

$$X^-(c) + h\nu \rightarrow X(c) + e^-(c)$$

where X is the halogen atom and (c) represents the crystalline state. The electrons are trapped in the lattice imperfections of the type of anion vacancies, imparting colour to the halide. Hersh[20] has reported that irradiated pellets of KCl and KBr resemble the large single crystals in many ways. The number of F-centres produced is larger in pellets than in single crystals for the same exposure and the pellets behave as though they contain more electron and

* Written in collaboration with S. R. Yoganarasimhan.

171

hole traps than the corresponding single crystals. In these pellets the V-bands are more pronounced and well developed.

The ultra-violet and visible absorption spectra of irradiated alkali halides were first studied by Pohl[21], who observed an intense band between 400 and 800 mμ. The centres responsible for this absorption were called F-centres and the band F-band. The fact that only one band was observed in the absorption range indicated that only one electron was involved in the transition.

De Boer[22] suggested that the F-centres are properly represented by a model consisting of an electron trapped at an anion vacancy. This view is held valid even now. Kleinschrod[23] showed that the absorption curve due to F-centres is not strictly Gaussian and that there is a shoulder towards the short wavelength region called the K-band. Konitzer and Markham[24] have obtained curves, which they believe to be due only to F-absorption, by subtracting the 'base line' and the K-band contributions. But the method used to eliminate the K-band is only arbitrary, resulting in an uncertainty in the ultra-violet region. In coloured samples, the number of F-centres measured optically is nearly equal to the stoichiometric excess of metal taken up during coloration.

One other evidence for the De Boer model of an F-centre is the existence of paramagnetism in coloured alkali halides as expected if an unpaired electron is trapped in a vacancy. The static paramagnetism of coloured alkali halides was observed by Jensen[25]. Kip and Kittel[26] have extended and analysed the earlier experiments. Kahn and Kittel[27] have shown that the g factor which determines the splitting of the energy per unit magnetic field is less than the value expected for a free electron, indicating that the ground state of the F-centre cannot be exclusively a $1s$ state. The observed shift in g factor has been explained by assuming that the ground-state wave function of the F-centre is at the centre of the vacancy distributed equally between s and g functions.

So far, no equation which is rigorously valid for correlating the concentration of F-centres to the intensity of the band is proposed. But the equation given by Rauch and Heer[28] is useful

$$Nf = 0.821 \times 10^{17} \, [n/(n^2 + 2)^2] \, A \text{ cm}^{-3}$$

where N = number of F-centres per cm^3, f = oscillator strength, n = refractive index and A = area of the absorption curve in eV cm^{-1}. Using this equation, the oscillator strength of F-centres has been calculated by measuring the amount of hydrogen liberated on dissolving additively coloured KCl in water[29]. The value of f was found to be 1.17 ± 0.15.

The coloration of alkali halides is bleached either partially or completely by the application of heat or irradiation in the F-band or both. The bleaching proceeds in two stages. The initial stage is very fast and the later stages are very slow. It has been shown by Casler, Pringsheim and Yuster[30] that the stability of the F-centres depends on the temperature at which the specimen is coloured. The lower the temperature of irradiation, the more unstable the colours will be. On warming the low-temperature irradiated samples, Casler, Pringsheim and Yuster[31] found that the bleaching of the F-centres was associated with bleaching of the V-band at low temperatures. The V$_1$-centres liberate holes at the time of their disappearance; these holes annihilate a part of the F-centres accounting for the rapid bleaching in the beginning. Once all the V_1-centres are destroyed, the remainder of the holes may be tied up with V_2 and V_3 centres which are more stable. This renders the bleaching at later stages difficult.

During irradiation in the F-band at low temperatures, extinction gradually decreases and the additively coloured salts show a broad band at low temperatures towards the long wavelength side. On warming, this broad F'-band is bleached accompanied by the intensification of the F-band. The quantum yields for the two processes are the same.

As a result of the irradiation with light lying in the F-band, anion vacancies are produced by ionization of the F-centres[32]. These join the cation vacancies forming pairs and move about in the lattice. The products of the coagulation are the R_1, R_2 and M bands. These are represented by Seitz[32] as combination products of an F-centre with a vacant anion site, with another F-centre and with a pair of vacancies of opposite signs respectively. Thus, the R and M bands may be assumed to be associated with aggregates of electrons and atoms.

The presence of impurities or foreign ions in KCl has a marked effect on the coagulation of F-centres. Watson and Scott[33] have shown that the introduction of alkaline earth ions into additively coloured KCl enhances the stability of F-centres. Markham and Hersh[34] have found that the optical and thermal bleaching properties of potassium halides are radically affected by doping with thallium ions.

Besides alkali halides, alkali and alkaline earth azides have been most thoroughly investigated for radiation coloration. By irradiation of freshly precipitated potassium azide at $-196°C$ with radiation of $\lambda = 2537$ Å, Tompkins and Young[19] obtained bands due to the presence of F-centres and V-centres. Ageing was found to have marked influence on these bands. The proposed mechanism of ageing involves the formation of anion and cation vacancy pairs

$$\square \, O + (N_3^-)^* + E \rightarrow \boxed{e} + ON_3$$

$\square$ = anion vacancy, O = cation vacancy, $(N_3^-)^*$ = exciton, E = phonon, $\boxed{e}$ = F-centre. The F-centre later decomposes to form nitrogen gas, R'-centre etc.

Rosenwasser, Dreyfus and Levy[35] have found that NaN_3, when irradiated by γ-rays at room temperature, develops a band at 360 mμ. This band may also be excited thermally although to a lesser extent. On the other hand, neutron irradiation gives bands at 660 mμ and 760 mμ. However, near the decomposition point, the spectra of NaN_3 subjected to any of the irradiation processes are the same. Apparently, many of the bands observed in NaN_3 spectra may be connected with the decomposition of the compound. Cohen and Smith[36] could excite a band at 275 mμ by x-irradiation of Ge-doped synthetic quartz. This band was absent in pure quartz. The colour centre absorption is supposed to be caused by an electric dipole transition. Exhaustive investigations have been carried out on the colour centres in silver halides in connection with photography[37].

Understanding of the nature of F-centre has advanced since the first postulate by De Boer, without any necessity for a radical change in the viewpoint. Considerable information is now available on the nature of the V-centres and particularly on the V_1-centres, which Seitz[32] has called the antimorphs of the F-centres. There is still need for critical experimental studies on the factors causing and affecting the coloration of alkali halides.

Radicals and Ions

In free radicals (I), carbanions (II) and carbonium ions (III), the carbon atoms are supposed to carry unhybridized p-orbitals which can form molecular orbitals with p-orbitals of unsaturated systems. The molecular orbitals

$$\overset{\diagdown}{\underset{\diagup}{-}}\text{C} \cdot \qquad \overset{\diagdown}{\underset{\diagup}{-}}\text{C}\overset{-}{:} \qquad \overset{\diagdown}{\underset{\diagup}{-}}\text{C}^{+}$$

I   I   III

and the energy levels of these three systems should be very similar. In fact, the triphenylmethyl free radical, the triphenylmethyl carbanion and the triphenylmethyl carbonium ion exhibit absorption bands in the same region, 400–500 mμ[38,39]. The absorption spectra of radicals and ions have been termed electron-resonance spectra and charge-resonance spectra respectively[38,40] and these phenomena are responsible for the long wavelength absorption in the visible region of triphenylmethane dyes[41,42], cyanine dyes[43] and polyene-Lewis acid complexes[44–47]. Theoretical considerations[124] show that the cation and the anion of an alternant system (even or odd) should have the same wavelength absorption. The spectra of the anions vary with the solvent as well as the alkali metal gegenion[125]. The effect of ion pairing may be eliminated by extrapolating the λ_{max} to the infinite gegenion radius. Aromatic hydrocarbons give the mono- and the di-anions which show large differences in their spectra[51] and form protonated species in acid solu-

Table 12.3. Absorption Data of Carbonium ions and carbanions

		λ_{max}, mμ	ϵ_{max}
Di- and tri-alkyl carbonium ions		295	5,000
Dialkylphenyl carbonium ions		400	10,000
Diphenylmethyl	cation	441	42,800
	anion	434	22,000
Triphenylmethyl	cation	441,434	37,800; 36,200
	anion	475,410	15,000; 7,500
Tropylium cation		274,217	4,500; 41,000
Cyclo-octatetraene dianion		340,275	3,000; 10,000
Allyl cation		273	4,700
Cinnamoyl cation		440	4,000
Anthracene	cation	710	9,600
	anion	714	9,000
	dianion	614	27,000
	proton adduct in HF	445	37,000

tions which are oxidized to the cation[55]. The site of protonation can be found by comparing the spectrum of the proton adduct with that of a model alternant hydrocarbon. The absorption spectra of several ions and radicals have been studied in recent years[48] (*Table 12.3*). Deboer[134] has recently reviewed the absorption spectra of anions and dianions in detail.

174

Newman and Deno[49] have observed that mono-, di-, and triphenylmethyl carbonium ions absorb in the same wavelength region, thus indicating incomplete coplanarity in the di- and triphenyl derivatives. Heilbronner and co-workers[50] studied the absorption spectra of benzotropylium series. The absorption spectra of a number of tropylium salts have been recorded (Chapter 5).

Some of the ions recently investigated are: aromatic positive and negative ions[51,52]; arylmethyl cations[53]; methyl substituted aromatic cations[54]; aromatic carbonium ions in HF[55]; the styrene anion[56]; the triphenylcyclopropenyl cation[57]; and the nitrosonium ion[58]. The appearance of a strong absorption band around 300 mμ in solutions of olefins in sulphuric acid was considered to be due to the presence of carbonium ions. Leftin and Hall[59] have pointed out that the long wavelength band may be due to the oxidation of the olefins. Aliphatic carbonium ions are electron-deficient species and are stabilized by hyperconjugation. Of these, the secondary and tertiary ions are more stable and may be considered to be quasi-π systems. The nor bornadienyl cation (III A) shows absorption at 350 mμ (ϵ 5,000), while the ion III B shows two bands at 355 (ϵ 600) and 290 mμ (ϵ 8,000), the former corresponding to that of III A and the latter to alkyl carbonium ions[126,127].

III A   III B

Pigments, Dyes[116,117] and Colouring Principles in Organic Compounds[60,121]

Several theories of colour have appeared since the first dye was isolated[60]. Witt, in 1876, proposed that certain chromophoric groups should necessarily be present to lend colour to organic compounds. Such chromophoric groups were unsaturated linkages. Armstrong, in 1888, suggested that compounds with quinoid structures were coloured, basing his idea on the observation that a simple compound like *para*-benzoquinone was coloured. But now it is known that the $n \rightarrow \pi^*$ transition (R-band) of the conjugated carbonyl group is responsible for the colour of p-benzoquinone (Chapter 4). The $n \rightarrow \pi^*$ transitions of chromophoric groups (C=S, N=N etc.) are responsible for colours in some of the simple organic compounds (thiobenzophenone, λ_{max} 600 mμ; azobenzene, λ_{max} 450 mμ).

In polyenes (Chapter 4), the colour deepens (larger λ_{max}) with the increasing length of the chain (i.e. increase in the number of double bonds in conjugation). Several relations of λ_{max} with the number of unsaturated linkages were already discussed. The most extensively studied class of polyenes is the carotenoids. Typical of these pigments are: carotene (from carrots), lycopene (from tomatoes), xanthophyll (from green leaves). Carotenoids show distinct and characteristic absorption maxima in the visible region, 400–630 mμ (*Figure 7.4*). Electronic spectroscopy has been an important tool in the structure elucidation of carotenoid pigments. A typical example would be the formulation of the structures of rhodoxanthin and its derivatives[61]. The *cis-trans* isomerism in carotenoids has been discussed by Zechmeister[62]. The absorption data of several carotenoids have been summarized by Gillam and Stern[63]. Because of the high intensity of the absorption bands only small quantities of these pigments (30 μg or less) will be necessary for their spectrophotometric analyses.

The effect of various reagents on the absorption spectrum of flavonols has been employed to determine the position of the OH group[120]. The spectrum is recorded successively in (*a*) ethanol, (*b*) ethanolic sodium acetate, (*c*) ethanolic boric acid-sodium acetate and (*d*) sodium ethoxide and the information is used to find out whether the OH group is in the 3, 5, 7, 3' or the 4' position of the flavone nucleus.

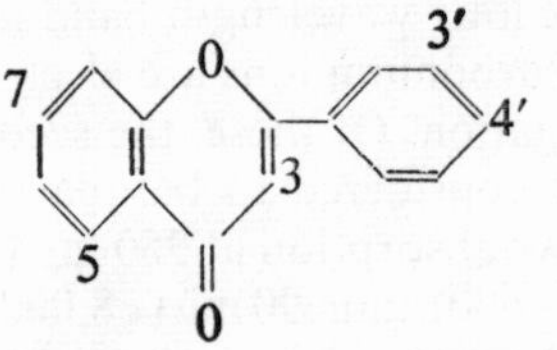

Solution	$-$OH	250 mμ band	370 mμ band
(*a*)	—	0 mμ shift	0 mμ shift
(*b*)	7	8–20	0
(*c*)	3', 4'	0	15–30
(*d*)	3, 4'	0	disappears
(*e*)	4' (and alkyl group at 3)	0	15–30

The spectrum in aluminium chloride–ethanol solution is also used to determine the OH at 3 or 5 position. A typical example of the use of the ultra-violet spectrum in the elucidation of flavonol structures is that of azalein[129]. Coumarin shows three absorption bands in the near ultra-violet region with maxima at 266, 282 and 318 mμ (ϵ_{max} 10,000, 8,000 and 5,000).

Anthocyanins, which are responsible for the (red, blue, and violet) colours of flower petals and berries, are glycosides of the parent substances called anthocyanidins. Anthocyanidins are derivatives of four parent substances: pelargonidin chloride, cyanidin chloride, delphidin chloride and apigenidin

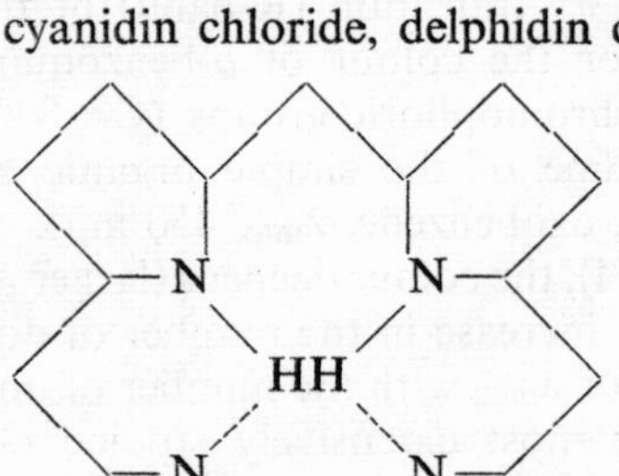

IV

chloride. The absorption spectra of anthocyanins consist of one absorption maximum in the region 500–545 mμ which is affected by the pH of the medium[64]. Thus, the red colour of rose and the blue colour of cornflower are both due to cyanin. In roses, cyanin is present as the oxonium salt, while it is in the form of the alkali metal salt in the case of cornflowers.

There is an important class of natural pigments which contains the porphyrin ring system (e.g. chlorophyll and haemin). The porphyrin ring, IV, contains four pyrrole nuclei connected by four C—H bridges and is found to be highly aromatic in character. Porphyrin exhibits absorption bands at 430*, 487, 518, 561 and 613 mμ[65], of which only the first and the last bands are considered to be due to pure electronic interactions[66]. The absorption spectra of chlorophyll and related derivatives have been reviewed by Aronoff[67]. The absorption curves of chlorophyll a and b are shown in *Figure 12.5*[68]. The position and intensity of the porphyrin absorption bands vary markedly with substitution.

Haemoglobin, which is the colouring principle of human venous blood, shows absorption bands at about 430 and 560 mμ. When haemoglobin absorbs oxygen from the air, changing to the bright red oxyhaemoglobin, the

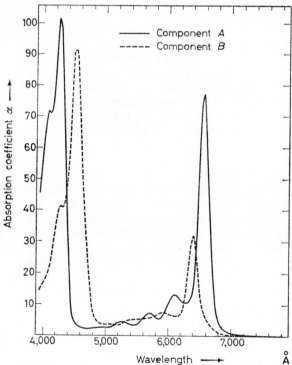

Figure 12.5. Absorption curves of chlorophyll a and b[68]

absorption spectrum changes markedly. Oxyhaemoglobin has absorption maxima at 415, 538 and 578 mμ. The literature values for the absorption

* The 400–450 mμ intense band of porphyrins is referred to as the 'Soret' band (see reference 122).

177

maxima of the blood pigments vary from one another[63]. The absorption spectra of the blood pigments are used for the detection of blood and blood stains. Presence of carbon monoxide in blood may be detected by the characteristic absorption bands of carboxyhaemoglobin at 540 and 570 mμ.

It was mentioned earlier that charge-resonance or electron-resonance phenomena[38,40] explain the colours of triphenylmethane dyes[41,42], cyanine dyes[43] and polyene-Lewis acid complexes[44−47]. Auxochromic substituents affect the colours of these dyes markedly because they provide greater opportunity for resonance[41,42]. Steric effects on the absorption properties of di- and triphenylmethane dyes and cyanine dyes have been discussed by Barker[69] and Dewar[70]. The blue and green colours of carotene with Lewis acids and bases have been reviewed by Körösy[47].

Various dyes including cyanines, merocyanines, triphenylmethane dyes, azines, etc., have been found to undergo association in aqueous solution and the association phenomenon has been investigated by spectrophotometry[71−75]. A typical example would be 1,1'-diethyl-2,2'-cyanine[74,75], which in aqueous solutions of concentrations below 0·001M shows two absorption bands at 485 and 523 mμ. At higher concentrations, a new sharp band appears at 572 mμ, the intensity of which is temperature-dependent. The appearance of the 572 mμ band is accompanied by an increase in the viscosity which is due to the formation of the polymers of the dye molecule. The existence of the polymeric species has been verified by other physical methods[76].

Formanek[77] has collected the data on the absorption spectra of a great number of dyes and has developed a method for their identification on the basis of their absorption spectra in various solvents and on the colour changes produced by the addition of different reagents. The absorption data of dyestuffs have been tabulated in the literature[63,77,78]. The absorption data of carotenoids and visual pigments have been discussed by Zechmeister[118] and Morton[119].

Optical Rotatory Dispersion

The variation of the optical rotation with the wavelength of light is called optical rotatory dispersion. For the past few years, optical rotatory dispersion has been used widely in structural and stereochemical studies and the sudden upsurge in the use of this technique is due to the availability of commercial photoelectric spectropolarimeters. Optical rotatory dispersion is of immense value for the study of the asymmetric organic and inorganic compounds, reaction mechanisms and macromolecules. The theory and application of optical rotatory dispersion have been fully discussed in a masterly manner by the leading expert in the field, Djerassi, in his recent book[79]. Klyne[80,81] has written excellent reviews on the subject.

The basic components of a spectropolarimeter are: a light source, monochromator, polarizer, cell, analyser and a device for measuring the rotation of the plane of polarization. In a simple spectropolarimeter, one adjusts the analyser manually to measure the rotation at different wavelengths. The same principle is also employed in certain automatic recording spectropolarimeters. In some spectropolarimeters, the rotation is compensated by an equal and opposite rotation produced electromagnetically in a Faraday cell. Some of the instruments are based on the symmetrical angle principle. The spectropolarimeters usually cover the wavelength region between 250 or 270 mμ and 700 mμ.

For compounds which do not absorb light within the range of wavelengths employed, the relation between the specific rotation [a] and λ is given by the one-term Drude equation

$$[a] = A_0/(\lambda^2 - \lambda^2_0)$$

where A_0 and λ_0 are constants for a compound. That is, a plot of [a] against λ would be a smooth curve, [a] increasing with decreasing λ. Such a curve is called a simple dispersion curve. In more complicated cases, a two-term, three-term or multiple-term Drude equation will have to be used

$$[a] = A_0/(\lambda^2 - \lambda^2_0) + A_1/(\lambda^2 - \lambda^2_1) + \ldots$$

A plot of [a] *versus* λ would then be a complex curve with maxima and minima. The author completely agrees with the view expressed by Djerassi[79] that the usefulness of the Drude equation for structural studies is limited.

Specific rotation [a] = $100a/lc$, where a is the observed rotation, l is the path length in dm and c is the concentration of the solution in g per 100 ml. Molecular dispersion, ϕ, is defined as [a] $\times$ molecular weight/100.

For compounds that absorb in the wavelength region studied, the dispersion curves are complicated and one or more maxima or minima may appear in the neighbourhood of the absorption bands. The optical rotation of the compounds can be measured through the absorption bands only if

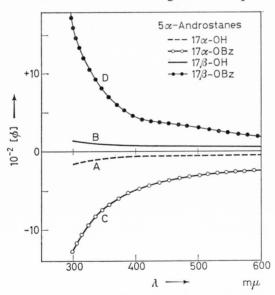

Figure 12.6. Plain curves[81]. A, 5a-androstan-17a-ol; B, 5a-androstan-17β-ol; C, 5a-androstan-17a-yl benzoate; D, 5a-androstan-17β-yl benzoate

the extinction coefficients are low. The most exhaustively studied systems are asymmetric ketones and aldehydes which exhibit the $n \to \pi^*$ band (R-band) of the carbonyl group with λ_{max} in the region of 270–300 mμ (ϵ_{max} < 100). Other types of compounds studied are nitro compounds and thiocarbonyl derivatives, both of which exhibit weak $n \to \pi^*$ bands.

179

G

Two principal types of rotatory dispersion curves have been classified: plain curves which do not show maxima or minima in the wavelength range studied (*Figure 12.6*) (the plain curves are called positive or negative depending on whether they rise or fall as one goes from longer to shorter λ) and Cotton-effect curves showing one or more maxima or minima in the neighbourhood of the absorption band (*Figure 12.7*). The maxima and minima in the rotatory dispersion curves are referred to as 'peaks' (P) and 'troughs' (T). The algebraic difference between the rotation values of the peak and the trough of a Cotton-effect curve is defined as the amplitude, *a*.

Rotatory dispersion has potential analytical uses, since the rotation increases multifold in the region of the absorption band compared to the value at the sodium D line. Dispersion measurements may be employed for studying the kinetics of reactions like epimerizations. Rotatory dispersion may be employed for the recognition and location of functional groups. Djerassi and co-workers have shown that every position in steroid ketones has a characteristic dispersion curve (value of *a*). Comparison of dispersion curves is valuable in determining the relative configurations in a molecule (e.g. steroids and the 19-norsteroids) and also in the assignment of absolute configurations. Recently, Moffitt and Moscowitz[82] have related the optical activity of absorbing compounds to the interactions between the absorbing function and attached atoms and groups. For the cyclohexanone system, the 'octant rule' which generalizes the relation between the positions of the substituent with the rotation, has been proposed and verified. Optical rotatory dispersion measurements have been employed in studies on proteins and

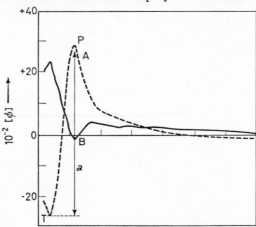

Figure 12.7. Saturated ketones[81]. Cotton-effect curves, illustrating differences due to stereochemistry. A, 5α-cholestan-3-one; B, 5β-cholestan-3-one

polypeptides and inorganic co-ordination complexes. With the availability of improved commercial spectropolarimeters, there is no doubt that optical rotatory dispersion will become a very important structural tool in chemistry.

Solvent Effects

The wavelength and the intensity of absorption bands are both affected when a molecule is in a solvent environment compared with its spectrum in the gas phase. This is due to the unequal perturbation of the ground and excited electronic states of the molecule which depends on the nature of the solvent–solute interactions in the two states. The absorption spectra in highly non-polar solvents (e.g. hydrocarbon solvents) generally retain most of the features of the gas phase spectra and the position and intensity of the absorption maxima are scarcely affected (*Figure 3.2*). The interpretation of solvent effects is often made difficult because they are small and not easy to measure precisely and also because several individual effects, superimposed on one another, contribute to the observed changes.

Kasha[83] and McConnell[84] have proposed solvent effects as a criterion for distinguishing the $n \to \pi^*$ and the $\pi \to \pi^*$ transitions (see Chapter 2). They defined bands as 'red-shift' or 'blue-shift' bands according to their displacement in the solvent order, paraffin, alcohol, water, without reference to the gas phase frequency. McConnell[84] and a number of other authors have found that all the known $n \to \pi^*$ transitions give blue-shift bands (see Chapters 2 and 3 for illustrations). But all $\pi \to \pi^*$ transitions do not necessarily give rise to red-shift bands (e.g. 260 mμ band of C_6H_6).

Bayliss[85] has made a quantitative approach to the study of solvent effects on the absorption spectra. Treating the solvent as a continuous dielectric medium, an expression has been developed for its effect on the Franck-Condon absorption of light, in terms of the polarization forces of the solvent. The same result was obtained by employing methods based on quantum theory and classical dispersion theory. Bayliss[85] has derived the following expression for the frequency shift, $\Delta \nu$, caused by the solvent

$$\Delta \nu = \text{const.} \times (f/\nu a^3) \frac{n^2 - 1}{n^2 + 1} \quad \cdots \cdots \quad (1)$$

where f = oscillator strength of the transition, a = radius of the spherical molecule, n = solvent refractive index, and ν = the frequency of absorption in the gas phase. This equation has been tested with the experimental data for isoprene, benzene, bromine and iodine. Good agreement has been found for the $\pi \to \pi^*$ transitions of benzene and isoprene. In the case of iodine and bromine, a quantitative approach was not possible due to the inherent limitations of the treatment.

In a later paper, Bayliss and McRae[86] have presented a scheme by which the solvent effects on absorption spectra can be interpreted qualitatively in terms of dipole-polarization and hydrogen-bonding forces between the solute and the solvent, superimposed on one another. A general polarization red shift which is due to the solvent polarization by the transition dipole and which depends on the solvent refractive index, is observed in the electronic spectra of all organic molecules in solution. When the solute is polar, other effects due to dipole-dipole and dipole-polarization forces come into operation. Application of the Franck–Condon principle shows that the solvent cage around the solute molecule is strained. This consists of orientation strain and packing strain, of which the former is more important in the case of polar solute and polar solvent. A decrease of the dipole moment of the solute during the transition leads to a blue shift (relative to the gas phase) of the absorption maxima (e.g. $n \to \pi^*$ transitions). On the other hand, if the dipole moment increases during the transition, the absorption maxima will

181

have a red shift. The blue shift observed by McConnell[2] in the case of the 260 mμ band of benzene is really a red shift (relative to the gas phase) since the refractive index increases in the order, water, alcohol and paraffin hydrocarbon. Four possible causes of solvent effects have been discussed, depending on whether the solute and the solvent are polar or non-polar.

McRae[87,88] has derived an expression for the solvent-induced frequency shift, from the second order perturbation theory, taking into account all the types of interactions suggested by Bayliss and McRae[86]. On the basis of a simple electrostatic model, the frequency shift, $\Delta\nu$, is related to the refractive index and the static dielectric constant of the solvent by an equation consisting of four terms. The first term in the equation represents the contribution from dispersive interactions which give rise to a general red shift; the second term represents the contribution from the solute dipole-induced solvent dipole interactions; the third term accounts for the solute dipole-solvent dipole interactions; and the fourth term represents the contribution from the interactions between the solvent permanent dipole and the solute dipole induced thereby. Since the fourth term is proportional to the square of the field intensity produced by the solvent dipoles, it may be taken to represent the quadratic Stark effect. Application to the 550 mμ band of phenol blue in a variety of solvents showed that the data in all non-polar and polar non-hydrogen bonding solvents fit well into the McRae expression and exceptions are found only in hydroxylic solvents. Several applications have been discussed by McRae. An alternative, but not fundamentally different relationship has also been derived by Longuet-Higgins and Pople[89].

Brealy and Kasha[90] have concluded, from their studies on the absorption spectra of benzophenone and pyridazine, that in the case of hydroxylic solvents, the observed solvent-induced blue shift is primarily due to hydrogen bonding between the solute and the solvent. But Pimentel[91] has pointed out that the hydrogen bonding in the excited state may be considerable and also that the importance of Franck–Condon principle in discussing the solvent blue shifts should not be minimized. Recently, Krishna and Goodman[92] have investigated solvent effects on the absorption and emission spectra of pyrazine and the alkyl substituted pyrazines, to understand the nature of the solute–solvent interactions in the ground and electronically excited states of the solute. Their results indicate that the weak hydrogen bonding in the ground state and the Franck–Condon strain resulting therefrom contribute to the blue shift, an observation which supports Pimentel's view[91].

Attempts have been made by several workers to generalize the effect of solvents on spectra in an empirical manner. Kosower[93] has proposed that the transition energies in kcal/mole (Z-values) be adopted as empirical measures of solvent polarity, taking the highly solvent-sensitive charge-transfer absorption band of 1-ethyl-4-carbomethoxy pyridinium iodide as the standard. Recently, Schubert, Steadly and Gaven[94] have suggested that the effect of solvent on the energy of the principal electronic transition of a particular nitrobenzene could also be used as a measure of solvent polarity. Since such parameters are themselves derived from the spectral shifts, they do not throw much light on the exact nature and magnitude of the various interactions responsible for the observed solvent effects. Further, these parameters use the same polarity scale for the hydrogen-bonding solvents and other non-hydrogen bonding solvents.

Weigang[95] has measured the solvent shifts for all the electronic transitions of phenanthrene, naphthalene and azulene in a series of paraffin hydrocarbon solvents. The effect of branching and cyclization was studied by the inclusion of various structural isomers. Normal hydrocarbons give remarkable linear shifts, and these shifts fit well into the McRae theory[87]. The corresponding non-cyclic branched and cyclic hydrocarbons produce lesser shifts. These small shifts have been attributed to the change in the physical conformation of the molecule and the resultant opportunity for closer interactions with the chromophore.

Ito, Inuzuka and Iminishi[96] and Balasubramanian and Rao[99] have recently measured the solvent blue shifts of a few carbonyl and other chromophores and have analysed the results in terms of a modified McRae equation[87]:

$$\Delta\nu = \text{Dispersion term} + B\left[\frac{n_D^2 - 1}{2n_D^2 + 1}\right] + C\left[\left(\frac{D-1}{D+2}\right) - \left(\frac{n_D^2 - 1}{n_D^2 + 2}\right)\right]$$

where the quadratic Stark effect term is ignored. The shifts of the $n \to \pi^*$ transitions in non-polar and polar (non-hydrogen bonding) solvents could be satisfactorily correlated with the electrostatic interations between the solute and the solvent molecules by the above equation. Excited state dipole moments of molecules have been calculated[99] employing the McRae expression. Hydroxylic solvents produce large blue shifts and the electrostatic interactions could account only for a small portion of the spectral shift. Infra-red studies in the same solvents indicate that the ground electronic state of the solute is stabilized by hydrogen bonding. An isobestic point has been observed in ethanol-hydrocarbon mixtures, which means that two species exist in equilibrium, i.e. the free molecule and the hydrogen-bonded complex. These observations have been interpreted in terms of the co-operating effects of both hydrogen bonding and electrostatic interactions between the solute and the solvent.

The solvent effects on the $n \to \pi^*$ transitions of aliphatic carbonyl and nitro compounds have been investigated in detail in the author's laboratory[97-99]. In the case of hydroxylic solvents, the solvent blue shifts are found to decrease in the order H_2O, CF_3CH_2OH, CH_3OH, C_2H_5OH, $i\text{-}C_3H_7OH$ and $t\text{-}C_4H_9OH$. The extent of solute–solvent hydrogen bonding is apparently dependent on the acidity of the alcohol. A similar trend has also been found by Basu[100,131]. Recently these trends have been definitely established by a quantitative study of the thermodynamics of hydrogen bonding employing infra-red spectroscopy[130].

Merocyanine dyes which have non-polar and zwitter ionic structures of similar energies show interesting solvent effects[88]. These dyes show red shifts and then blue shifts in polar solvents as the polarity is progressively increased. The ϵ_{max} also first increases and then falls. The oscillator strength is, however, nearly constant. The observations can be explained on the basis that the zwitter ionic structures are more stable in polar solvents than the neutral species.

183

Temperature Effects

Small changes in laboratory temperature may normally be ignored in routine spectrophotometry. However, in certain physico-chemical studies like the determination of equilibrium or rate constants, careful control of temperature is necessary, since the concentration of a particular absorbing species will be markedly affected by temperature changes. Thermostated cells are employed in such studies. Large variations in temperature cause profound

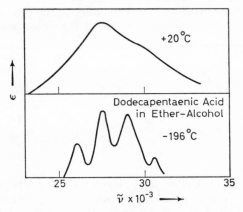

Figure 12.8. Temperature effect on the spectrum of dodecapentaenic acid[60]

changes in the absorption spectra. Lowering the temperature results in greater resolution and fine structure. In general, absorption bands possess fine structure at low temperatures and broaden at higher temperatures. This is illustrated by *Figure 12.8*, where the absorption curves of dodecapentaenic acid at 20° and −196°C are reproduced[60]. The extinction often decreases linearly with increasing temperature. Some substances change their colour on heating, a phenomenon referred to as thermochromism (see Chapter 10 for discussion).

Haupt[101] has recorded the absorption spectra of dichromate in aqueous solution at 25° and 50°C and has suggested that the data may be used for the calibration of spectrophotometers. Sager and Siewers[102] have reported the absorbance values, dissociation constants and related thermodynamic properties of some organic bases derived from spectrophotometric measurements in the 10°–40°C range. The variations of absorbance with temperature in the ultra-violet absorption spectra of 19 typical organic compounds have been studied in the temperature range 5°–33°C, employing methanol and *iso*-octane as solvents[103]. The variation ranges from 0·0% per °C for acetone to 0·74% per °C for toluene. Sager and Byers[104] have investigated the ultra-violet and visible absorption spectra of aqueous solutions of potassium nitrate, potassium dichromate, diphenyl sulphone, diphenyl phosphate, 4,4′-diaminobenzophenone and *m*-cresosulphonaphthalein, at 10°C, 25°C and 40°C. The ϵ_{max} has generally been found to increase slightly (though not linearly) with decrease in temperature, with the exception of diphenyl phosphate. The results indicate that temperature should be controlled within ± 2°C if the ϵ values are to be obtained within 0·5%. Ito and co-workers[105,106] have recently studied the effect of temperature on ultra-violet absorption spectra in relation to hydrogen bonding.

Nowadays, temperature-regulated cell holders are available for many commercial spectrophotometers and it is hoped that more extensive researches of temperature effects will be undertaken in the near future.

Hydrogen Bonding

Three types of hydrogen bonding may be studied by spectroscopic methods: intermolecular hydrogen bonding between solute molecules, intermolecular hydrogen bonding between solute and solvent molecules, and intramolecular hydrogen bonding. Most of the studies on electronic spectra reported in the literature relate to solute–solvent hydrogen bonding. The effect of hydrogen-bonding solvents on $n \to \pi^*$ and $\pi \to \pi^*$ transitions was briefly discussed earlier (Chapters 2, 3 and above). Recently, solute–solvent hydrogen bonding of the types, O—H . . . S, S—H . . . O, S—H . . . S, N—H . . . O, etc. have been studied by employing the blue-shifts of $n \to \pi^*$ transitions[130]. Equilibrium constants of formation of hydrogen-bonded complexes have been calculated employing electronic spectroscopy[130,131]. In the present discussion, we shall only deal with the effects of intermolecular hydrogen bonding between solute molecules (self association) on their ultra-violet absorption spectra.

Forbes and Templeton[107] have deduced evidence for different types of hydrogen bonding from ultra-violet absorption spectra and have discussed the implications of the spectral analyses. Forbes and Knight[108] have studied monomer-dimer equilibria of benzoic acid, p-toluic acid, p-hydroxybenzoic acid and salicylic acid in cyclohexane and cyclohexane-ether solutions. They have found that the intensity (in terms of ϵ_{max}) of the 230 mμ band increases with increase in benzoic acid concentration in cyclohexane or in cyclohexane containing small amounts of ether. If the proportion of ether in the cyclo-hexane-ether system is large, the concentration dependence of the intensity is diminished, thus indicating competitive intermolecular hydrogen bonding. In 100% ether solution, there is no concentration dependence of the ϵ_{max}. This seems to suggest that the monomeric form predominates when there is competitive solute–solvent hydrogen bonding. A similar suggestion has also been made by Unganade and Lamb[109]. Intramolecular hydrogen bonding in salicylic acid also decreases the strength of the dimeric hydrogen bond. Forbes and Knight[108] have clearly shown that the concentration limit ($\sim 10^{-3}$ mole per litre in the case of benzoic acid) above which the ϵ_{max} becomes approximately independent of concentration changes, is related to the strength of the dimeric hydrogen bond. Thus, the lower the concentration limit, the stronger is the dimeric hydrogen bond. Employing this ϵ_{max}-concentration relation as the basis, Forbes, Knight and Coffen[110] have compared the strengths of dimeric hydrogen bonds in a number of substituted benzoic acids and found them to vary with the nature and position of the substituent. Ito[111] has studied the effect of concentration on the 'benzenoid' band (around 280 mμ), of benzoic acid and its derivatives. Absorption bands associated with dimeric molecules seem to appear at longer wavelengths than those of the monomeric species. This observation has also been confirmed by studying the temperature effect on the absorption spectra. Rao and Murthy[112] have found that the λ_{max} values of both the 230 mμ and the 280 mμ bands of benzoic acid increase with concentration and attain limiting values around the same concentration as that reported by Forbes and Knight[108].

Von Keussler[113] has shown that the 'benzenoid' band (around 270 mμ) of phenol shows a concentration dependence in cyclohexane solution. Dearden and Forbes[114] have studied hydrogen bonding in anilines and phenols in great detail. Hydrogen bonding is not appreciable below a concentration of 0·01 mole per litre and the strength of the intermolecular hydrogen bond is probably weaker than in the case of benzoic acids. The concentration dependence of the aniline spectrum is much less than that of phenol[114,132]. Ito[115] has studied the association of phenols in non-polar solvents at different temperatures employing the 270 mμ band. The absorption bands of the associated molecules occur at shorter wavelengths than those of free molecules. Rao and Murthy[112] have found that the λ_{max} values of both the 210 mμ and the 270 mμ bands of phenol decrease with increase in concentration and attain limiting values at fairly high concentrations. Self-association of thiophenol has been found to be negligible by studying the concentration-dependence of the λ_{max} and ϵ_{max} as well as the spectrum in ether[132]. Similar results have been obtained with thiolbenzoic acid[133].

REFERENCES

[1] ILSE, F. E. and HARTMANN, H., *Z. Physik. Chem.*, 1951, **197**, 239.

[2] BETHE, H., *Ann. Physik*, 1929, **3**, 133.

[3] VAN VLECK, J. H., *Phys. Rev.*, 1932, **41**, 208; *J. Chem. Phys.*, 1935, **3**, 813.

[4] SCHLAPP, R. and PENNEY, W. G., *Phys. Rev.*, 1932, **42**, 666.

[5] ABRAGAM, A. and PRYCE, H. M. L., *Proc. Roy. Soc. (London)*, 1951, **206A**, 173.

[6] ORGEL, L. E., *J. Chem. Soc.*, 1952, 4756; *J. Chem. Phys.*, 1955, **23**, 1004; GRIFFITH, J. S. and ORGEL, L. E., *Quart. Revs.*, 1957, **11**, 381.

[7] JØRGENSEN, C. K., *Report to the Xth Solvay Council*, Brussels, 1956.

[8] TANABE, Y. and SUGANO, S., *J. Phys. Soc.*, *Japan*, 1954, **9**, 753, 756.

[9] VAN SANTEN, J. H. and VAN WIERINGEN, J. S., *Rec. trav. chim.*, 1952, **71**, 420.

[10] MOFFITT, W. and BALLHAUSEN, C. J., *Ann. Rev. Phys. Chem.*, 1956, **7**, 134.

[11] TSUCHIDA, R., *Bull. Chem. Soc.*, *Japan*, 1938, **13**, 388, 436 and 471.

[12] DUNN, T. M., in *Modern Coordination Chemistry*, Edited by LEWIS, J. and WILKINS, R. G., Interscience, New York, 1960, p. 245.

[13] JØRGENSEN, C. K., *Energy Levels of Complexes and Gaseous Ions*, Copenhagen, 1957.

[14] JØRGENSEN, C. K., *Acta Chem. Scand.*, 1958, **12**, 903.

[15] JAHN, H. A. and TELLER, E., *Proc. Roy. Soc. (London)*, 1937, **A161**, 220.

[16] BJERRUM, J., BALLHAUSEN, C. J. and JØRGENSEN, C. K., *Acta Chem. Scand.*, 1954, **8**, 1275.

[17] NYHOLM, R. S., *Proc. Roy. Inst. G. Brit.*, 1960, **38**, 25.

[18] JACOBS, P. W. M. and TOMPKINS, F. C., in *Chemistry of the Solid State*, Edited by GARNER, W. E., Butterworths Scientific Publications, 1955, Chapter 3.

[19] TOMPKINS, F. C. and YOUNG, D. A., *Discussions Faraday Soc.*, 1957, No. 23, 202.

[20] HERSH, H. N., *J. Chem. Phys.*, 1957, **27**, 1330.

[21] POHL, R. W., *Proc. Phys. Soc. (London)*, 1937, **49**, extra number, 3.

[22] DE BOER, J. H., *Rec. trav. chim.*, 1937, **56**, 301.

[23] KLEINSCHROD, F. G., *Ann. Physik*, 1936, **27**, 97.

[24] KONITZER, J. D. and MARKHAM, J. J., *J. Chem. Phys.*, 1960, **32**, 843.

[25] JENSEN, P., *Ann. Physik*, 1939, **34**, 161.

[26] KIP, A. F. and KITTEL, C., *Phys. Rev.*, 1951, **83**, 657.

[27] KAHN, A. H. and KITTEL, C., *Phys. Rev.*, 1953, **89**, 315.

[28] RAUCH, C. J. and HEER, C. V., *Phys. Rev.*, 1957, **105**, 914.

[29] SCOTT, A. B. and HILLS, M. E., *J. Chem. Phys.*, 1958, **28**, 24.

[30] CASLER, R., PRINGSHEIM, P. and YUSTER, P., *J. Chem. Phys.*, 1950, **18**, 887.

[31] CASLER, R., PRINGSHEIM, P. and YUSTER, P., *J. Chem. Phys.*, 1950, **18**, 1564.

[32] SEITZ, F., *Rev. Mod. Phys.*, 1954, **26**, 7.

[33] WATSON, L. R. and SCOTT, A. B., *J. Chem. Phys.*, 1959, **30**, 342.

[34] MARKHAM, J. J. and HERSH, H. N., *J. Chem. Phys.*, 1960, **32**, 1885; HERSH, H. N., *J. Chem. Phys.*, 1959, **30**, 790.

[35] ROSENWASSER, H., DREYFUS, R. W. and LEVY, P. W., *J. Chem. Phys.*, 1956, **24**, 184.

[36] COHEN, A. J. and SMITH, H. L., *J. Chem. Phys.*, 1958, **28**, 401.

[37] MITCHELL, J. W. in *Chemistry of the Solid State*, Edited by GARNER, W. E., Butterworths Scientific Publications, 1955, Chapter 13.

[38] ANDERSON, L. C., *J. Amer. Chem. Soc.*, 1935, **57**, 1673.

[39] CHU, T. L. and WEISSMAN, S. I., *J. Chem. Phys.*, 1954, **22**, 21.

[40] MULLIKEN, R. S., *J. Chem. Phys.*, 1939, **7**, 14, 20, 121, 339, 353, 356, 364, 570.

[41] BURY, C. R., *J. Amer. Chem. Soc.*, 1935, **57**, 2115.

[42] PAULING, L., *Proc. Natl. Acad. Sci.*, *U.S.*, 1939, **25**, 577.

[43] BROOKER, L. G. S., *Rev. Mod. Phys.*, 1942, **14**, 290.

[44] COLLINS, F. D., *Nature (London)*, 1950, **165**, 817.

[45] KRAUSS, W. and GRUND, H., *Naturwissenschaften*, 1953, **40**, 18.

[46] JACOBS, T. L. and TUTTLE, W. P., *J. Amer. Chem. Soc.*, 1949, **71**, 1313.

[47] KÖRÖSY, F., *Acta. Chim. Acad. Sci. Hungary*, 1958, **15**, 35.

[48] PLATT, J. R., *Ann. Rev. Phys. Chem.*, 1959.

[49] NEWMAN, M. S. and DENO, N. C., *J. Amer. Chem. Soc.*, 1951, **73**, 3644.

[50] MEUCHE, D., STRAUSS, H. and HEILBRONNER, E., *Helv. Chim. Acta*, 1958, **41**, 57.

[51] HOIJTINK, G. J., BALK, P., SCHREURS, J. W. H., WEIJLAND, W. P., BOUMAN, N. and DE BRUIJN, S., *Rec. trav. chim.*, 1957, **76**, 813, 836, 841, 860, 869, 907.

[52] BALK, P., DE BRUIJN, S. and HOIJTINK, G. J., *Mol. Phys.*, 1958, **1**, 151.

[53] DENO, N. C. and GOODMAN, L., *J. Amer. Chem. Soc.*

[54] MCCAULAY, D. C. and LIEN, A. P., *Tetrahedron*, 1959, **5**, 186.

[55] DALLINGA, G., MACKOR, E. L. and STUART, A. A. V., *Mol. Phys.*, 1958, **1**, 123.

[56] HIROTA, K., KUWATA, K. and MORIGAKI, K., *Bull. Chem. Soc. Japan*, 1958, **31**, 538.

[57] BRESLOW, R. and YUAN, C., *J. Amer. Chem. Soc.*, 1958, **80**, 5991.

[58] TURNEY, T. A. and WRIGHT, G. A., *J. Chem. Phys.*, 1958, **29**, 252.

[59] LEFTIN, H. P. and HALL, W. K., *J. Phys. Chem.*, 1960, **64**, 382.

[60] LEWIS, G. N. and CALVIN, M., *Chem. Revs.*, 1939, **25**, 273.

[61] KUHN, R. and BROCKMANN, H., *Ber.*, 1933, **66**, 828.

[62] ZECHMEISTER, L., *Chem. Revs.*, 1944, **34**, 267.

[63] GILLAM, A. E. and STERN, E. S., *Electronic Absorption Spectroscopy*, Edward Arnold, London, 1957.

[64] ROBINSON, R. and TODD, A. R., *J. Chem. Soc.*, 1932, 2293, 2488 and later papers.

[65] STERN, A. and WENDERLEIN, H., *Z. Physik. Chem.*, 1936, **A176**, 81.

[66] JACOBS, E. E., HOLT, A. S. and RABINOWITCH, E., *J. Chem. Phys.*, 1954, **22**, 142.

[67] ARONOFF, S., *Chem. Revs.*, 1950, **47**, 175.

[68] ZSCHEILE, F. P., Jr., *J. Phys. Chem.*, 1934, **38**, 95.

[69] BARKER, C. C. in *Steric Effects in Conjugated Systems*, Edited by GRAY, G. W., Butterworths, London, 1958, Chapter 4.

[70] DEWAR, M. J. S., in *Steric Effects in Conjugate Systems*, Chapter 5.

[71] SHEPPARD, S. E., *Revs. Mod. Phys.*, 1942, **14**, 303, 410.

[72] SHEPPARD, S. E. and GEDDES, A. L., *J. Amer. Chem. Soc.*, 1944, **66**, 2003.

[73] MATTOON, R. W., *J. Chem. Phys.*, 1944, **12**, 268.

[74] SCHEIBE, G., *Angew. Chem.*, 1939, **52**, 631 and earlier papers.

[75] JELLY, E. E., *Nature (London)*, 1936, **138**, 1009; 1937, **139**, 631.

[76] DICKINSON, H. O., *Trans. Faraday Soc.*, 1947, **43**, 486.

[77] FORMANEK, J., *Untersuchung und Nachweis Organischer Farbstoffe auf Spectroskopischem Wege*, Springer, Berlin, Part I, 1908; Part II, 1911–1927.

[78] HOLMES, W. C., *International Critical Tables*, 1930, **7**, 173.

[79] DJERASSI, C., *Optical Rotatory Dispersion*, McGraw-Hill, New York, 1959.

[80] (a) KLYNE, W., in *Advances in Organic Chemistry: Methods and Results*, Edited by RAPHAEL, R. A., TAYLOR, E. C., and WYNBERG, H., Interscience, New York, 1960, Vol. I, p. 239.
(b) KLYNE, W. and PARKER, A. C. in in *Physical Methods of Organic Chemistry*, Edited by WEISSBERGER, A., Interscience, New York, 1960, Third Edition.

[81] KLYNE, W., *J. Roy. Inst. Chem.*, 1960, **84**, 50.

[82] MOFFITT, W. and MOSCOWITZ, A., *J. Chem. Phys.*, 1959, **30**, 648.

[83] KASHA, M., *Disc. Faraday Soc.*, 1950, **9**, 14.

[84] McCONNELL, H., *J. Chem. Phys.*, 1952, **20**, 700.

[85] BAYLISS, N. S., *J. Chem. Phys.*, 1950, **18**, 292.

[86] BAYLISS, N. S. and McRAE, E. G., *J. Phys. Chem.*, 1954, **58**, 1002, 1006.

[87] McRAE, E. G., *J. Phys. Chem.*, 1957, **61**, 563.

[88] McRAE, E. G., *Spectrochim. Acta*, 1958, **12**, 192.

[89] LONGUET-HIGGINS, H. C. and POPLE, J. A., *J. Chem. Phys.*, 1957, **27**, 192.

[90] BREALY, G. J. and KASHA, M., *J. Amer. Chem. Soc.*, 1955, **77**, 4462.

[91] PIMENTEL, G. C., *J. Amer. Chem. Soc.*, 1957, **79**, 3323.

[92] KRISHNA, V. G. and GOODMAN, L., *J. Chem. Phys.*, 1960, **33**, 381.

[93] KOSOWER, E. M., *J. Amer. Chem. Soc.*, 1958, **80**, 3253.

[94] SCHUBERT, W. M., STEADLY, H. and GAVEN, J. M., *J. Amer. Chem. Soc.*, 1960, **82**, 1353.

[95] WEIGANG, O. E., Jr., *J. Chem. Phys.*, 1960, **33**, 892.

[96] ITO, M., INUZUKA, K. and IMINISHI, S., *J. Amer. Chem. Soc.*, 1960, **82**, 1317.

[97] RAO, C. N. R., GOLDMAN, G. K. and BALASUBRAMANIAN, A., *Can. J. Chem.*, 1960, **38**, 2508.

[98] BALASUBRAMANIAN, A. and RAO, C. N. R., *Chem. & Ind. (London)*, 1960, 1025.

[99] BALASUBRAMANIAN, A. and RAO, C. N. R., *Spectrochim. Acta*, 1962, **18**, 1337.

[100] CHANDRA, A. K. and BASU, S., *Trans. Faraday Soc.*, 1960, **56**, 632.

[101] HAUPT, G. W., *J. Research Nat. Bur. Standards*, 1952, **48**, 414.

[102] SAGER, E. E. and SIEWERS, I. J., *J. Research Nat. Bur. Standards*, 1952, **49**, 7.

[103] YARBOROUGH, V. A., HASKIN, J. F. and LAMBDIN, W. J., *Anal. Chem.*, 1954, **26**, 1576.

[104] SAGER, E. E. and BYERS, F. C., *J. Research Nat. Bur. Standards*, 1957, **58**, 33.

[105] ITO, M., TSUKIOKA, H. and IMANISHI, S., *J. Amer. Chem. Soc.*, 1960, **82**, 1559.

[106] ITO, M., *J. Mol. Spec.*, 1960, **4**, 106.

[107] FORBES, W. F. and TEMPLETON, J. F., *Canad. J. Chem.*, 1958, **36**, 180.

[108] FORBES, W. F. and KNIGHT, A. R., *Canad. J. Chem.*, 1959, **37**, 334.

[109] UNGANADE, H. E. and LAMB, R. W., *J. Amer. Chem. Soc.*, 1952, **74**, 3789.

[110] FORBES, W. K., KNIGHT, A. R. and COFFEN, D. L., *Canad. J. Chem.*, 1960, **38**, 728.

[111] ITO, M., *J. Mol. Spec.*, 1960, **4**, 144.

[112] RAO, C. N. R. and MURTHY, A. S. N., *J. Sci. Industr. Res.*, India, 1961, **20B**, 290.

[113] VON KEUSSLER, V., *Z. Elektrochem.*, 1954, **58**, 136.

[114] DEARDEN, J. C. and FORBES, W. F., *Canad. J. Chem.*, 1960, **38**, 896.

[115] ITO, M., *J. Mol. Spec.*, 1960, **4**, 125.

[116] VENKATARAMAN, K., *Chemistry of Synthetic Dyes*, Academic Press, New York, 1952.

[117] KUHN, H., *Fortschr. Chem. org. Naturstoffe*, 1958, **16**, 169; 1959, **17**, 404 (Electron Gas Theory of Colour of Natural and Artificial Dyes).

[118] ZECHMEISTER, L., *Fortschr. Chem. org. Naturstoffe*, 1958, **15**, 31; 1960, **18**, 223.

[119] MORTON, R. A. and PITT, G. A. J., *Fortschr. Chem. org. Naturstoffe*, 1957, **14**, 245.

[120] VENKATARAMAN, K., *Fortschr. Chem. org. Naturstoffe*, 1959, **17**, 1.

[121] MACCOLL, A., *Quart. Revs.*, 1947, **1**, 16 (Colour and Constitution).

[122] SCHWARTZ, S., BERG, M. H., BOSSENMAIER, I. and DINSMORE, H., in *Methods of Biochemical Analysis*, Ed. by GLICK, D., Interscience, New York, 1960, Vol. 8, p. 227.

[123] BALLAHAUSEN, C. J., *Ligand Field Theory*, McGraw Hill Co.

[124] LONGUET–HIGGINS, H. C. and POPLE, J. A., *Proc. Phys. Soc.*, 1955, **68A**, 591.

[125] CARTER, H. V., McCLELLAND, B. J. and WARHURST, E., *Trans. Faraday Soc.*, 1960, **56**, 455.

[126] LEAL, G. and PETTIT, R., *J. Amer. Chem. Soc.*, 1959, **81**, 3160.

[127] WINSTEIN, S. and ORDRONNEAU, C., *J. Amer. Chem. Soc.*, 1960, **82**, 2084.

[128] MASON, S. F., *Quart. Revs. (London)*, 1961, 287.

[129] JURD, L. and HOROWITZ, R. M., *J. Org. Chem.*, 1957, **22**, 1618.

[130] SINGH, S., MURTHY, A. S. N. and RAO, C. N. R., *Trans. Faraday Soc.*, 1966, **62**, 1056.

[131] BHOWMIK, B. B. and BASU, S., *Trans. Faraday Soc.*, 1963, **59**, 813; 1964, **60**, 1038.

[132] MURTHY, A. S. N., *Indian J. Chem.*, 1965, **3**, 143.

[133] MURTHY, A. S. N., RAO, C. N. R., RAO, B. D. N. and VENKATESWARLU, P., *Trans. Faraday Soc.*, 1962, **58**, 855.

[134] DEBOER, E., in *Advances in Organometallic Chemistry*, Vol. 2. Ed. by STONE, F. G. A. and WEST, R., Academic Press, New York, 1964.

CHAPTER 13
AMINO ACIDS, PROTEINS AND RELATED COMPOUNDS*

PROTEINS show absorption in the near and far ultra-violet regions. In the near ultra-violet region, the absorption above 250 mμ is mainly due to the aromatic amino acids such as tyrosine, tryptophan and phenylalanine (*Figure 13.1*). The absorption between 210 and 250 mμ has a variety of contributions while the far ultra-violet absorption below 210 mμ is mainly due to the peptide bond. There has been increasing activity in the study of the electronic absorption spectra of amino acids, proteins and related compounds in recent years. Several new techniques have been developed for the estimation of various types of groups in proteins, and ultra-violet spectroscopy is becoming more useful because of the versatility and better wavelength range of the modern commercial spectrophotometers. In addition to absorption spectra, fluorescence and phosphorescence spectra have also been employed in the study of proteins.

In this chapter, an attempt will be made to summarize the highlights of the studies on the electronic spectra of amino acids, proteins and related compounds. For a detailed treatment of the subject the reader is referred to the reviews of Beaven[1] and Wetlaufer[2].

Instrumentation and Techniques

Many of the spectrophotometric studies in proteins involve measurements of small differences in absorptivity and wavelength and it therefore becomes imperative that the instruments and the methods of analysis employed should be as foolproof as possible. Some of the main instrumental problems in the study of proteins are: stray radiation, reproducibility of absorptivity and the use of proper standards, turbidity and light scattering and errors due to luminescence. All these problems have been discussed in the reviews of Beaven[1] and Wetlaufer[2].

The use of high resolution spectrophometers gives considerably better information on the fine structure bands and several methods have been reported in the literature for the precise location of these bands. By recording the spectra at low temperatures generally the fine structure bands get sharpened. However, there are very few solvents available for the study of proteins at low temperatures. Proteins have been studied in glasses and in non-aqueous solvents such as HF, hydrazine and formamide. Spectra of sublimed films have also been recorded, although they are not as satisfactory as dilute solutions.

As was pointed out earlier in Chapter 9, the far ultra-violet range has become accessible in recent years and the peptide absorption band at $\sim$ 190 mμ can be employed fruitfully for structural and analytical work. However, one has to

* Written in collaboration with K. R. Bhaskar.

take care to eliminate interference from oxygen dissolved in solvents, ions such as Cl⁻ and OH⁻ which show absorption in this region.

Differential spectrophotometry has been employed in the study of proteins to study small wavelength displacements and intensity changes. In this procedure, the spectrum of a protein under a particular set of conditions is taken with respect to a solution of the same protein under a different set of conditions (employed as reference). The absorbance difference between the two solutions, ΔA or ΔE, is plotted against the wavelength to obtain the difference spectrum. ΔA may be positive or negative. The difference spectra obtained in this way are essentially derivative or first differential spectra. This procedure assumes that there is no loss in accuracy in the measurement of optical densities with respect to concentrated solutions, provided Beer's law holds. Further, the intensity of the incident light must be sufficiently high at higher

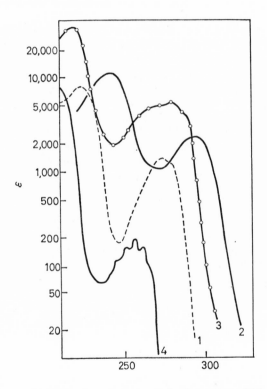

Figure 13.1. Ultra-violet absorption spectra of: tyrosine (curve 1, at pH 2; curve 2, at pH 12); tryptophan (curve 3, at pH 2) and phenylalanine (curve 4, at pH 2)

concentrations to be able to make the zero setting. If these conditions are satisfied, the precision of the measurement by the 'differential' technique will be six times greater than by the ordinary method. This method has been particularly useful in the study of hydrogen bonds in proteins. In these studies,

191

the concentration of the protein solute is kept the same in both the reference and the sample solutions but conditions like the pH or the ionic strength of the sample solution are varied.

True derivative spectra can be obtained by differentiation of the absorption bands (see Chapter 1). True differential spectrophotometry can be carried out by using reference solutions containing absorbing species identical with the sample solutions but at slightly lower concentrations.

Aromatic Amino Acids and Related Compounds

The absorption spectra of tyrosine, tryptophan and phenylalanine are all quite similar (*Figure 13.1*) and show the characteristic aromatic absorption in the regions 210–220 and 260–280 mμ. Both the bands probably arise from the $\pi \to \pi^*$ transitions of the aromatics. In tyrosine, the bands show bathochromic shifts and intensification in solutions of high pH due to the ionization of the phenolic OH group (*Figure 13.1*) and are therefore useful for the study of the hydrogen ion equilibria of tyrosyl residues in proteins. A number of difference spectral studies has been carried out on tyrosine and related compounds. Modification of the tyrosyl residue in proteins causes shifts and intensification of the aromatic absorption bands. Thus, iodination increases the absorptivity and shifts the phenolate peak to 320 mμ[3]. Formation of the ether or ester derivatives of the phenol also causes small shifts in tyrosine spectra. NBS oxidation of tyrosyl residues can also be studied by the variation of the spectrum[4]. Oxidation of the tyrosyl residues by tyrosinase gives rise to intermediates with absorption bands[5] at 305 and 480 mμ and a final product with λ_{max} at 325 mμ by the dopachrome sequence. The dopa quionone sequence gives an intermediate with λ_{max} at 390 mμ and a final product with a shoulder at 470 mμ. Tyrosinase can distinguish between the C-terminal and N-terminal residues since the oxidation proceeds by the dopa quionone and dopachrome sequence respectively.

Tryptophan is the strongest absorber of the aromatic amino acids (*Figure 13.1*). Several difference spectral studies on tryptophan derivatives have been reported in the literature[1,2]. The absorption spectrum of polytryptophan is similar to that of the parent amino acid[6]. Oxidation of tryptophyl residues can be followed by the changes in spectrum just as in the case of the tyrosyl group[4,7].

Phenylalanine shows the weakest absorption bands of the three aromatic amino acids and its absorption bands are generally masked by the strong bands of tyrosine and tryptophan (*Figure 13.1*). Difference spectra of phenylalanine have been reported in the literature[1,8–10].

Electronic absorption spectra of cysteine, cystine and methionine show long wavelength absorption due to $n \to \sigma^*$ transitions. Ionization of the SH group in cysteine gives rise to a new band at ~ 235 mμ[11]. The spectrum of methionine is similar to that of cysteine. The model for the absorption spectrum of cystine residues in proteins is not clearly understood. Oxidation of the S—H to disulphide causes a substantial change in the spectrum. Oxidation of S—H with iodine gives rise to sulphenyl iodides (λ_{max}, 350 mμ).

Thiazolines which are supposed to be present in proteins, show absorption at 250 mμ (log ϵ, 3·4). The imidazole group of histidine absorbs around 205 mμ and acetyl imidazole shows a band at ~ 244 mμ. Ultra-violet absorption spectra of several other amino acids have also been reported in the literature and the reader is referred to the original papers and reviews on the subject.

The Peptide Bond

The peptide bond in amino acids and simple peptides absorbs in the 200–240 mμ region due to the $n \to \pi^*$ transition of the carbonyl group. Bands are found in the regions of 190 and 160 mμ due to $\pi \to \pi^*$ transitions. The peptide bands show marked conformational dependence and can be employed for the study of helix-coil transitions. By employing polarized ultra-violet radiation one can study the dichroism of polypeptides in the 190 as well as the 220 mμ bands. The helical content of a protein can be estimated in this way and the estimates compare well with those from optical rotatory dispersion. The peptide bond absorption can also be used successfully for the spectrophotometric estimation of proteins. The molecular extinction coefficient at 205 mμ per peptide bond is in the range 2,500–2,800. This value varies with pH and other environmental conditions.

Spectrophotometric Titrations

Titration of ionizable groups of proteins can be carried out spectrophotometrically. The most common spectrophotometric titration has been for the tyrosyl groups employing the 295 mμ band. Ionizations of the amino, carboxyl and sulphydryl groups are also accompanied by marked changes in absorbance, but the regions of absorption of these groups have large interferences from other species. The studies of Martin and co-workers[12] on the ionization of tyrosine derivatives have shown that it is possible to obtain microscopic ionization constants by spectrophotometry. Thus, the twelve ionization constants interrelating the eight microscopic forms of tyrosine were obtained. Polytyrosine and other tyrosyl polymers have also been titrated in a similar fashion[13].

Mixtures of tyrosine and tryptophan have been analysed by study of the absorption spectra in neutral and alkaline solutions (*Figure 13.1*). Tryptophan and tyrosine contents in proteins have been estimated by studying the absorbance changes on treating proteins with NBS[4,7].

Ionization of cysteine and related thiols and the associated microconstants have been studied by spectrophotometric titrations[11]. The heat of ionization of the sulphhydryl groups in this acid has also been determined by the spectrophotometric procedure[11]. Ionization of sulphhydryl groups has been examined in gelation[14]. Ionization of carboxyl and amine groups cannot be studied directly by spectrophotometry[2].

Ionization studies of proteins by spectrophotometry have been carried out extensively in recent years, particularly with respect to the tyrosyl content. Wetlaufer[2] has given a detailed tabulation of all the spectrophotometric titrations carried out with proteins.

Difference Spectra

By precise measurement of difference spectra, valuable structural information on proteins has been obtained. The use of the tandem two-compartment cells are particularly useful in these studies[15]. Typical difference spectra are shown in *Figures 13.2* and *13.3*. Difference spectra were first employed by Laskowski and colleagues[16] in the study of hydrogen bonding in proteins. The differential ultra-violet absorption spectra of insulin[16] had the following features. When the spectrum of a tryptic digest was taken with respect to

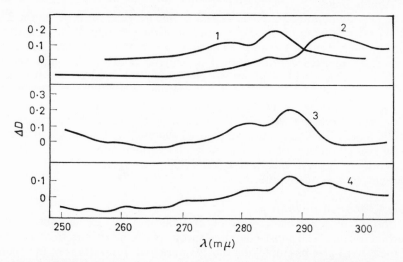

Figure 13.2. Difference spectra of aromatic amino acids of proteins: In the sample beam a solution of pH 6 to 7 was kept while in the reference beam a solution of pH 1 to 1·5 was taken. Curve 1, glycyl-L-tyrosine (2·5 × 10^{-3}M); curve 2, glycyl-L-tryptophan (5 × 10^{-4}M); curve 3, ribonuclease (0·3%) and curve 4, ovalbumin (0·2%). (From S. Yanari and Bovey, F. A.[9] by courtesy of The American Society of Biological Chemists Inc.)

native insulin at pH 7 as the reference, a shift from 287 mμ to 279 mμ was observed. Again when the spectrum of insulin at pH 2 was taken with reference to insulin at pH 7, a similar shift was observed. The maximum difference in optical density was found at 287 mμ which cannot possibly be due to the ionization of tyrosine. If it were due to the ionization of tyrosine, the maximum shift should have occurred at 294 mμ. Vicinal effect cannot explain this observation because the tyrosyl residue is farther away from both the ruptured peptide bonds. The observed shift has therefore been attributed to the breaking up of the tyrosyl hydrogen bonds due to tryptic digestion, assuming that the tyrosine in the native protein is hydrogen bonded at some point to the rest of the molecule. Since the magnitude of the shift observed in the spectrum of insulin in the case of tryptic digestion is the same as when the pH is reduced from 7 to 2, it has been concluded[16] that the hydrogen bonds present at pH 7 are broken at pH 2. Employing an insulin solution at pH 7 as the reference and by varying the pH of a solution with the same insulin concentration, the difference in optical density, ΔD, was measured at 287 mμ. The pK of the ionizing group was obtained from the titration curve (ΔD versus pH). The pK value for the acceptor group was approximately 3 in the case of insulin. This value should be lower than the intrinsic p$K°$ value for the acceptor group, due to hydrogen bonding[17]. The acceptor group may therefore, be either a C-terminal carboxyl group (p$K°$ = 3·6)[18], or a side-chain carboxyl group (p$K°$ = 4·7)[18] of a glutamyl or aspartyl residue. On this basis, Laskow-

194

ski and colleagues[16] have proposed a hydrogen bond between B_{26} tyrosyl residue and a carboxyl, either at the C-terminal or at the side-chain. Following the same treatment, a similar conclusion has been arrived at in the case of ribonuclease[19], as the pK value for the acceptor group was about 2.

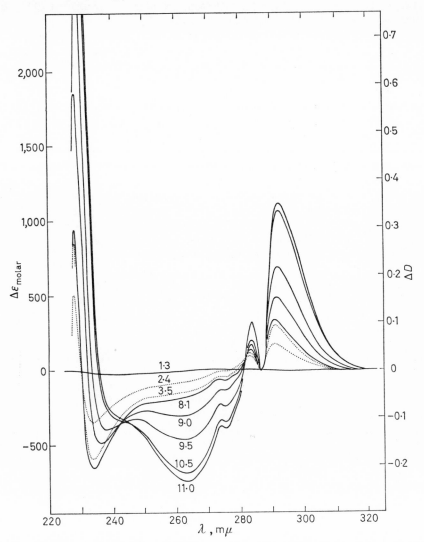

Figure 13.3. Difference spectra of tryptophan at 22°. The solutions are $3 \cdot 14 \times 10^{-4}$M, the ionic strength, $0 \cdot 10$. Samples at the indicated values of pH were measured against the pH $1 \cdot 3$ reference, using a Cary 15 Recording Spectrophotometer. Spectral band width was $0 \cdot 3$ mμ from 320 to 235 mμ, increasing to 3 mμ at 225 mμ (By courtesy of Dr. J. M. Donovan)

In the pH region of carboxyl ionization, lysozyme exhibited a peak at 295 mμ in its differential spectrum[20]. The absence of the peaks at 280 mμ and 287 mμ seems to indicate that no tyrosyl-carboxylate ion hydrogen bonds are present in lysozyme. The peak at 295 mμ is characteristic of tryptophan residue.

As tryptophan is a non-ionizable chromophore, the spectral changes have been attributed to the changes of charge on the neighbouring groups. This may occur in the native protein by the hydrolysis of the peptide bond near the chromophore or by the ionization of a side-chain group one or two residues away[20]. From the pK value obtained from the plot of ΔD against pH, it has been concluded that the ionizing groups are only carboxyls.

Recently, studies on the ultra-violet absorption spectra of bovine plasma albumin[21], bovine serum albumin and ovalbumin[22] indicated that the spectral perturbations cannot be attributed only to tyrosyl-carboxylate ion hydrogen bonding[23]. The effects of pH, ionic strength and intrinsic anion-binding ability on the differential spectra have been investigated. A plot of the differential absorption coefficient, ΔE, as a function of pH showed a small increase in ΔE above pH 7, in addition to the increase at lower pH values. This result cannot be explained simply as due to the protonation of groups involved in hydrogen bonding. Williams and Foster[21] have attributed the significant rise in ΔE above pH 7 to the disruption of other hydrogen bonds by deprotonation of donor groups and to the disruption of tyrosyl hydrogen bonds due to co-operative changes in the protein structure[24,25].

An increase in the ionic strength and anion binding should facilitate the protonation of the carboxyl group and thus the shift in the spectrum must follow this order. But the experimental results showed an opposite trend[21] in the shift which is in accord with the effects on the expansion of proteins[25]. This has been confirmed by plotting ΔE at 287 mμ against the radii calculated from viscosity and sedimentation coefficient measurements. The results are explained on the basis of the co-operative changes in the protein structure, namely isomerization and expansion.

The effect of urea on the differential ultra-violet spectra[21] also points out that the perturbations are only due to structural changes. Below pH 5, an increase in the urea concentration increases the ΔE and above pH 5, a 2M urea solution depresses ΔE while a 4M solution enhances ΔE. The effect of 2M urea has been attributed to its intermolecular hydrogen-bonding ability with some of the non-bonded tyrosyl residues in the native protein. This result, combined with other observed effects on viscosity and optical rotation, shows that 2M urea is incapable of producing co-operative structural changes in the native protein. Glazer, MacKenzie and Wake[22] could not obtain a differential absorption spectrum for ovalbumin at low pH's since the protein is incapable of expansion in acidic solutions. These results force one to the conclusion that the carboxyl group may, or may not, be an acceptor in the hydrogen-bonded structure and that the spectral perturbations are essentially due to structural changes in the native protein in the different environments. Although the difference in the absorption spectra has hitherto been interpreted on the basis of the changes in the intramolecular hydrogen bonding, Williams and Foster[21] have pointed out the importance of the polarity of the medium (D-effect) and electronic polarizability (P-effect) in determining spectral changes.

Bigelow and Geschwind[8] have pointed out good correlation between spectral perturbation and refractive index of aqueous solutions. Yanari and Bovey[9] have shown that solvents affect the absorption bands by altering the energy of the electronic transitions and that difference spectra can be generated by comparing protein chromophores in aqueous solutions with the same concentration of chromophore in micellar detergent solutions. The chromophore containing micelle appears to be a good spectral model for the chromophore containing protein interior. Yanari and Bovey[9] further point out that ionization of the aromatic amino acids cannot account for the observed difference spectra in proteins. Recent studies of Donovan, Laskowski and Scheraga[10] have shown that the large spectral perturbation of tryptophyl groups in the acid titration of lysozyme was dependent on ionic strength.

By employing the solvent perturbation technique it has been possible to estimate the number of exposed and buried groups in proteins. By employing this technique Herskovits and Laskowski[15] have studied ribonuclease and serum albumin. They also critically discuss the various assumptions and limitations of the solvent perturbation techniques for the estimation of buried and exposed groups in proteins.

Difference spectra have been recorded in the 220–240 mμ region as well[2,26]. Thus, denaturation of proteins can be studied in this region.

Wetlaufer[2] has given a tabular summary of the difference spectral studies related to proteins.

Fluorescence, Phosphorescence and Energy Transfer

The fluorescence of proteins originate from their amino acid residues (*Figure 13.4*). The visible fluorescence reported in many proteins are probably due to impurities[28]. Proteins containing tyrosine but no tryptophan show tyrosine fluorescence in low yield (e.g. insulin). Proteins containing tryptophan show characteristic tryptophan fluorescence (e.g. human serum albumin). The phenylalanine fluorescence is not seen in proteins.

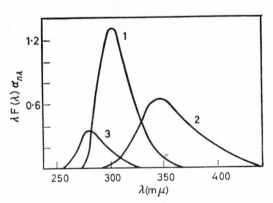

Figure 13.4. Fluorescence spectra of the aromatic amino acids in neutral aqueous solution. Curve 1, tyrosine; curve 2, tryptophan; curve 3, phenylalanine. (From F. W. J. Teale and G. Weber[27] by courtesy of Cambridge University Press)

Increase in viscosity of the solvents increases the quantum yield of most proteins. The mechanisms of quenching of the tyrosine, and the effect of urea in increasing the tryptophan fluorescence yield have been examined[1,28,29]. Effect of substitution on tyrosine and tryptophan fluorescence as well as the alkaline quenching of fluorescence in these derivatives have been studied in detail.

The overlap between the absorption and fluorescence bands of tyrosine is similar to that in certain dyes. It is likely that energy transfer can occur in proteins[27]. Thus tryptophan fluorescence can be stimulated by excited phenylalanine.

Polarization of fluorescence of tyrosine, tryptophan as well as of proteins have been studied by Weber[30]. Phosphorescent emission from proteins has also been reported[31].

REFERENCES

[1] BEAVEN, G. H., in *Advances in Spectroscopy*, Edited by Thompson, H. W., Vol. II, p. 331, Interscience, New York, 1961.

[2] WETLAUFER, D. B., in *Advances in Protein Chemistry*, Vol. 17, Academic Press, New York, 1962.

[3] GEMMILL, C. L., *Arch. Biochem. Biophys.*, 1956, **63**, 177, 192.

[4] RAMACHADRAN, L. K. and WITKOP, B., *J. Amer. Chem. Soc.*, 1959, **81**, 4028.

[5] YASUNOBU, K. T., PETERSON, E. W. and MASON, H. S., *J. Biol. Chem.*, 1959, **234**, 3291.

[6] PATCHORNIK, A., SELA, M. and KATCHALSKI, E., *J. Amer. Chem. Soc.*, 1954, **76**, 229.

[7] PETERS, T., Jr. *Compt. rend. Trav. lab. Carlsberg, Ser. Chim.*, 1959, **31**, 227.

[8] BIGELOW, C. C. and GESCHWIND, I. I., *Compt. rend. trav. lab. Carlsberg. Ser. Chim.*, 1960, **31**, 283.

[9] YANARI, S. and BOVEY, F A., *J. Biol. Chem.*, 1960, **235**, 218.

[10] DONOVAN, J. W., LASKOWSKI, M., Jr., and SCHERAGA, H. A., *J. Amer. Chem. Soc.*, 1961, **83**, 2686.

[11] BENESCH, R. E. and BENESCH, R., *J. Amer. Chem. Soc.*, 1955, **77**, 5877.

[12] MARTIN, R. E. and EDSALL, J. T., *Bull. Soc. Chim. Biol.*, 1958, **40**, 1763.

[13] SELA, M. and KATCHALSKI, E., *J. Amer. Chem. Soc.*, 1956, **78**, 3986.

[14] BENESCH, R. and BENESCH, R. E., *Proc.Natl. Acad. Sci. U.S.*, 1958, **44**, 848.

[15] HERSKOVITS, T. T. and LASKOWSKI, M., Jr, *J.. Biol. Chem.*, 1962, **237**, 2481.

[16] LASKOWSKI, M., Jr., WIDOM, J. M., McFADDEN, M. L. and SCHERAGA, H. A., *Biochem. et Biophys. Acta*, 1956, **19**, 581.

[17] LASKOWSKI, M., Jr. and SCHERAGA, H. A., *J. Amer. Chem. Soc.*, 1954, **76**, 6305.

[18] TANFORD, C. and EPSTEIN, J., *J. Amer. Chem. Soc.*, 1954, **76**, 2163.

[19] SCHERAGA, H. A., *Biochem. Biophys. Acta*, 1957, **23**, 196.

[20] DONOVAN, J. W., LASKOWSKI, M., Jr. and SCHERAGA, H. A., *Biochem. Biophys. Acta*, 1958, **29**, 455.

[21] WILLIAMS, E. J. and FOSTER, J. F., *J. Amer. Chem. Soc.*, 1959, **81**, 865.

[22] GLAZER, A. N., MACKENZIE, H. A. and WAKE, R. G., *Nature*, 1957, **180**, 1286.

[23] FOSTER, J. F. and AOKI, K., *J. Phys. Chem.*, 1957, **61**, 1369.

[24] FOSTER, J. F. and AOKI, K., *J. Amer. Chem. Soc.*, 1958, **80**, 1117.

[25] STERMAN, M. D. and FOSTER, J. F., *J. Amer. Chem. Soc.*, 1956, **78**, 3652.

[26] GLAZER, A. N. and SMITH, E. L., *J. Biol. Chem.* 1960, 235, PC 43.

[27] TEALE, F. W. J. and WEBER, G., *Biochem. J.*, 1957, **65**, 476.

[28] WEBER, G., *Advances in Protein Chemistry*, vol. 8, Ed. by M. L. Anson, K. Bailey and J. T. Edsall, Academic Press, New York, 1963.

[29] TEALE, F. W. J., *Biochem. J.*, 1960, **76**, 381.

[30] WEBER, G., *Biochem. J.*, 1960, **75**, 345.

[31] DEBYE, P. and EDWARDS, J. O., *Science*, 1952, **116**, 143.

BIBLIOGRAPHY

Collections of Absorption Spectral Data
Absorption Spectra in the Ultraviolet and Visible Region, Edited by LANG, L. and others, Vols. 1, 2, 3 and 4, Academic Press, New York

FORMANEK, J. *Untersuchung und Nachweis Organischer Farbstoffe auf Spektroskopischem Wege*, Springer, Berlin, Part I, 1908; Part II, 1911– 1927.

FREIDEL, R. A. and ORCHIN, M., *Ultra-violet Spectra of Aromatic Compounds*, John Wiley, New York, 1951.

International Critical Tables, McGraw-Hill, 1929, Vol. V, pp. 359–379.

International Critical Tables, McGraw-Hill, 1930, Vol. VII, pp. 173.

Landolt-Börnstein's Zahlenwerte und Funktionen aus Physik, Chemie, Astronomie, Geophysik und Technik, Springer Verlag, Berlin, 1951, Vol. I, Part 3, pp. 89–358.

Organic Electronic Spectral Data, Vols. 1 and 2 (1946–1955), Ed. by KAMLET, M. J., and UNGANADE, H. E., Interscience, New York, N.Y., 1960.

Tables Annuelles de Constantes et Données Numériques, Gauthier-Villars et Cie, Paris. Data up to 1934.

Ultra-violet Spectral Data, American Petroleum Institute Research Project 44.

Indices
American Society for Testing Materials, Committee E-13, *Punched Cards* (see *J. Opt. Soc. Amer.*, 1957, **47**, 672).

HERSHENSON, H. M., *Ultra-violet and Visible Absorption Spectra*, Index for 1930–1954, Academic Press, New York, 1954; Index for 1955–1959, Academic Press, New York, 1959.

Books and Reviews
BAUMAN, R. P., *Absorption Spectroscopy*, John Wiley, New York, 1962.

BEAVEN, G. H., in *Advances in Spectroscopy*, Vol. II, edited by Thompson, H. W., Interscience, New York, 1961 (Proteins).

BEAVEN, G. H. and JOHNSON, E. A., in *Molecular Spectroscopy*, Heywood, London, 1961.

BRAND, J. C. D. and EGLINTON, G., *Applications of Spectroscopy to Organic Chemistry*, Oldbourne Press, London, 1964.

BRAND, J. C. D. and SCOTT, A. I., in *Elucidation of Organic Structures by Physical Methods*, Ed. by K. W. Bentley, Chapter II, Part I, Interscience, New York, 1963.

BRAUDE, E. A., in *Determination of Organic Structures by Physical Methods*, Edited by Braude, E. A. and Nachod, F. C., Academic Press, New York, 1955, Chapter 4.

BRAUDE, E. A., in *Chemistry of Carbon Compounds*, Edited by Rodd, E. H., Elsevier, Amsterdam, 1951, Vol. I.

BRAUDE, E. A., *Ann. Repts. on Progr. Chem.*, 1945, **42**, 105.

BRODE, W. R., *Chemical Spectroscopy*, John Wiley, New York, 1943.

BRODE, W. R., *Enzymology*, 1944, **4** (Absorption spectra of vitamins, hormones and enzymes).

DUNCAN, A. B. F. and MATSEN, F. A., in *Chemical Applications of Spectroscopy*, Edited by West, W., Interscience, New York, 1956, Chapter V.

DYER, J. R. *Applications of Absorption Spectroscopy of Organic Compounds*, Prentice Hall, Englewood Cliffs, N.J., 1965.

BIBLIOGRAPHY

FARNOW, H., *Absorption Spectroscopy*, Dragoco, Holzminden.

FERGUSON, L. N., *Electronic Structures of Organic Molecules*, Prentice Hall, New York, 1952, Chapter 9.

FORBES, W. F., in *Interpretive Spectroscopy*, ed. by FREEMAN, S. K. Chapter I. Reinhold, New York, 1965.

GILLAM, A. E. and STERN, E. S., *Electronic Absorption Spectroscopy*, Edward Arnold, London, 1958.

HIRT, R. C., *Anal. Chem.*, 1962, **34**, 276.

JAFFE, H. H. and ORCHIN, M., *Theory and Applications of Ultraviolet Spectroscopy*, John Wiley, New York, 1964.

LEWIS, G. N. and CALVIN, M., *Chem. Revs.*, 1939, **25**, 273 (The colour of organic substances).

MACCOLL, A., *Quart. Revs.*, 1947, **1**, 16 (Colour and constitution).

MASON, S. F., *Quart. Revs.*, 1961, 287 (Review on Electronic Absorption Spectra of Molecules).

MELLON, M. G., Light absorption spectrometry, *Anal. Chem.*, 1949, **21**, 3; 1950, **22**, 2; 1951, **23**, 2; 1952, **24**, 2; 1954, **26**, 2; MELLON, M. G. and BOLTZ, D. F., *ibid.*, 1956, **28**, 559; 1958, **30**, 554; 1962, **34**, 232.

MILLER, F. A., *Quantitative Biological Spectroscopy*, Burgess, Minneapolis, 1940.

MORTON, R. A., *The Application of Absorption Spectra to the Study of Vitamins, Hormones and Coenzymes*, Hilger, London, 1942.

MURRELL, J. N., *The Theory of the Electronic Spectra of Organic Molecules*, Methuen, London, 1963.

PHILLIPS, J. P., *Spectra-Structure Correlation*, Academic Press, New York, 1964.

PLATT, J. R., Electronic spectra of organic compounds, *Ann. Rev. Phys. Chem.*, 1959.

REID, C., *Excited States in Chemistry and Biology*, Butterworths, London, 1957.

ROSENBAUM, E. J., Ultra-violet spectrophotometry, *Anal. Chem.*, 1949, **21**, 16; 1950, **22**, 14; 1951, **23**, 12; 1952, **24**, 14; 1954, **26**, 20; HIRT, R. C., *ibid.*, 1956, **28**, 579; 1958, **30**, 589.

SCOTT, J. F., in *Physical Techniques in Biological Research*, Edited by Oster, G. and Pollister, A. W., Academic Press, New York, 1955, Vol. I.

SINSHEIMER, R. L., in *Radiation Biology*, Edited by Hollaender, A., McGraw-Hill, New York, 1955, Vol. II.

Steric Effects in Conjugated Systems, Edited by Gray, G. W., Butterworths, London, 1958.

STUCKEY, R. E., *J. Pharm. Pharmacol.*, 1952, **4**, 345 (Spectrophotometry in pharmaceutical analysis).

TURNER, D. W., in *Determination of Organic Structures by Physical Methods*, ed. by NACHOD, F. C. and PHILLIPS, W. D., Chapter 5, Academic Press, New York, 1962.

WEST, W., in *Physical Methods of Organic Chemistry*, Edited by Weissberg, A., Interscience, New York, 1949, Part II, Chapter 21.

WEST, W., in *Chemical Applications of Spectroscopy*, Edited by West, W., Interscience, New York, 1956, Chapter VI.

WETLAUFER, D. B., in *Advances in Protein Chemistry*, Vol. 17, Academic Press, New York, 1962 (Proteins and amino acids).

INDEX

Abietic acid, 37, 92
Absorbance, 3
  standard values, 7
Absorption
  intensity, 3
  irrelevant, 100
Acetaldehyde, 24, 134
Acetanilides, 69
Acetone, 15, 24, 26, 32, 134, 184
  photochemical decomposition, 134
Acetonitrile, 23
Acetophenone, 26, 63, 67, 69, 116
  substituted, 117
Acetylacetone, 99
Acetylenes, 23, 128
Acetylenic compounds, naturally occur-
  ring, 53
Acidity function, 105
Acids, 133
  αβ-unsaturated, 44
  dissociation constants, 104
Acraldehyde, 43
Acridine, 78, 136
  dyes, 136
Acridone, 136
N-Acyldihydroindoles, 91
N-Acylindoles, 91
Adenine, 83
Ajamalicine, 91
Alcohols, 21, 125, 133
Aldazine, 32
Aldehydes, 103
  aliphatic, 134
  asymmetric, 179
  αβ-unsaturated, 41
Alkali
  azides, 171, 173
  halides, 138, 171
Alkaline earth
  azides, 171, 173
  halides, 138
Alkaloids, 91
Alkenes, 127
cis-2-Alkenes, 127
trans-2-Alkenes, 127
Alkyl azides, 55
Alkyl iodides, 20, 22
Alkyl nitrates, 31
Alkyl nitrites, 31
Alkyl substitution, 25
2-Alkyl-1-alkenes, 127
Allenes, 55, 128
Alloxan, 82
Allowed bands, 5

Alloyohimbine, 91
Amethyst violet, 137
Amides, 190
  cylic, 129
Amine picrates, 103
Aminoacids, 191
Amino ketones, 27
Aminopyrene sulphonic acids, 139
Aminopyrimidines, 82
Amino-1,2,3,4-thiatriazoles, 85
Ammonia, 21, 22
Angstrom unit, 1
Aniline, 61, 62, 65
Anilines, 69, 186
Anisoles, 69
Anthocyanidins, 176
Anthocyanins, 176
Anthracene, 71, 78, 128, 134, 136, 140
Anthraquinone, 136
Arachidonic acid, 107
Aromatics, 123, 128
  carbonium ions, 174
  far ultra-violet spectra, 128
  negative ions, 174
  positive ions, 174
  substitution, orientation in, 69
  complexes with oxalyl chloride, 153
  non-benzenoid, 72
Arsenic iodide, 21
Aryl sulphides, 142
Aryl sulphones, 69
Aryl sulphoxides, 69
Association
  constants, 107
  phenomenon, 178
Auxochromes, 13, 15, 20–24
Aza acyloins, 27
Azalein, 176
Azides, 55, 69
Azine dyes, 136
Azines, monocyclic, 79
Azobenzene, 32, 63, 175
Azoxy compounds, 31
Azulenes, 72, 183

Baker–Nathan order, 67
Balchanolide, 95
Bands
  A-bands, 16
  α,β and p-bands, 16, 58
  change-transfer bands, 63
  E-bands, 15
  F-bands, 172

201